INTEGRATED PEST MANAGEMENT FOR

AVOCADOS

INTEGRATED PEST MANAGEMENT FOR

AVOCADOS

UNIVERSITY OF CALIFORNIA
STATEWIDE INTEGRATED PEST MANAGEMENT PROGRAM

AGRICULTURE AND NATURAL RESOURCES
PUBLICATION 3503

2008

PRECAUTIONS FOR USING PESTICIDES

Pesticides are poisonous and must be used with caution. READ THE LABEL BEFORE OPENING A PESTICIDE CONTAINER. Follow all label precautions and directions, including requirements for protective equipment. Use a pesticide only on the plants or site specified on the label or in published University of California recommendations. Apply pesticides at the rates specified on the label or at lower rates if suggested in this publication. In California, all agricultural uses of pesticides must be reported, including use in many non-farm situations, such as cemeteries, golf courses, parks, roadsides, and commercial plant production including nurseries. Contact your county agricultural commissioner for further details. Laws, regulations, and information concerning pesticides change frequently, so be sure the publication you are using is up-to-date.

Legal Responsibility. The user is legally responsible for any damage due to misuse of pesticides. Responsibility extends to effects caused by drift, runoff, or residues.

Transportation. Do not ship or carry pesticides together with food or feed in a way that allows contamination of the edible items. Never transport pesticides in a closed passenger vehicle or in a closed cab.

Storage. Keep pesticides in original containers until used. Store them in a locked cabinet, building, or fenced area where they are not accessible to children, unauthorized persons, pets, or livestock. DO NOT store pesticides with foods, feed, fertilizers, or other materials that may become contaminated by the pesticides.

Container Disposal. Consult the pesticide label, the County Department of Agriculture, or the local waste disposal authorities for instructions on disposing of pesticide containers. Dispose of empty containers carefully. Never reuse them. Make sure empty containers are not accessible to children or animals. Never dispose of containers where they may contaminate water supplies or natural waterways. Offer empty containers for recycling if available. Home use pesticide containers can be thrown in the trash only if they are completely empty.

Protection of Nonpest Animals and Plants. Many pesticides are toxic to useful or desirable animals, including honey bees, natural enemies, fish, domestic animals, and birds. Certain rodenticides may pose a special hazard to animals that eat poisoned rodents. Plants may also be damaged by misapplied pesticides. Take precautions to protect nonpest species from direct exposure to pesticides and from contamination due to drift, runoff, or residues.

Permit Requirements. Certain pesticides require a permit from the county agricultural commissioner before possession or use. When such materials are mentioned in this publication they are marked with an asterisk (*).

Plant Injury. Certain chemicals may cause injury to plants (phytotoxicity) under certain conditions. Always consult the label for limitations. Before applying any pesticide, take into account the stage of plant development, the soil type and condition, the temperature, moisture, and wind. Injury may also result from the use of incompatible materials.

Personal Safety. Follow label directions carefully. Avoid splashing, spilling, leaks, spray drift, and contamination of clothing. NEVER eat, smoke, drink, or chew while using pesticides. Provide for emergency medical care IN ADVANCE as required by regulation.

Worker Protection Standards. Federal Worker Protection Standards require pesticide safety training for all employees working in agricultural fields, greenhouses, and nurseries that have been treated with pesticides, including pesticide training for employees who do not work directly with pesticides.

ORDERING

For information about ordering this publication and/or a free catalog, contact
University of California
Agriculture and Natural Resources
Communication Services
6701 San Pablo Avenue, 2nd Floor
Oakland, California 94608-1239
Telephone 1-800-994-8849
(510) 642-2431
FAX (510) 643-5470
E-mail: danrcs@ucdavis.edu
Visit the ANR Communication Services Web site at http://anrcatalog.ucdavis.edu

Publication 3503

Other books in this series include:
Integrated Pest Management for Alfalfa Hay, Publication 3312
Integrated Pest Management for Almonds, Second Edition, Publication 3308
Integrated Pest Management for Apples and Pears, Second Edition, Publication 3340
Integrated Pest Management for Citrus, Second Edition, Publication 3303
Integrated Pest Management for Cole Crops and Lettuce, Publication 3307
Integrated Pest Management for Cotton, Second Edition, Publication 3305
Integrated Pest Management for Floriculture and Nurseries, Publication 3402
Integrated Pest Management for Potatoes, Second Edition, Publication 3316
Integrated Pest Management for Rice, Second Edition, Publication 3280
Integrated Pest Management for Small Grains, Publication 3333
Integrated Pest Management for Stone Fruits, Publication 3389
Integrated Pest Management for Strawberries, Second Edition, Publication 3351
Integrated Pest Management for Tomatoes, Fourth Edition, Publication 3274
Integrated Pest Management for Walnuts, Third Edition, Publication 3270
Natural Enemies Handbook: The Illustrated Guide to Biological Pest Control, Publication 3386
Pests of Landscape Trees and Shrubs, Second Edition, Publication 3359
Pests of the Garden and Small Farm, Second Edition, Publication 3332

ISBN-13: 978-1-60107-420-1
Library of Congress Control Number: 2006906787
©2008 by the Regents of the University of California

Division of Agriculture and Natural Resources
All rights reserved.

This publication has been peer reviewed for technical accuracy by University of California scientists and other qualified professionals. This review process was managed by the ANR Associate Editor for Pest Management.

3M-1/08-WJC/CM

Contributors and Acknowledgments

Steve H. Dreistadt, Writer

Photographs by David Rosen (except as noted)

Mary Louise Flint, Technical Editor

Prepared by the University of California Statewide IPM Program at Davis.

Photographs were obtained with financial support from the California Avocado Commission and through the cooperation of California avocado growers.

Technical Advisors

Gary S. Bender, University of California Cooperative Extension, San Diego

Ben Faber, University of California Cooperative Extension, Ventura

Mark S. Hoddle, Department of Entomology, University of California, Riverside

Reuben Hofshi, Hofshi Foundation, Fallbrook

Rex E. Marsh, Department of Wildlife, Fish and Conservation Biology, University of California, Davis

John A. Menge, Department of Plant Pathology, University of California, Riverside

Joseph G. Morse, Department of Entomology, University of California, Riverside

Pascal Oevering, University of California Cooperative Extension, Ventura

Howard D. Ohr, Department of Plant Pathology, University of California, Riverside

Phil A. Phillips, UC IPM Program and University of California Cooperative Extension, Ventura

Contributors

Entomology: Matthew Blua, David H. Headrick, Mark S. Hoddle, Dave Machlitt, Joseph G. Morse, Pascal Oevering, Phil A. Phillips, Tom Roberts

Horticulture: Mary Lu Arpaia, Mary L. Bianchi, Ben Faber, Reuben Hofshi, Carol J. Lovatt, Peggy Mauk, Guy W. Witney

Plant Pathology: Gary S. Bender, James A. Downer, John A. Menge, Howard D. Ohr, Joseph S. Semancik

Vegetation Management: W. Thomas Lanini, Anil Shrestha, Cheryl A. Wilen

Vertebrates: Rex O. Baker, Rex E. Marsh, Terrell P. Salmon

Special Thanks

The following have generously provided information, offered suggestions, reviewed draft manuscripts, identified pests, or helped obtain photographs: Duncan Abbott, Robert Abbott, Jodi Azulai, Lori Berger, Michael J. Costello, David Crowley, Joseph M. DiTomaso, Allan J. Dodds, Greg W. Douhan, Pauli Galin, Raymond J. Gill, David A. Grantz, Justine Haessly, David R. Haviland, Bob Heath, Ellie Hengehold, Raymond L. Hix, Christine Joshel, David Kellum, Shawn King, John H. Klotz, Robert F. Luck, Alex Lyon, Richard S. Melnicoe, Patrick J. O'Connor-Marer, Barbara L. P. Ohlendorf, Steve Peirce, Charles Robins, Lindsay Robinson, Richard Roush, Tom Shea, Nick Stehly Sr., Nick Stehly Jr., Richard Stehly, Kathy Stewart, Larry L. Strand, Brian Taylor, Gillian W. Watson, and Jim Wiseman.

Production

Design: (this volume): Celeste Marquiss, ANR Communication Services

Design: (IPM manual series): Seventeenth Street Studios

Digital Photo Processing: Steven Lock, Jack Kelly Clark

Drawings: Valerie Winemiller, Celeste Marquiss, and Robin Walton

Editing: Jim Coats

Contents

Integrated Pest Management for Avocados

This manual is designed to help growers and pest control professionals apply the principles of integrated pest management (IPM) to avocado production. IPM puts the emphasis on anticipating and avoiding potential problems whenever possible. Integrated pest management decisions are based on established monitoring techniques and treatment guidelines. Management relies primarily on methods that are the least disruptive to natural enemies and that minimize adverse environmental effects.

California has more than 5,000 avocado growers who together produce more than 90% of the avocados grown in the United States. Florida and Hawaii produce most of the rest. Approximately 400 million pounds of avocados are harvested annually in California. The farm-level value of California-grown avocados was $368 million during 2004. Most of California's 62,000 acres (25,000 ha) of bearing trees are in southern interior and south coastal regions, but at least some production is reported in 20 counties (Figure 1). San Diego County produces the most avocados, followed in order by Ventura, Santa Barbara, Riverside, San Luis Obispo, and Orange Counties.

The United States is the world's second largest avocado producer after Mexico. Historically, most avocados consumed in the United States have been California-grown,

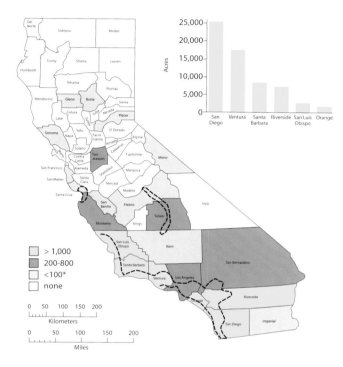

Figure 1. Avocado-producing counties in California and the acres bearing fruit, 2004. California produces more than 90% of the avocados grown in the United States. Primary commercial growing areas are indicated by dotted lines. *Sources:* CAS 1976, National Agricultural Statistics Service 2005, various California county Agricultural Crop Reports.

* The specific acreage is unreported in some counties with few growers.

IPM Is . . .

Integrated pest management (IPM) is an ecosystem-based strategy that focuses on the long-term prevention of pests or their damage. Pests include fungi and other pathogens, insects, mites, vertebrates, and weeds that damage avocados. IPM combines techniques such as biological control, habitat modification, changes in cultural practices, and use of pest-resistant rootstock cultivars. Pesticides are applied only when monitoring indicates they are needed according to established guidelines, and applications are made with the goal of controlling only the target pest organism. Pesticides are selected and applied in ways that minimize risks to human health, beneficial and nontarget organisms, and the environment.

but imported fruit and exotic pests are dramatically altering the economics and management of California avocados. Avocados are native to Central America and the Caribbean but have been planted throughout the world's tropical and semitropical regions. There are more than 30 countries that produce over 10 million pounds of fruit every year (Figure 2). Worldwide avocado production increased by almost 50% from 1994 to 2004, going from 4.6 billion pounds in 1994 to 6.8 billion pounds in 2004.

Increased commerce and travel have facilitated the introduction of new pests. Invertebrates caused only occasional problems in California avocado groves until the 1990s, when avocado thrips and persea mite were inadvertently introduced. Avocado thrips and persea mite are now key avocado pests, often causing substantial economic loss. Most avocado growers in the past relied on effective natural enemies to biologically control invertebrate pests. Now growers use pesticides more frequently. More-recently introduced pests may further disrupt avocado pest management programs.

Integrated pest management can help growers resolve the challenges of foreign competition and new pests. IPM programs improve fruit quality and yield and increase the grower's ability to predictably and reliably produce marketable fruit.

The manual's first few chapters summarize avocado growth and development, general crop management practices, and basic IPM principles. Subsequent chapters cover the management of avocado diseases, abiotic (non-infectious) disorders, insects and mites, weeds, and vertebrate pests. These chapters provide descriptions and photographs of individual pests and the damage they cause. IPM recommendations include guidelines for monitoring pests, enhancing natural controls, and taking effective control actions.

New homes are being constructed adjacent to a large avocado grove on the slope. Adopting IPM methods can reduce potential conflicts with neighbors concerned about pesticide drift and runoff.

For pesticide recommendations, new techniques, and other time-sensitive information, you can consult the most current revisions of *Avocado: UC IPM Pest Management Guidelines* and *Avocado Year-Round IPM*, available online at www.ipm.ucdavis.edu. Check regularly with your University of California Cooperative Extension farm advisor for new developments.

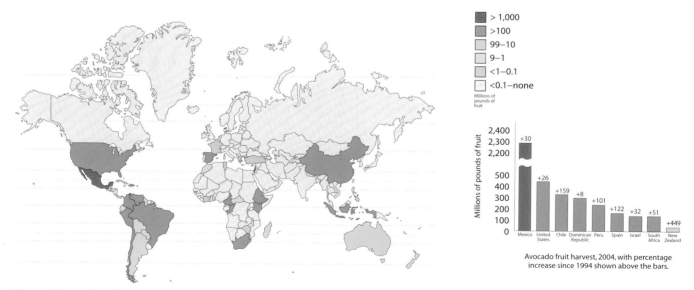

Figure 2. Avocado-producing countries and their harvests during 2004, in millions of pounds of fruit. Many producing countries do not currently meet fruit quality standards for export to the United States and other developed markets. Bars show the 2004 harvest of key avocado-exporting countries. Percentage increases in harvest from 1994 to 2004 for exporting countries are shown on top of bars. *Source*: Food and Agriculture Organization 1994, 2004.

The Avocado Tree: Development and Growth Requirements

Avocado growers strive to produce numerous large, unblemished fruit. In order to deliver attractive and flavorful avocados to consumers, a grower's management and harvest practices must also favor good postharvest qualities. Optimal fruit quality and yield result when trees are well-managed and healthy. Growing healthy, high-yielding trees requires an understanding of the crop's seasonal development and its specific requirements for good growth. Growers also need to know how environmental factors and cultural practices affect trees and fruit and their pests. This chapter and those that follow will help growers to meet these challenges.

The Seasonal Cycle of Avocado

The avocado tree *(Persea americana)* is a tropical evergreen with three horticultural races (Guatemalan, Mexican, and West Indian). Trees grow up to about 60 feet (18 m) tall and develop throughout the year. The timing and length for each crop stage depend mostly on temperature. As a result, crop development dates vary among locations and from year to year.

Flower buds are initiated during late summer or fall and develop through winter. Blossoming and fruit set occur from late winter through early summer, but most harvested fruit develop from flowers that are pollinated during about two months in spring. Fruit grow slowly through midsummer and then rapidly increase in size during late summer and fall. Leaf flush and root growth begin after flowering. Root and shoot growth continue from spring through fall, but both slow during summer. The average seasonal development cycle for avocados is summarized in Figure 3.

Avocado flowers occur in groups as a much-branched panicle. Each of these compound inflorescences is about 4 to 10 inches (10–25 cm) wide and can produce hundreds of flowers over a several-week period. A mature tree can produce hundreds of inflorescences and thus many thousands of flowers a year. Individual flowers are about ⅖ inch (1 cm) wide. Avocado flowers are bisexual. Female and male parts of the flower mature and open once for several hours at separate times (Figure 4). The female parts open first. Male parts open the next day. Any given tree in bloom will have many flowers open at the same time, some in the female phase and others as males. There is great genetic variability among the flowers within a single tree.

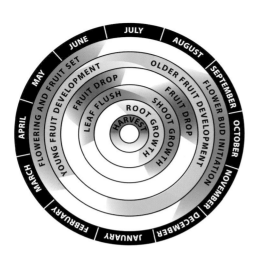

Figure 3. Average seasonal development of avocado growing in Santa Barbara and Ventura Counties. In warmer interior Riverside and San Diego Counties, each stage begins and ends on average about 2 to 4 weeks sooner than shown here. In these warmer interior areas, certain crop stages may require less time to complete development. Further north in San Luis Obispo and Monterey Counties, stages begin and end about 2 to 6 weeks later than shown. *Adapted from:* CAC and CMCC 2003.

Individual avocado flowers are about ⅔ inch (1 cm) wide. Each flower has both male and female parts, which mature and open at separate times.

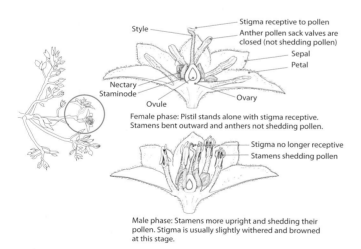

Figure 4. Avocado flowers occur in a much-branched group or compound inflorescence *(left illustration).* Several hundred short-lived blossoms are produced over a several-week period. Each flower has female and male parts that mature and open on different days. During the female (first) phase *(top),* the stigma (pollen receptacle) is rigid and upright. Petals and stamens are relatively flat. The male phase *(bottom)* usually occurs the next day. Stamens become upright and shed pollen and the stigma is withering. *Sources:* McGregor 1976, P. Fawcett in Tomlinson 1980.

Avocado flowers occur in a much-branched group. Blossoming occurs during an extended period from late winter through early summer, but most harvested fruit develop from flowers that are pollinated during about two months in spring.

Pollinators of avocado include hummingbirds and various fly, wasp, and wild bee species. Domesticated honey bees (*Apis mellifera*) are the most economically important avocado pollinators. Most growers place honey bee hives in groves. The presence of honey bees greatly increases flower pollination and fruit yield. Even under optimal conditions, however, the majority of fruit that does set will fall from the tree when still small and immature (fruit drop). Avocado fruit take at least 6 to 7 months to go from pollination to fruit maturity.

Mature fruit keep well for months on the tree. Although mature on the tree, avocados do not ripen until after they are picked. Harvest can begin in late fall or early winter and may not end until the subsequent fall. Two years' crops can easily overlap on a tree, so fruit may be on the tree through-

Domesticated honey bees are the most important avocado flower pollinators. Fruit yield is greatly reduced unless hives of domesticated honey bees are placed in groves during flowering.

Even under optimal growing conditions, the majority of fruit that set will fall from the tree during about May to June when fruit are small. A tree can set several thousand fruit, but about 200 mature fruit per average-sized tree is a good harvest.

Fruit increase in size slowly during the first month or two after fruit set. Small fruit, those about ¾ inch (19 mm) or less in length, are susceptible to feeding damage from avocado thrips, a key pest.

Avocado fruit increase in size rapidly from late summer through fall. Fruit keep well on the tree and do not ripen until after they are picked.

out the year. Harvest of previous-season fruit may or may not be completed by the time the subsequent year's fruit has set. Avocados are hand-picked by clipping (cutting) or snapping (breaking) fruit stems. Pickers work from the ground, use ladders, or cut fruit using a pole equipped with a pull-cord–operated terminal blade and fruit-catching bag.

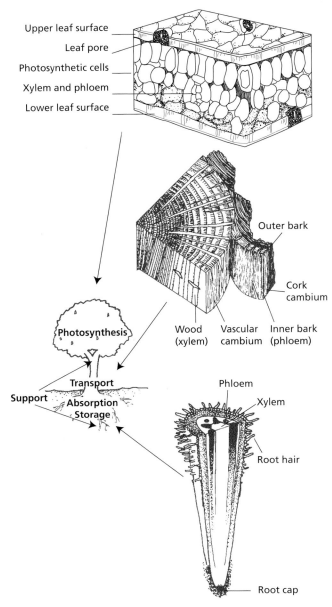

Avocado trees grown commercially in California are grafted. Only the most cold tolerant rootstocks (those of Mexican origin) are widely grown. Productivity (fruit yield), resistance to pathogens (Phytophthora root rot, Dothiorella canker, and Phytophthora canker and crown rot), and salt tolerance are key rootstock selection criteria. Over 95% of the scions (the aboveground, fruit-producing part of the tree) grown commercially in California are Hass, a cultivar developed in California. Avocados are typically grown on hillsides, often on very steep slopes. Hilly terrain improves soil drainage and reduces the risk of frost. Rugged terrain is often less costly to purchase because very hilly sites are suitable for relatively few crops. Hilliness does increase the cost of pumping and uniformly applying irrigation water, however, and rugged terrain restricts the use of mechanized equipment such as tractors and ground-spray rigs.

Growth Requirements

Good fruit quality and yield require proper care and healthy functioning of the trees' non-fruiting parts. Vital vegetative parts include the leaves, limbs, roots, and trunk (Figure 5). All plant parts are closely interdependent, as illustrated by the relationship between the flush of new leaves and the drop of fruit and old leaves (Figure 6).

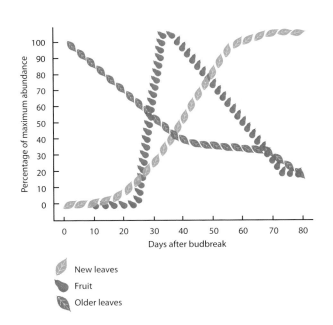

Figure 5. The basic anatomy and functions of key vegetative parts of a tree. The limbs, trunk, and roots support the plant and provide its vascular (transport) system. Fine roots absorb water and nutrients, which are transported upward in the xylem. Leaves produce carbohydrates, which are used immediately for tissue growth and maintenance or transported down in phloem as sugars. Sugars are converted to other carbohydrates, such as cellulose and starch, and stored in roots, limbs, and the trunk. Cambium is vital tissue that grows to enlarge the plant and differentiate into other tissues.

Figure 6. The peak (maximum) flush of new leaves occurs at about the peak drop of older leaves and the end of summer fruit drop. This example illustrates how all parts of the tree are closely interrelated. Good fruit quality and yield depend on the proper care and functioning of trees' nonfruiting plant parts. *Adapted from:* Arpaia 2000.

Most avocado leaf flush occurs during spring, beginning shortly after blossoming. Shoot growth is indeterminate and can occur continuously and almost any time. Shoots primarily grow from spring through fall, slowing during midsummer.

After leaves flush, root growth begins and continues through fall, slowing during midsummer. Avocados have a very shallow root system, revealed here by brushing away the leaf mulch. A thick layer of organic mulch is critical for healthy tree growth and good fruit yield. Mulch helps reduce certain pest problems such as Phytophthora root rot and weeds.

Tree growth and fruit development require adequate temperatures, appropriate soil conditions, and sufficient light, nutrients, and water. Light is essential for photosynthesis, the process by which green plant tissue manufactures sugars (Figure 7). Sugars are synthesized in the leaves using water taken from the soil, carbon dioxide from the air, and light energy from the sun. Sugar provides the energy for tree growth, development, and maintenance. Sugars are used immediately or stored as other carbohydrates such as cellulose and starch in leaves, stems, and roots.

Regular irrigation is necessary for avocado tree survival and fruit production in semiarid California. Avocado groves are watered by sprinkler, microsprinkler, or drip systems. Only a fraction of the water taken up by trees is retained; most of it passes through the plant and out the leaf pores during transpiration. Transpiration is a process that supplies water to the leaves for photosynthesis, carries nutrients to all parts of the tree, and cools the plant. Climatic factors such as the amount of sunshine, humidity, heat, and wind affect the rate of transpiration.

Carbon, hydrogen, and oxygen (supplied by air and water) and 14 soil-derived elements are essential for good tree growth and fruit production. California orchard soils contain

Figure 7. Photosynthesis is a chemical process within green plant tissue. Energy in sunlight is used to convert carbon dioxide and water into oxygen and carbohydrates.

sufficient amounts of most essential elements either because they are already present in the soil or because they return to the soil periodically through leaf decay, atmospheric deposition, or other means. Other nutrients, primarily modest amounts of nitrogen and occasionally potassium, phosphorus, and zinc (and perhaps boron in some locations) are replenished by fertilization.

Avocado trees grow best under mild to warm temperatures. Trees and fruit are highly sensitive to cold and freezing. Excess salinity and high pH in soil and water and inappropriate irrigation are key environmental and cultural factors that can adversely affect avocado trees. This is discussed in the fourth chapter, "Cultural Practices and Abiotic Disorders."

Managing Pests in Avocados

Integrated pest management (IPM) is a strategy to prevent and minimize pest damage while avoiding adverse impacts on human health and the environment. Pests include damaging insects, mites, pathogens, vertebrates, and weeds. Abiotic disorders induced by adverse environmental conditions and inadequate cultural practices also injure avocado fruit and trees.

An IPM program applies knowledge of crop and pest biology to coordinate pest management with cultural practices. IPM emphasizes preventing problems and seeks to achieve economical, long-lasting pest control. Careful monitoring of pests and of plant and environmental conditions gives the grower valuable information to help determine whether and when control action is needed. Biological, cultural, mechanical, chemical, and physical (also called environmental) techniques are applied in various combinations to prevent problems or manage their severity. Pesticides are used only if monitoring indicates that they are needed. When pesticides are applied, they are chosen and used in ways that minimize disruption to biological control and other IPM practices. Figure 8 is a checklist of cultural and pest management practices a grower is likely to use during the year.

No single program works for all avocado groves. Grove history, local climate, rootstock, soil characteristics, surroundings, water quality, and grower preferences are among the factors that determine the best management program. This IPM for Avocados manual will help you to

- prevent problems
- accurately diagnose the cause of problems and identify pests and beneficials
- regularly monitor crops and growing areas
- use control action thresholds or guidelines
- employ effective management methods

Pest Prevention

There are many crop problems that you can anticipate and avoid. Prevention is often the least expensive and most effective method, and for certain problems, prevention is the only control option. For example, most diseases can only be effectively managed by preventive action during an early stage of disease development. Once symptoms become obvious or severe, treatment options are more limited and the tree or fruit may have already sustained serious damage. Pest prevention includes choosing a good growing site, preparing

Pre-bloom, Open Flower, Pollination, and Fruit Set (December through June)

❑ Protect water quality by managing runoff and drift.

❑ Scout for and manage diseases, especially: Armillaria, Avocado root rot, Dothiorella and Phytophthora cankers, Sunblotch.

❑ Monitor and if warranted manage invertebrates, during spring and summer including: Avocado thrips, Greenhouse thrips, Persea and Sixspotted mites.

❑ Monitor weeds, especially during spring through fall. If warranted manage vegetation, especially weeds near trunks.

❑ Monitor for and manage vertebrates, especially during spring and summer.

❑ Apply gypsum and mulch to reduce avocado root rot and improve soil.

❑ Manage irrigation: Inspect irrigation systems by late winter. Monitor and adjust scheduling to meet trees' varying water needs.

❑ Promote pollination: Place honey bee hives in groves. Manage pesticides to avoid killing bees.

Young Fruit Development (March through July)

❑ Protect water quality by managing runoff and drift.

❑ Scout for and manage diseases, especially: Armillaria, Avocado root rot, Dothiorella and Phytophthora cankers, Sunblotch.

❑ Monitor and if needed manage pests that damage fruit: Abiotic disorders, Invertebrates, Pathogens, Vertebrates.

❑ Monitor and if warranted manage invertebrates, during spring and summer, including: Avocado thrips, Caterpillars, Greenhouse thrips, Persea and Sixspotted mites.

❑ Monitor and if needed manage other invertebrates: Avocado brown mite, Branch and twig borer, False chinch bug, Fuller rose beetle, Glassy-winged sharpshooter, Lace bug, Mealybugs, Scales, Whiteflies.

❑ Monitor weeds, especially during spring through fall. If warranted manage vegetation, especially weeds near trunks.

❑ Monitor for and manage vertebrates, especially during spring and summer.

❑ Manage pesticides to avoid killing bees.

❑ Manage irrigation: Monitor and adjust scheduling to meet trees' varying water needs.

Older Fruit Development (June through January, but fruit may remain on trees though October)

❑ Protect water quality by managing runoff and drift.

❑ Scout for and manage diseases, especially: Armillaria, Avocado root rot, Dothiorella and Phytophthora cankers, Sunblotch.

❑ Monitor and if needed manage pests that damage fruit: Abiotic disorders, Invertebrates, Pathogens, Vertebrates.

❑ Monitor and if warranted manage invertebrates, including: Avocado brown mite, Caterpillars, Persea and Sixspotted mites.

❑ Monitor for and manage vertebrates, especially: Coyote, Ground squirrel, Pocket gopher, Roof rat.

❑ Reduce disease and manage tree growth by proper pruning.

❑ Manage nutrition: Test foliar nutrients. Fertilize if needed.

❑ Test frost control system by November. Apply frost protections when warranted through March, especially if growing on flat land.

❑ Inspect trees or sample foliage or soil during late summer or fall to assess salinity from alkaline soils, poor quality water, and fertilizers.

❑ Manage irrigation: Monitor and adjust scheduling to meet trees' varying water needs.

Figure 8. Seasonal checklist of major monitoring and management activities for avocado. See also Figures 9 and 13. For current information, consult the *Avocado Year-Round IPM Program* online at www.ipm.ucdavis.edu.

Many problems can be anticipated and prevented during planting. The small trees (foreground) with drooping, slightly pale foliage are infected with avocado root rot. They were planted near the base of a slope where waterlogged soil and pathogen-contaminated runoff from above are problems. By choosing *Phytophthora*-resistant rootstocks, planting on a raised soil berm, amending soil with gypsum, and applying a thick layer of coarse organic mulch, the grower could have avoided the problems seen here.

The history of pest problems and soil conditions at a site are among the important factors to consider when you are choosing a new avocado planting site. This young avocado is dying from Armillaria root rot. The fungus persists for many years in infected roots and wood in soil, such as the stump in the foreground. This pathogen-infested state of the soil could have been determined before planting, and a different site or crop chosen. It will be very difficult to obtain good avocado fruit yield here.

the site well before planting, and selecting disease-resistant rootstock cultivars. Key preventive management practices (summarized in Table 1) include using good sanitation, applying and maintaining organic mulch, and providing appropriate irrigation.

Identification and Diagnosis

You have to be able to correctly identify the cause of any damage or stress symptoms and the species of any pests before you can choose the most appropriate management strategies. Most pest management methods, including pesticides, effectively manage only a select group of species. Even related species are managed differently: for example, avocado thrips and greenhouse thrips. Other similar species (such as flower thrips) are harmless and require no management. Some species are beneficial predators (*Franklinothrips* and sixspotted thrips) and should be conserved. In some cases, the symptoms caused by pest organisms closely resemble damage caused by nutrient deficiencies or adverse soil conditions. Make a habit of regularly looking on and around trees for disease symptoms, invertebrates, vertebrates, and weeds, and learn how to recognize them. When you know how to distinguish pests from important beneficial organisms, you are more able to assess the effectiveness of biological control.

Many different pests and disorders have the potential to damage fruit or trees. However, most damage in avocado is caused by just a few common problems:

Table 1. Cultural Practices and Growing Conditions That Growers Can Manipulate (Y) in an IPM Program to Help Prevent and Control Avocado Pests and Disorders.

Pest or problem	Site selection	Soil preparation	Rootstock cultivar	Scion cultivar	Rootstock certified pathogen-free	Irrigation water quality	Irrigation amount and frequency	Water placement, irrigation method	Sanitation	Border vegetation management	Fertilization	Mulching	Pruning	Dust control	Ant control	Harvest methods and timing
Diseases																
Armillaria root rot	Y	Y					Y	Y	Y							
avocado black streak				Y		Y	Y									
bacterial canker				Y		Y	Y									
Dothiorella canker			Y		Y		Y	Y	Y				Y			Y
fruit rots				Y			Y	Y	Y			Y	Y			Y
Phytophthora canker, crown rot		Y	Y				Y	Y	Y				Y			
Phytophthora root rot	Y	Y	Y			Y	Y	Y	Y				Y			
sunblotch				Y	Y				Y				Y			
Verticillium wilt	Y								Y							
Disorders																
aeration, root asphyxiation	Y	Y					Y	Y								
frost tolerance	Y		Y	Y			Y				Y		Y			
nutrient disorders	Y	Y				Y	Y	Y			Y	Y				
poor drainage	Y	Y	Y				Y	Y								
sunburn	Y	Y					Y				Y	Y	Y			Y
salinity	Y	Y	Y	Y		Y	Y				Y	Y				
Invertebrates																
avocado brown mite				Y			Y				Y		Y			
avocado thrips											Y	?*	Y			Y
caterpillars	Y									Y			Y			Y
glassy-winged sharpshooter	Y									Y						Y
greenhouse thrips													Y	Y		Y
Homoptera											Y			Y	Y	
persea mite	Y			Y			Y			Y	Y					
pests of young trees only	Y									Y					Y	
sixspotted mite				Y									Y			
Other																
vertebrates	Y								Y	Y			Y			
water contamination, soil loss	Y	Y					Y	Y		Y	Y	Y				
weeds	Y	Y					Y	Y	Y	Y		Y				

* ? = The effectiveness of mulching for thrips control is uncertain.

- adverse growing conditions (frost, poor drainage, and salinity)
- inadequate cultural practices (inappropriate amounts and frequency of irrigation)
- invertebrates (avocado thrips and persea mite)
- pathogens (root and crown rots and canker diseases)

Some additional organisms (vertebrates, weeds, and certain insects) generally are pests only when trees are young. Later chapters show how to identify and diagnose these and other less-common problems. Consult the latest update of *Avocado: UC IPM Pest Management Guidelines* and the *Avocado Year-Round IPM Program*, both available online at www.ipm.ucdavis.edu, for the most current, well-illustrated information.

Diagnosing the cause of problems often requires appropriate tools, such as a hand lens, hatchet, or shovel. The causes of some problems can be identified only when you send appropriate samples for testing at a laboratory, so it is important that you know proper sample collection procedures. You may need additional collection materials—such as bags or containers and a cooler with ice—in order to obtain and submit adequate samples to a laboratory for diagnosis.

To identify the causes of some problems you will need to rely on the assistance of experienced professionals. Do not hesitate to seek their help if you are not sure what is causing a problem. UCCE farm advisors (listed under "University of California Cooperative Extension Service" or "Cooperative Agricultural Extension, University of California" in the county government listing of many local telephone directories), county agricultural commissioners, and professional pest control advisors can help you or direct you to other specialists when necessary. Other information sources are listed in the suggested reading.

Monitoring

Check groves regularly for pest or disease problems, such as when you are in the grove for other routine cultural practices. Monitor tree and fruit health, weather conditions, and the growing environment. Systematically look for damage symptoms, pests, and conditions and practices that can injure fruit or trees. Monitoring certain pests, such as small insects and mites, requires at least the use of a good hand lens. A binocular dissecting microscope makes it easier to find and identify tiny creatures on samples brought in from the grove.

Keep written records of your monitoring results, including grove conditions (such as soil moisture), management activities, and weather. Record the presence of damage and pests, and when appropriate, record some quantification of the abundance or severity of damage and the population levels of pest and beneficial organisms. (Subsequent chapters describe specific methods for monitoring important pests.)

During the season, consult your records to discern whether damage and pest or natural enemy populations are rising or falling. Use this information to evaluate and predict potential problems, plan management actions, assess the efficacy of control, and determine whether more action is needed. Simple tables and graphs of data can help you to recognize patterns. Maps help to identify localized problems

Diagnosing the cause of problems often requires appropriate tools. A chisel, hatchet, pocket knife, and shovel are used to help diagnose many diseases and disorders and to collect samples for submission to a diagnostic laboratory.

Successful pest management requires correct identification of the cause of damage or stress symptoms. Mechanical injuries (shown here) from wind abrasion and avocado thrips are common causes of similar-looking scars on fruit, but the methods for preventing these maladies are very different.

and pest distribution. Over the years, these records will provide valuable historical data that you can use as a basis for improving long-term grove management.

Monitoring Units. Conditions favoring pest development often vary within a grove and between neighboring groves. Differences such as tree age, rootstock cultivar, environmental conditions, and management history cause pests and disorders to differ from one location to another. Monitor each grove separately. Divide large or variable groves into several subsections and monitor these units separately. Mark the boundaries of any monitoring units (grove subsections) on a map and in the field, for instance with colored flagging or spray paint on tree trunks. Record the results for each grove or monitoring unit on a separate recordkeeping form.

Monitoring Pests. When and how often to monitor varies, depending for instance on the pest species, growing location, season, and the age of trees. Start sampling well before you expect populations to begin to build. Continue sampling through the pest's damaging stages.

Invertebrates need to be monitored only during certain times of the year, as summarized in Figure 9. On mature trees, certain invertebrates generally can be ignored (read under "Pests of Young Trees" in the sixth chapter, "Insects, Mites, and Other Invertebrates"). On both young and old trees, scout periodically throughout the year for diseases and disorders and for conditions that promote their development. Monitor for vertebrate pests and weeds regularly throughout the year when trees are young. Vertebrates and weeds generally constitute minor problems in mature groves, but even

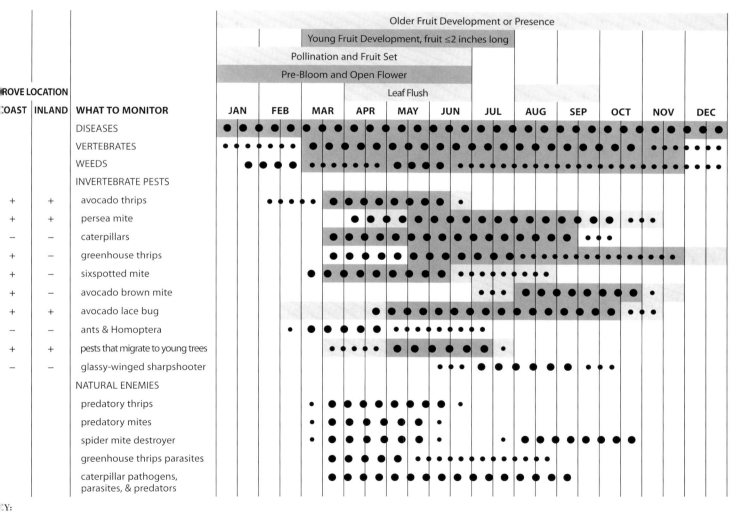

Figure 9. When to monitor for pests, damage, and key natural enemies in avocado. Consult the latest *Avocado: UC IPM Pest Management Guidelines* and *Avocado Year-Round IPM Program* online at www.ipm.ucdavis.edu for more current, well-illustrated information.

then monitoring for weeds at least twice a year (during mid-winter and late spring) and scouting for vertebrates at least during spring and summer can be helpful.

Specific quantitative sampling methods have been developed for certain invertebrates, including avocado thrips, caterpillars, and persea mite. More qualitative monitoring methods are suggested for diseases, vertebrates, weeds, and most other invertebrates. At a minimum, it is important that you note pests' presence and watch for changes in their status. Unless other methods are suggested, prepare a record once each quarter (fall, winter, spring, and summer) for each grove, noting the dominant pests and disorders and any other significant stresses. Correct identification of these problems is essential. For current monitoring recommendations and suggested recordkeeping forms, consult the latest update of *Avocado: UC IPM Pest Management Guidelines* and the *Avocado Year-Round IPM Program* online at www.ipm.ucdavis.edu.

Monitoring Weather. Weather greatly influences the development of avocado trees and their pests. Wetness from irrigation and rainfall is a primary factor favoring development of certain diseases. Temperature in particular controls the rate at which avocados, insects, and mites develop. For example, at warm temperatures persea mite can complete one generation in about 7 to 10 days, compared with a month or more if temperatures are cool. As average temperatures increase, invertebrate and pathogen damage can develop more quickly, monitoring may need to be more frequent, and control actions (when warranted) must be applied more promptly in order to prevent unacceptable damage. Daily temperatures recorded in degree-day (DD) units provide an accurate estimate of the number of days required for invertebrates such as avocado thrips, caterpillars, and persea mite to complete one generation, as discussed in the sixth chapter, "Insects, Mites, and Other Invertebrates."

Significant local variations in weather are common, especially variations in temperature and rainfall. A reliable source of local weather information is critical to decisions such as whether and when to protect trees from cold injury or how much irrigation water to apply, based on local rainfall and evapotranspiration data.

Many newspapers and radio stations provide local weather information. The National Weather Service broadcasts local and regional weather on NOAA Weather Radio, VHF channels 162.42, 162.50, and 162.55 MHz. Evapotranspiration information is available from the California Department of Water Resources' CIMIS program and from UC IPM online at www.ipm.ucdavis.edu.

For the most accurate weather data, set up a weather station in or near your grove. Instruments available for your use vary from simple maximum-minimum thermometers to electronic devices that continuously monitor and record weather information for transfer to a computer. More sophisticated stations transmit the data to a remote computer. Set up and maintain the weather instruments according to manufacturers' instructions. Calibrate the instruments regularly to ensure accuracy. Compare weather information to your other monitoring records to help plan your crop and pest management programs.

Year-Round IPM

Crop and pest management practices vary according to avocado growth development stage and time of year. You must also coordinate them with cultural practices (such as fertilization, irrigation, and harvest). Several pests—avocado root rot, mites, and avocado thrips, for example—must often be monitored and managed at the same time (see Figure 9). Each management practice can help prevent, or may

JACK KELLY CLARK

A reliable source of local weather information is critical to making good management decisions such as protecting trees from cold injury and when to schedule irrigations. This weather monitoring unit continuously checks the weather in the grove and automatically transmits information to a conveniently located, remote computer.

inadvertently cause, several different problems (see Table 1). The specific combination of practices that you need to integrate at any given time varies throughout the year.

This manual organizes information by practice, disorder, and pest species. This topical organization makes information easy to find in some ways, but it can make it difficult for advisors and growers to determine all the different actions that need to be taken and when. The *Avocado Year-Round IPM Program* online at www.ipm.ucdavis.edu addresses this need and so facilitates implementation of a comprehensive IPM program. This Internet service for advisors and growers presents the major activities you might need to conduct during each crop growth development period. The *Avocado Year-Round IPM Program* guides users through a full year cycle of monitoring pests, making management decisions, and planning for the following season. In addition to helping advisors and growers improve crop yield and tree health and better manage pests, this program shows users how to reduce water quality risks and other environmental problems.

On the Web, the *Avocado Year-Round IPM Program* links to

- detailed monitoring instructions that include decision thresholds
- monitoring checklists and forms to print and use for recordkeeping
- photo galleries to help you identify pests and beneficials seen while monitoring
- pesticide recommendations, which are not included in this manual
- a pesticide checklist to identify ways to prevent or minimize negative impacts of pesticide applications
- pest management guidelines, which identify management alternatives

Use this IPM for Avocados manual in combination with the latest update of *Avocado: UC IPM Pest Management Guidelines* and *Avocado Year-Round IPM Program* online at www.ipm.ucdavis.edu.

Control Action Guidelines

Growers and pest control professionals use control action guidelines, when available, to help decide whether management actions are necessary to prevent tree damage or fruit loss due to pests. Action guidelines are meaningful only when used in combination with careful field monitoring and accurate identification of pests and beneficials. For certain pests, such as avocado thrips and omnivorous looper, numerical thresholds have been developed that indicate economically damaging population levels, and these can be used as a basis for control action guidelines. Some monitoring guidelines, such as those for caterpillars and avocado brown mite, involve the assessment of population levels for pests and for beneficial species that act as biological control agents.

Numerical control action guidelines have been developed for certain pests, such as avocado thrips. You can use monitoring data on thrips abundance on succulent, young leaves to help you decide whether to treat before thrips move to feed on fruit when leaves harden.

There are no numerical guidelines for diseases, vertebrates, weeds, and most invertebrates, so treatment decisions for these are based on qualitative assessments of the problems. The extent of pest damage or infestation, the potential for effective and economical control, the time delay between the time you take a management action and the time that control becomes effective, the history of a grove or a region, the stage of crop development, and weather are among the factors to consider in deciding whether and when to act. Control action guidelines may change as new cultivars, cultural practices, and pests are introduced and as new information becomes available.

Management Methods

The best IPM program prevents pest outbreaks and provides long-term, economical control. Select an appropriate growing site and prepare the soil well before planting. Choose disease-tolerant rootstock cultivars. Plant certified, pathogen-free stock where available. Install and maintain an appropriate irrigation system. Use good methods to determine the appropriate amount and frequency of irrigation. Adjust scheduling to meet the trees' changing need for water. Apply and maintain a thick layer of coarse organic mulch beneath the trees. Conserve natural enemies, in part by using pesticides only when careful field monitoring indicates that an application is needed to prevent economic loss.

Site Selection and Preparation

Healthy, vigorous trees are best able to tolerate pests and stresses. Plant avocado trees only where they will be able to develop well, both above and below the ground. Availability of an adequate supply of good-quality irrigation water, a reasonable distance to a packinghouse, a ready supply of labor to help manage and harvest your crop, local weather history, and soil conditions are among the important considerations when choosing the grove location.

Avocado trees are less tolerant of cold, poor drainage, and salinity than most other California tree crops. Avocados do best when planted where soil is well-drained and not too alkaline and where they can be irrigated with water low in salts. Trees planted on upper slopes or hillsides generally have good drainage and a reduced risk of frost injury.

Before preparing the planting site, plan your pest management program and take actions to avoid common problems:

- Consult field records for cropping history, cultural practices, pesticide use, and problems with pests and soil conditions.
- Survey the site for weeds starting at least one year before planting. Perennial weeds in particular are easier to control before planting.

- Collect samples of irrigation water and soil and analyze them for alkalinity, overall salinity, and any specific ions that may be of concern.
- Check for soil compaction and poor drainage.
- Survey adjacent areas for pests that may move into the grove, including vertebrates such as deer, ground squirrels, rabbits, and voles that can seriously damage recently planted trees. Nearby abandoned groves or unmanaged vegetation may be sources of pest insects that you will want to take precautions against.

Many site problems, if you detect them before planting, can be overcome by careful preplant preparations. Preplant techniques include amending the soil, choosing rootstock cultivars that are resistant or tolerant to anticipated problems, and eradicating perennial weeds. Install subsurface drains and backhoe or rip through any impervious subsoils where warranted, especially if planting on lower slopes or

Good planting methods can prevent many pest problems and shorten the time required for young trees to begin bearing fruit. This tree was planted on a slight mound to improve drainage. Mulch applied near trunks helps to control weeds, conserve soil moisture, and reduce problems with avocado root rot.

Apply whitewash to the trunk and main limbs of all young trees at planting time to prevent sunburn.

Use cultivars with disease-resistant rootstock and, if available, obtain certified, pathogen-free stock. This avocado tree was killed by Dothiorella canker caused by infection of the graft union in the nursery. The young tree shown here died later, after it was planted.

valley floors, which often have subsurface layers that cause poor drainage. Properly grade sites and consider planting on a broad, raised mound or soil berm to improve drainage. If planting on raised soil, loosen and otherwise properly prepare subsurface layers so roots can penetrate the soil beneath mounds to anchor the trees well and avoid tipping trunks. Be aware that by moving soil you can spread pathogen and weed propagules that persist in the soil and so induce these pests to develop into problems, such as by causing weeds to germinate by exposing their buried seeds to light. Coordinate preplanting pest management with other site preparation operations, such as installing an efficient irrigation system that is carefully designed and maintained for the climatic and physical conditions of the site.

Rootstock Cultivar Selection

Most scion cultivars grown commercially in California are Hass avocados. Many different rootstocks are available, and rootstock cultivar selection is a critical planning decision. The rootstock choice affects management practices, pest problems, and fruit yield and profits throughout the life of the grove. Your grove's irrigation water quality, local climate, and soil characteristics will affect your choice of rootstock cultivar. Certain rootstock cultivars are resistant to or more tolerant of Dothiorella canker, frost, Phytophthora canker, Phytophthora root rot, and salinity (Table 2). Because a rootstock cultivar that is resistant to one problem may be more susceptible to another, consider planting a mixture of the recommended rootstock cultivars. Consult your Cooperative Extension farm advisor or avocado propagators for the latest information on suitable rootstocks.

Table 2. Rootstock Cultivars, Origin, and Approximate Pathogen and Stress Susceptibility.

Origin, pathogen, or stressor	Barr Duke	Borchard	Duke 7	Duke 9	Dusa (Merensky 2)	G-6	Lula	Latas (Merensky 1)	Martin Grande[1]	Thomas	Topa Topa	Toro Canyon	Uzi (PP15)	Zentmyer (PP4)
Cultivar[2]	Mex	Mex	Mex	Mex	Mex × G	Mex	G × WI	Mex × G	×[1]	Mex	Mex	Mex	Mex	Mex
Propagation	clonal	clonal	clonal	clonal	clonal	seed	seed	clonal	clonal	clonal	seed	clonal	clonal	clonal
Phytophthora cinnamomi	3.5	0.5	3	3.5	5	2	?	4.5	5	4.5	0	2.5	5	5
Phytophthora citricola	3	3	4	4	?	3	?	?	3	2	3	5	4	3
Dothiorella	5	5	5	5	5	2	?	5	?	2	5	5	3	4
Salinity	2	3	3	3	4	2	?	5	2	1	2	3	4	1
Frost	4.5	4.5	4	4.5	4.5	4.5	1	4.5	1	4.5	4.5	4.5	?	5

Key: 0 = poor or least tolerant, 5 = best or most tolerant, ? = information unknown
1. Martin Grande (also identified as G755A,B,C) is a hybrid of *Persea americana* × *P. schiedeana*.
2. Cultivar or horticultural race is Mex = Mexican, G = Guatemalan, WI = West Indian, × = a hybrid of cultivars or species.
Relative tolerance ratings are approximate and based on observations and studies under a variety of field and greenhouse conditions.
Ratings of newer rootstocks are preliminary; check with your advisor or supplier for the latest information on rootstock tolerances. Adapted from: Bender, Menge, and Arpaia 2003.

Excluding Foreign Pests

Many of our worst pests were carelessly introduced from other states or countries. Exotic (foreign) pests cause major problems for avocado growers. Until the 1990s when avocado thrips and persea mite were inadvertently introduced into California, invertebrates caused only occasional damage to avocado fruit and trees. The Caribbean, Central America, Florida, and Mexico have many avocado pests that do not naturally occur in California. For example, avocado lace bug has been a pest in the Caribbean and Florida for many years, but it only became established in San Diego in 2004. Exotic fruit flies such as Mexican fruit fly and Mediterranean fruit fly are discovered periodically in California and have been eradicated many times.

New pests are introduced during trade and travel. Do not bring uncertified fruit, plants, or soil into California. Vegetative avocado plant parts are likely to pose a much greater risk of introducing exotic pests than are legally imported fruit. Buy stock only from reputable, local sources. Report suspected fruit or plant smugglers to local authorities. Take any unfamiliar pests to your county agricultural commissioner or Cooperative Extension office for identification. Telephone 1-800-491-1899 or visit www.cdfa.ca.gov/phpps for more information on exotic pests.

Clean bins, equipment, and vehicles before bringing them in from another area to avoid introducing certain pests. Fruit rot decay fungi, soilborne pathogens, weed propagules, and insects such as giant whitefly and weevils can arrive on the debris in dirty bins like this one.

Sanitation

Sanitation reduces the buildup and spread of insects, pathogens, vertebrates, and weeds. Obtain certified, pathogen-free nursery stock if possible. Diseased nursery stock historically has been a major source of pathogens that cause Dothiorella canker and Phytophthora root rot. To avoid spreading the Phytophthora root rot pathogen, stay out of groves when the soil is wet. Prevent movement of soil or water from contaminated areas to uninfested areas of the grove. Clean all equipment and bins brought in from other areas to avoid introducing insects, pathogens, and weeds. If you find a small infestation of a perennial weed in or around the grove, eradicate it before it spreads throughout the grove. Manage vegetation in and near groves to reduce problems with invertebrates that move from weeds to damage young trees. Reduce debris and weeds to minimize vertebrate cover and habitat. Remove abandoned citrus trees to reduce the likelihood that insects such as amorbia, glassy-winged sharpshooter, and orange tortrix will move from citrus into nearby avocado groves.

Mulch

Mulch is a layer of material covering the soil. Mulching beneath trees conserves soil moisture, controls weeds by excluding sunlight, and moderates the root-growing environment. By applying coarse organic material beneath the tree canopy, you reduce the incidence of Phytophthora root rot, the most important disease of avocado. Mulching may also reduce the incidence and severity of stress-related diseases and disorders such as black streak. Mite damage may be reduced because of the decrease in dust and drought stress that occurs with mulch. Where substantial organic material is added beyond the avocados' own dropped tree leaves, the survival of avocado thrips pupating in soil declines, perhaps helping to control this serious fruit pest.

Apply a thick layer of coarse organic mulch when trees are planted, keeping it several inches away from the trunk. Reapply mulch periodically during at least the first few years of tree growth or whenever the mulch becomes thin. Prevent mulch from blowing or washing away. Provide trees with appropriate cultural care and good growing conditions to keep them healthy so they will develop a dense canopy, which as the trees mature naturally provides mulch when leaves drop. See under "Mulch" in the seventh chapter, "Weeds," for more information.

Vegetation Management

Noncrop plants in and around groves can both cause problems and provide benefits. Weeds compete with trees for water and nutrients, primarily during the grove's early years of growth. Weeds can harbor pests such as rodents and snails (increasing damage to trees) and increase wildfire hazards.

Grove vegetation also provides many benefits, such as controlling soil erosion, improving water infiltration, and reducing movement of potential contaminants offsite into surface water. Vegetation provides alternative hosts and shelter for parasites and predators of invertebrate pests and reduces dust that can favor mite outbreaks and disrupt the effectiveness of natural enemies. Cover crops can be especially beneficial in young groves, among older trees that have been extensively pruned, on slopes, and when managed as vegetative filter strips along borders and roads

A cover crop consists of the resident vegetation (the least expensive choice), one or more seeded annual species (such as commercially available self-seeding mixes), or both resident and seeded vegetation. Competition from desirable cover crop species helps keep weedy species from building up, and in addition helps manage soil and water problems and certain pests. Primarily when trees are young, cover crops require good management to minimize

their competition with trees for nutrients and moisture and to minimize the need for additional water. Cover crops may increase the frost hazard, especially in low-lying areas, and may also favor buildup of certain pests that primarily damage young trees, including pocket gophers, voles, and snails. See the "Cover Crops" section in the seventh chapter, "Weeds," for more information.

Irrigation

Proper irrigation is critical for improving tree health and preventing and managing many diseases and disorders. Irrigation also affects weeds and certain invertebrates, such as mite outbreaks that occur more frequently under drought stress conditions. Irrigating too frequently or applying excessive amounts of water promotes Phytophthora root rot and directly injures trees by asphyxiating (suffocating)

Manage grove vegetation to control soil erosion, improve water infiltration, and reduce offsite movement of potential water contaminants. When trees are young, control weeds near trunks to minimize competition for water and nutrients.

Erosion causes loss of valuable topsoil and contaminates a stream (not visible here) at the base of this slope. Maintaining resident vegetation or a planted cover crop in between rows and good irrigation management can minimize these problems. Soil berms around the dripline to retain dropped leaves as mulch and culverts to divert runoff are also good options when growing avocados on steep slopes.

roots. Avoid directly wetting trunks and minimize soil waterlogging to reduce problems with Phytophthora canker and crown rot.

Schedule the frequency and amount of irrigation using reliable methods, such as basing your decisions on local evapotranspiration and soil moisture monitored with tensiometers or other effective devices. Modify your irrigation schedule according to the trees' changing needs for water. Periodically test water quality and use high-quality irrigation water without high overall salinity or an excess of specific minerals. Regularly inspect and adjust irrigation systems to provide good uniformity among emitters. Read the "Water Management" section in the fourth chapter, "Cultural Practices and Abiotic Disorders," for more information.

Fertilization

Modest amounts of nitrogen and occasional applications of potassium, phosphorus, and zinc (and perhaps boron at some locations) generally make up the only fertilization needed to promote avocado tree health and good fruit yield. Do not apply unneeded minor nutrients, as this can induce deficiencies of other nutrients. Avoid applying too much nitrogen: it can reduce fruit yield and pollute water. Excess fertilization, especially if you use quick-release nitrogen formulations, may increase avocado thrips populations and damage during late spring and summer in response to the increased leaf flush promoted by excess foliar nitrogen. When nutrient deficiency symptoms do occur, determine whether the actual cause is some problem other than a simple lack of nutrients. Unhealthy roots (resulting from inappropriate irrigation, Phytophthora root rot, and waterlogging of soil, for instance)

Pale new growth may be due to nitrogen deficiency. However, discolored foliage is most often caused by adverse soil conditions or unhealthy roots. Determine the actual cause of symptoms so you can select effective management actions.

and undesirable soil pH levels are common problems that prevent roots from absorbing adequate amounts of nutrients, even when they are present in sufficient quantities in the soil. Read the "Fertilization" and "Nutrient and Mineral Disorders" sections in the fourth chapter, "Cultural Practices and Abiotic Disorders," for more information.

Pruning

Pruning can help you control certain diseases and insects, but it can also increase some diseases and disorders, depending on when and how you prune. Prune to develop tree structure, limit tree height, improve air circulation and spray penetration, and remove dead and dying wood. To reduce pathogen infection of fresh pruning wounds, prune only when trees are dry. Where caterpillars, greenhouse thrips, or mealybugs are a problem, prune and thin the trees' canopies to reduce protected sites and canopy bridges that facilitate the pests' survival and movement between trees. If fruit rots have been a problem, prune away branches within about 3 feet (90 cm) of the ground to reduce pathogen propagules that splash up from the soil. Remove suckers only by cutting them above ground level, and then treat the pruning wound to prevent infections that can lead to Phytophthora canker and crown rot. Disinfect your pruning tools periodically, such as after you finish work on each tree, to avoid spreading pathogens on your equipment. Be aware that severe pruning may expose the bark and fruit to sunburn damage or induce expression of sunblotch viroid damage in trees that have been symptomless carriers.

Avocado is less tolerant of salinity than most other California tree crops. The marginal necrosis and white residue on these leaves near sprinkler emitters indicate low-quality irrigation water. Salty water can directly damage trees and increase stress-related maladies such as avocado black streak.

Pruning too severely often leads to extensive trunk and root decay, which causes trees to die within a few years despite temporary regrowth that appears healthy. Pruning can help to control certain pests or increase some diseases and disorders, depending on when and how it is performed.

Harvesting

Do not pick avocados when trees are wet, as wetness reduces the fruit's storage life. If caterpillars, greenhouse thrips, or mealybugs are a problem, you can reduce the potential for damage by selectively harvesting the larger fruit in each cluster and any fruit that touch leaves. The earlier the harvest, the less damage greenhouse thrips can cause to harvested fruit and the less damage they will cause to the next season's crop. Instruct pickers to clip off any fruit stems and cut them short to reduce the likelihood of mechanical injury to fruit and to prevent puncture wounds that promote fruit rots. Handle the harvested fruit gently and do not allow it to touch the ground. Shade the fruit in bins to prevent sunburn, but do not shade it with clipped avocado foliage as this may favor the spread of certain pests that move off the leaves and disperse to different parts of the grove or to other groves along the shipping route when you move the bins.

Biological Control

Biological control is the action of competitors, parasites, pathogens, and predators to control pests and reduce damage. Most insects and mites in avocado are usually suppressed by natural enemies, so they rarely cause economic damage. Notable exceptions are avocado thrips and persea mite. Predators apparently play a relatively minor role in keeping vertebrate pest populations low in avocados. The importance of natural enemies in pathogen control is not well known. See Table 3 for a list of common natural enemies that attack pest insects and mites in avocado.

Augmentation, conservation, and classical biological control are three tactics for using natural enemies. Augmentation is the purchase and release of commercially

Postharvest fruit quality is enhanced by good harvesting techniques. Pick only when trees are dry. Handle fruit gently. Do not allow fruit to touch the ground, where it can become contaminated.

Table 3. Pests with Complete or Substantial Biological Control and Their Major Natural Enemies in Avocado.

PEST		
Common name	Scientific name	Natural enemies
amorbia	*Amorbia cuneana*	*Eumea caesar*,[1] *Nilea erecta*,[1] NPV,[2] *Trichogramma* spp.
avocado brown mite	*Oligonychus punicae*	*Euseius hibisci*,[3] *Galendromus helveolus*,[3] *Stethorus picipes*[4]
brown garden snail	*Cantareus aspersus=Helix aspersa*	*Rumina decollata*[5]
black scale	*Saissetia oleae*	Coccinellidae,[4] *Coccophagus*, *Metaphycus* spp., *Scutellista caerulea*
giant whitefly	*Aleurodicus dugesii*	*Encarsiella noyesi*, *Entedononecremnus krauteri*, *Idioporus affinis*
greenhouse thrips	*Heliothrips haemorrhoidalis*	*Megaphragma mymaripenne*, *Thripobius semiluteus*
latania scale	*Hemiberlesia lataniae*	*Aphytis*, *Aspidiotiphagus*, *Comperiella*, *Signiphora* spp., Coccinellidae[4]
longtailed mealybug	*Pseudococcus longispinus*	*Anarhopus sydneyensis*
mulberry whitefly	*Tetraleurodes mori*	*Cales noacki*, various predators
omnivorous looper	*Sabulodes aegrotata*	*Apanteles caberatae*, granulosis virus, *Habrobracon xanthonotus*, *Meteorus tersus*, spiders, *Trichogramma* spp.
orange tortrix	*Argyrotaenia citrana*	*Apanteles aristoteliae*, *Exochus nigripalpis*,[1] *Trichogramma* spp.
redbanded whitefly	*Tetraleurodes perseae*	*Cales noacki*
sixspotted mite	*Eotetranychus sexmaculatus*	*Amblyseius limonicus*, *Galendromus helveolus*, *Euseius hibisci*, *Stethorus picipes*,[4] *Scolothrips sexmaculatus*[6]

Other potential pests (e.g., scales and whiteflies) occur at low densities in avocado, perhaps due to biological control, but the importance of their natural enemies is undocumented in avocado. Commercially available natural enemies that may be effective when released in avocado include green lacewings (*Chrysoperla* spp.), mealybug destroyer lady beetle (*Cryptolaemus montrouzieri*), moth egg parasitic wasp (*Trichogramma platneri*), and predaceous mites (*Galendromus* spp., *Neoseiulus californicus*).
The natural enemies are parasitic wasps except as indicated.
1. parasitic fly
2. nuclear polyhedrosis virus
3. predatory mite
4. lady beetle
5. predatory snail
6. predatory thrips

available beneficials. When resident natural enemies are insufficient, releases of *Trichogramma* egg parasites can control the subsequent caterpillar populations. Predatory mite releases help to control pest mites. See the sixth chapter, "Insects, Mites, and Other Invertebrates," for more discussion.

Classical biological control (sometimes called importation) involves the foreign collection and local release and establishment of exotic natural enemies. Many organisms that are not pests in their native habitats become unusually abundant when they are unintentionally introduced into new areas where their native natural enemies do not occur. Many of the natural enemies listed in Table 3 were deliberately imported. By law, importation can only be done by qualified university or government scientists using strict quarantine procedures. Before they make any releases in the new country, researchers use field research in the native habitat and controlled tests in quarantine facilities to confirm that the natural enemies are beneficial and will have little or no negative impact. Industry and taxpayer financial and political support are critical for the success of classical biological control.

Conservation. Preservation of resident natural enemies is the most important biological control method. Many naturally occurring parasites and predators are easily disrupted by pesticide applications, and this can result in outbreaks of pests

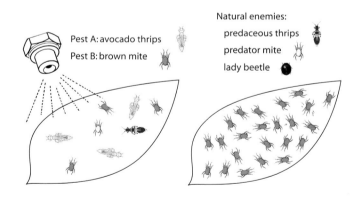

Figure 10. Disruption of biological control often results in secondary outbreaks of insects and mites. For example, many potential pests such as avocado brown mite are present on leaves at low densities but become abundant and cause damage only when ants, dust, or broad-spectrum pesticides prevent natural enemies from being effective. Here a nonselective, persistent pesticide applied for avocado thrips (Pest A) also killed predaceous thrips, predatory mites, and the spider mite destroyer lady beetle (*Stethorus*), leading to a secondary outbreak of avocado brown mite (Pest B).

such as caterpillars, mealybugs, mites, scales, and whiteflies (Figure 10). Make limited and carefully considered use of pesticides, as discussed below. Carefully select the location, material, method, rate, and timing of any insecticide or miticide application so the treatment will be least disruptive to natural enemies.

To improve your overall IPM program, choose pesticides that have the least impact on natural enemies, as summarized in Table 4. Use the most selective and shortest residual (least-persistent) materials when possible. Make spot applications if feasible to minimize harm to nontarget species and provide unsprayed reservoirs from which beneficials can recolonize trees. An occasional, single application of broad-spectrum pesticides is less harmful to natural enemies than multiple broad-spectrum treatments.

Minimize dust in the grove. Dusty conditions reduce the reproduction and host-finding ability of many natural enemies, and this in turn causes outbreaks of pests such as mites and scales and other Homoptera (plant juice-sucking pests). Control ants if Homoptera are a problem. Ants tend Homoptera and will attack any natural enemies they encounter.

See the sixth chapter, "Insects, Mites, and Other Invertebrates," for more discussion of biological control and photographs of important natural enemies. Consult the *Natural Enemies Handbook* (Flint and Dreistadt 1998) for more details on biological control.

Most pest insects in avocado groves are under good biological control. This omnivorous looper has been killed by the gregarious, externally feeding larvae of the parasitic wasp, *Habrobracon* (=*Bracon*) *xanthonotus*. Many insects in avocado become problems only when their natural enemies are killed by pesticides applied to control other pests such as thrips or mites.

Table 4. Insecticide and Miticide Groups and Relative Toxicity to Natural Enemies and Pests in Avocado.

Material (with example trade names)	Group[1]	Range of activity[2]	Pests targeted	Natural enemies affected	Persistence[3]
abamectin (Agri-Mek)	M	intermediate	avocado thrips, persea mite	predatory thrips, predaceous mites	long
Bacillus thuringiensis, Bt	M	narrow	caterpillars	none	short
copper bands	CON	narrow	brown garden snail	none	long
imidacloprid	N	intermediate	glassy-winged sharpshooter, Homoptera	some beneficial insects	long
iron phosphate (Sluggo)	IO	narrow	snails and slugs	predatory decollate snail	short
malathion	OP	broad	chinch bug, Fuller rose beetle, grasshoppers, greenhouse thrips, June beetles	beneficial insects and mites	intermediate
metaldehyde (Deadline)	A	narrow	snails and slugs	predatory decollate snail	intermediate
oil, narrow-range	CON	broad	avocado lace bug, mites, scales	unprotected stages of beneficial insects and mites	short
pyrethrin (PyGanic)	B	broad	grasshoppers, greenhouse thrips	insects	short
sabadilla (Veratran-D)	B	narrow	avocado thrips, greenhouse thrips	few	short
spinosad (Success, Entrust)	M	narrow	avocado thrips	some predatory insects[4]	intermediate
sticky materials	CON	narrow	trunk climbers, e.g., ants, Fuller rose beetle	few	long
sulfur	IO	narrow	mites, thrips	beneficial insects and mites	intermediate

Pesticide registrations change. Determine which pesticides are currently legal and recommended before you make any applications. For current information, consult the county agricultural commissioner, product labels, and the *Avocado: UC IPM Pest Management Guidelines* online at www.ipm.ucdavis.edu.

1. Group = Pesticides in the same group may have the same mode of action (the way they kill pests), and pests resistant to one of these pesticides may be resistant to all pesticides in that group (called cross-resistance). The same mode of action does not apply to at least some materials within broad generic groups such as contact (CON), inorganic (IO), and microbials (M). Where pesticide resistance may be a problem, consult the latest *Avocado: UC IPM Pest Management Guidelines* (online at www.ipm.ucdavis.edu) and the sources of detailed information on pesticide groups: FRAC (2005), HRAC (2005), and IRAC (2005) listed in Literature Cited.

2. Range of Activity = the degree of selectivity for that material, the group of organisms primarily affected by the treatment.

3. Persistence = the length of time a material remains effective or toxic, categorized as short (days), intermediate (a few weeks), or long (many weeks or months).

4. Toxic against some natural enemies (predatory thrips, syrphid fly larvae) when sprayed and shortly thereafter (8–24 hours).

KEY
A = acetaldehyde
B = botanical
CON = contact including smothering or barrier effect
IO = inorganic
M = microbial by-products and pathogens
N = chloronicotinyl nitroguanidine
OP = organophosphate

Avocado groves are home to many general predators that help to prevent most invertebrates from becoming pests. This larva of the multicolored Asian lady beetle, *Harmonia axyridis*, preys on a variety of pests, including aphids, mites, scales, and whiteflies.

Pesticides are valuable IPM tools, but materials must be carefully selected and applied to achieve desired pest control and minimize disruptions of natural enemy populations.

Pesticides

Within an IPM program, pesticides are valuable tools because they can drastically reduce pest populations or prevent further damage within a short time after application. Where pests are expected to cause economic damage soon or have already reached damaging levels, pesticides may be the only effective tools available. Treat for specific pests only when monitoring indicates that economically damaging populations are present or anticipated.

Pesticides include fungicides, herbicides, insecticides, miticides (also called acaricides), and rodenticides. Pesticides belong to a variety of chemical groups with very different properties (Table 4). To control one pest, often you can choose among several active ingredients or several different formulations that contain the same active ingredient. You may also be able to select one chemical to control several pests at the same time, or mix compatible materials together. The choice will depend on the degree of control you need, the effect on beneficial species and other pests, and various economic and legal restrictions. Where possible, choose the material that is least disruptive to biological control.

The microbial insecticide *Bacillus thuringiensis* (Bt) is desirable in IPM programs because it selectively kills caterpillars that ingest it and is nontoxic to natural enemies and nontarget species. Certain insecticides that are toxic only when pests eat treated foliage (materials without contact toxicity) and commercially available predators and parasites also have a relatively narrow range of toxicity (Table 4). Pesticides that are broad-spectrum (i.e., they kill many types of organisms) but have little or no persistence can be considered "soft" pesticides because they are less harmful to nontarget species than other, more-persistent broad-spectrum "hard" pesticides. See the "Pesticides" section in the sixth chapter, "Insects, Mites and Other Invertebrates," for a discussion of the differences between some specific pesticides available to avocado growers.

Using Pesticides Effectively. Try to apply a pesticide when the target pest is at its most vulnerable state and when natural enemies are least likely to be affected. For example, when treating weeds after emergence, make sure they are at the growth stage recommended on the pesticide label. When applying baits for vertebrates such as ground squirrels, make sure it is a time of year when the pests are active and likely to feed on bait. Correct application is critical for effective control. Calibrate the equipment properly and place the chemical selectively where possible. Use the correct dosages. The recommended dosage (rate) and frequency of application given on the pesticide label may be higher than necessary for good control when properly timed and applied. In many cases, an herbicide's application rate must be adjusted for soil type, climatic conditions, and irrigation method. Consult your farm advisor for the lowest effective dosage and best application method for the pest problem in your grove.

Before choosing a pesticide, check the latest update of *Avocado: UC IPM Pest Management Guidelines* available on the internet at www.ipm.ucdavis.edu. Always read the pesticide label. The label lists legal requirements, registered uses for each product, and required safety precautions.

Problems Associated with Pesticides

The attributes that make a pesticide a valuable tool can in some circumstances cause problems that impede the success of an IPM program. Problems include the development of pesticide resistance, pest resurgence, and secondary pest outbreaks. Pesticide applications may also affect nearby crops, wildlife, and human health.

Pesticide Resistance. Repeated use of a pesticide promotes resistance by selecting for (i.e., favoring the survival and reproduction of) pest individuals that are less susceptible to the pesticide (Figure 11). Resistance renders ineffective any subsequent treatments of that pesticide or of other pesticides that have the same mode of action (the same way of killing pests). Resistance is especially likely to develop in populations of pests that reproduce rapidly, including insects, mites, and pathogens. Although it is less common, resistance also occurs in some weed species. The development of resistance is an acute problem in a crop for which only a limited number of pesticides are available, as is the case for avocado.

To slow the development of resistance, use control methods other than pesticides where feasible. Limit pesticide applications to only when needed. When you do apply pesticides, alternate (rotate) applications among several pesticides with different modes of action, as described in resources such as *Fungicides Sorted by Modes of Action* (FRAC 2005), *Classification of Herbicides According to Mode of Action* (HRAC 2005), and *Classification of Insecticides According to Mode of Action* (IRAC 2005), listed in the suggested reading. Limit the frequency of application and keep the area treated to a minimum. Leave some areas unsprayed to allow survival of beneficials as well as some untreated pests that can then be available to breed with pesticide-resistant pests, reducing the overall rate at which resistance develops.

Pest Resurgence. Pest resurgence is the rapid rebuilding of a pest population that was recently controlled by a pesticide application. Resurgence is a problem particularly in pest populations that have a short reproductive cycle, such as mites. If faced with resurgence populations, you may have to spray repeatedly, increasing both your production costs and the chances for secondary pest outbreaks and the development of pesticide-resistant pests.

Secondary Pest Outbreak. When a pesticide applied to control the target pest unintentionally causes the buildup of insects or mites that were previously controlled by natural enemies, this is termed a secondary pest outbreak (see Figure 10). Avocado brown mite, caterpillars, scales, and whiteflies are among the species that usually are present at innocuous population levels, but are likely to become problems after certain materials applied for other pests unintentionally eliminate natural enemies of these nontarget, potential pests. To reduce the chances for pest resurgence and secondary pest outbreak, choose selective materials when possible. Time your applications to be most destructive to the pest species but least destructive to beneficial species.

Hazards to Honey Bees. Certain insecticides used in avocado groves are toxic to honey bees and naturally occurring native pollinators. When avocado trees are in bloom or bees are in the grove, choose insecticides that are least toxic to bees. Apply sprays early in the morning or late in the evening when honey bees are less active. If you must apply an insecticide that is toxic to bees, check with your county agricultural commissioner's office to find out about any application restrictions intended to protect bees and to find out whether there are beekeepers in your area that should be informed of your scheduled spraying. Consult the latest update of *Avocado: UC IPM Pest Management Guidelines* (available online at www.ipm.ucdavis.edu) for information on the toxicity of various pesticides to bees.

Hazards to Water Quality and Wildlife. Pesticides applied to avocado groves may harm wildlife if runoff or spray drift contaminates water or nearby natural areas. The Federal Clean Water Act requires a written plan (called a Total Maximum Daily Load or TMDL) for every water body that is impaired

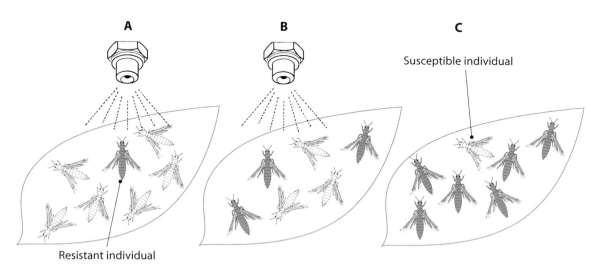

Figure 11. Resistance to pesticides develops through genetic selection in populations of pests, including insects, mites, pathogens, and weeds. A. Certain individuals in a pest population are naturally less susceptible to a pesticide than other individuals. B. These less-susceptible pest biotypes are more likely to survive an application and to produce progeny that are also less susceptible. C. After repeated applications over several generations, the pest population consists primarily of resistant or less-susceptible individuals. Applying the same pesticide or other chemicals with the same mode of action is no longer effective.

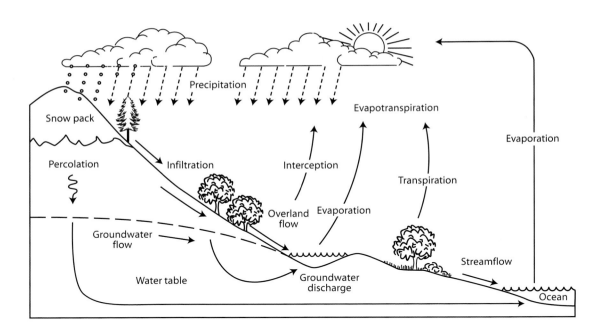

Figure 12. Pesticides and fertilizers applied in groves can contaminate groundwater or surface water by moving, as shown here by the hydrologic cycle. Avoid contamination by making good application decisions, carefully managing irrigation, and using cultural methods such as untreated buffers and vegetative filter strips to minimize offsite movement. *Adapted from:* M. Padgett-Johnson and T. Bedell 2002.

and does not meet water quality standards. Many California rivers and creeks are impaired. Managing the offsite movement of soil and water is recommended, and may even be required, especially for groves in watersheds with impaired waterways (Figure 12). Take special precautions, select less-harmful materials, or avoid using pesticides where runoff or spray drift is likely to contaminate nearby bodies of water or sensitive wildlife habitat areas. Stay informed about regulations that are designed to protect water supplies and wildlife in your area: sources of information include the California State Water Resources Control Board and your Regional Water Quality Control Board. Advice or funding to help you reduce the offsite movement of materials may be available from the federal Natural Resources Conservation Service (NRCS) or your local Resource Conservation District.

In areas where endangered species or protected wildlife species occur, special guidelines apply to the types of pesticides you can use and the ways you can apply them. A bulletin is available for each county in California, listing that county's endangered species, mapping their locations, and providing the specific guidelines for using pesticides near endangered species habitat. These bulletins are available from the Department of Pesticide Regulation (DPR) Web site (www. cdpr.ca.gov/docs/es/index.htm) or from your county agricultural commissioner. Consult Table 5 for summary guidelines to help you prevent adverse effects from pesticides used near sensitive wildlife habitat. Wildlife protection guidelines that apply when you use rodenticides are discussed in the eighth chapter, "Vertebrates."

Air Pollution. Air quality is below state and federal standards in much of California. Agricultural practices can contribute to air pollution. For instance, various cultural operations can generate respirable particulates that cause lung damage. Certain pesticides (fumigants and emulsifiable concentrate [EC] formulations), vehicles, and livestock waste emit volatile organic compounds (VOCs). VOCs and nitrogen oxides combine with sunlight to form ozone. Ozone present at ground level can reduce crop yields and harm human health, causing respiratory irritation and sicknesses.

The federal Clean Air Act requires that each state develop an implementation plan to improve air quality and meet air quality standards, including limits on ozone in the lower atmosphere. DPR and the California Air Resources Board are reducing VOC emissions from pesticides through research, regulations, and education to promote alternatives to VOC-generating practices.

Employ IPM techniques to minimize pesticide use. Especially avoid using soil fumigants. When you are selecting among pesticides, consider applying formulations other than emulsifiable concentrates. To the extent that it is compatible with your other IPM goals, minimize the size of the treatment area, reduce application rates, and use methods that minimize volatilization—for instance, apply materials through drip or low-volume irrigation systems instead of using aerial application or foliar sprays. If pests can be effectively controlled at various times of the year, consider avoiding applications during seasons or weather conditions when air quality is poor; instead, make applications when air quality is good.

Exposed roots indicate that erosion has caused the soil grade around this young tree to drop about 1 foot (30 cm). Consult the federal Natural Resources Conservation Service (NRCS) or your local Resource Conservation District for advice and possibly funding to help reduce erosion and runoff.

Avocados are often grown near to or up slope from riparian areas. Drift, erosion, and runoff can pollute water with fertilizers, pesticides, and soil unless groves and their borders are well managed.

Table 5. Guidelines to Prevent Adverse Effects of Fungicides, Herbicides, or Insecticides Used near Sensitive Wildlife Habitat.

☐ Avoid pesticide use in occupied habitat. Herbicides may be used in organized habitat recovery programs or for selective control of invasive exotic plants.

☐ Irrigate efficiently to prevent excessive erosion or runoff.

☐ Schedule irrigations and pesticide applications to maximize the amount of time between the pesticide application and the first subsequent irrigation.

☐ Allow at least 24 hours between pesticide application and an irrigation that may result in surface runoff into natural bodies of water.

☐ Time pesticide applications to allow aerial or foliar sprays to dry before rain or sprinkler irrigation.

☐ When air is calm or moving away from nearby wildlife habitat, begin spray or dust applications on the side of the grove nearest the habitat. When air is moving toward nearby habitat, do not make an aerial spray or dust application within 200 yards of the habitat or a ground application within 40 yards of the habitat. The probability of drift into nearby habitat (and the size of untreated buffer strip needed) can be reduced by intervening physical barriers such as hedgerows and windbreaks.

☐ Do not apply pesticide within 30 yards uphill of wildlife habitat unless a suitable method is used to contain or divert runoff.

☐ Provide a buffer strip of at least 20 feet of vegetation that is not treated with pesticides along rivers, streams, wetlands, vernal pools, stock ponds, and the downhill side of groves from which runoff may occur. The buffer can be unsprayed border rows of trees or borders of managed resident weeds or cover crops.

☐ Prepare the land to contain as much runoff as possible within the grove site, such as by creating soil berms.

☐ Mix pesticides in areas not prone to runoff, such as concrete pads, flat, disked soil, or gravel mixing pads, or use methods that contain spills and rinses.

☐ Triple-rinse and properly empty, store, and dispose of all pesticide containers.

Consult the "Vertebrates" chapter for wildlife protection guidelines when using rodenticides.

Table 6. Pesticide Safe Use Tips.

☐ Read labels before purchasing a pesticide and read the label again before using a pesticide.

☐ Select the right pesticide.

☐ Learn and follow all applicable regulations.

☐ Confirm the availability of emergency health care.

☐ Train mixers, applicators, handlers, and other workers.

☐ Transport pesticides safely.

☐ Wear appropriate personal protective equipment.

☐ Mix pesticides properly.

☐ Use appropriate application equipment.

☐ Apply pesticides safely.

☐ Plan for accidents.

☐ Clean any spills immediately.

☐ Dispose of containers properly.

☐ Keep good records.

For more details, consult *The Safe and Effective Use of Pesticides* (O'Connor-Marer 2000) and *Pesticide Safety: A Reference Manual for Private Applicators* (O'Connor-Marer and Cohen 2006).

Hazards to Humans. All pesticides are toxic (poisonous) in some way at a sufficient dose. Persons who handle, mix, and apply pesticides are the most heavily exposed, and they may be at risk of acute poisoning or chronic ailments. Employers must ensure that workers who apply, handle, or mix pesticides have been properly trained. Follow label directions and always use pesticides safely, as summarized in Table 6. Choose wisely how and when to apply pesticides. Select from among the least-hazardous pesticides available for your situation. Take steps to reduce drift and avoid water contamination, such as by checking and adjusting equipment calibration and nozzles and ensuring that the wind speed and direction are acceptable.

Every pesticide label has a signal word indicating its relative hazard of immediate or acute injury. The signal words are CAUTION (the least hazardous), WARNING, and DANGER. DANGER, the most hazardous, often includes a skull and crossbones and may also be labeled POISON. Pesticides labeled DANGER generally are available only to certified applicators and require special equipment, precautions, and training for use.

In addition to acute hazards, certain pesticides are suspected of causing long-term health problems. This type of information is not provided on the label, but you can find it on the material's Material Safety Data Sheet (MSDS). A MSDS is available for each pesticide, detailing its potential hazards. One way to obtain the MSDS is to input the pesticide's name and the abbreviation "MSDS" in an Internet search engine.

The restricted-entry interval (REI) is the required number of hours or days after application during which entry into treated areas is prohibited or restricted. REI regulations help minimize human exposure to pesticides. Consult your agricultural commissioner for the latest information on REIs and pesticide safety.

Cultural Practices and Abiotic Disorders

An abiotic (nonliving) or noninfectious disorder is caused by inappropriate cultural care or adverse environmental conditions. Certain abiotic disorders are often unavoidable or chronic because growers have a limited ability to manipulate the environment. However, plant damage from many noninfectious disorders and pest problems is preventable or manageable if you select an appropriate growing site, modify the site before planting, choose tolerant rootstock cultivars, and optimize cultural practices as summarized here and in the third chapter, "Managing Pests in Avocados." The most critical strategy for improving yield and avoiding damage to fruit and trees is to monitor and provide the basic requirements for tree growth (Figure 13).

The most common abiotic disorders affecting avocado are water- and soil-related problems, including inappropriate amount and frequency of irrigation, poor water placement, soil compaction, inadequate drainage, and excess salinity. Nutrient disorders, fire, frost, genetic disorders, herbicides and other pesticides, mechanical injury, and sunburn are also discussed in this chapter. In addition to causing direct damage to trees or fruit, many abiotic disorders increase avocados' susceptibility to pathogens such as canker diseases and Phytophthora root rot. Invertebrates such as borers, phloem-sucking Homoptera, and mites can also be more of a problem on trees stressed by nutrient- and water-related disorders.

The first step in remedying a noninfectious disorder is to identify its cause. Distinguish abiotic disorders from other causes of similar damage such as insects, mites, pathogens, and vertebrates. Noninfectious disorders sometimes can be recognized by characteristically distorted, discolored, or dying foliage on the affected plant. However, diagnosing the cause of a disorder can be difficult. Different causes can produce the same symptoms. In many cases, more than one cause is adversely affecting the plants at the same time. In addition to their direct damage to plants, abiotic disorders and pests can act in combination to the point that they kill plants. Read the "Monitoring" section in the third chapter, "Managing Pests in Avocados," and the "Monitoring and Diagnosis" section in the fifth chapter, "Diseases," to learn how to determine the specific causes of problems.

Water Deficiency and Excess

Inappropriate soil moisture is the most common problem affecting avocado trees. Applying too much or too little

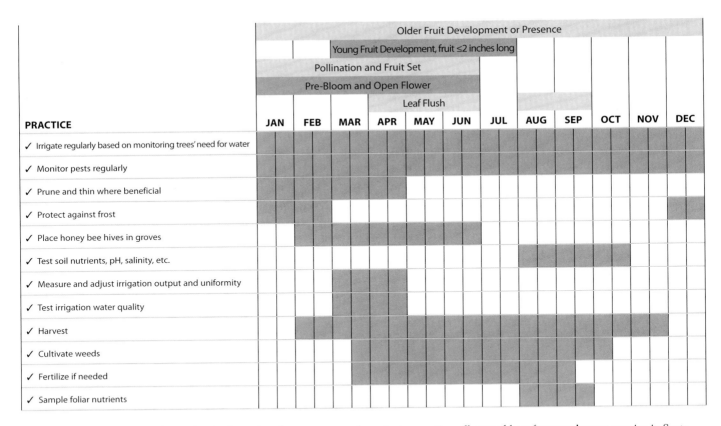

Figure 13. Approximate times for conducting key cultural management and monitoring practices, illustrated here for avocado trees growing in Santa Barbara and Ventura Counties. Optimal times vary according to location and weather. Testing foliage and soil generally are done once during the indicated period. Practices such as cultivation, frost protection, irrigation, and pest monitoring are ongoing or are repeated at appropriate intervals. *Adapted from*: CAC and CMCC 2003.

water during each irrigation, irrigating too frequently or not frequently enough, poor uniformity, and inadequate adjustment of irrigation according to the trees' varying needs for water are common causes of tree damage and reduced fruit yield.

Too little water early in the spring leads to small or wilting leaves and small fruit. During summer insufficient water causes leaf drop and sunburn on fruit and limbs. Applying excess amounts or irrigating too frequently waterlogs the soil and asphyxiates and kills roots. Decline and dieback of aerial plant parts and discolored, wilted, or prematurely dropping foliage can be caused by water deficiency or excess. In addition to causing direct damage to trees, inappropriate irrigation contributes to problems such as crown and root rot diseases, nutritional disorders, and salinity as summarized earlier in Table 1.

Rainfall, soil type, terrain, temperature, tree size, stage of crop development, water quality, wind, and method of irrigation are among the many factors that affect water availability and trees' needs for soil moisture. Appropriate irrigation is the most important cultural step growers can take to improve yield and minimize pest problems. Additional steps that help provide trees with appropriate moisture include keeping roots healthy, improving drainage, preventing soil compaction, and using good quality water.

Water Management

Overwatering means irrigating too frequently, applying excess amounts during an irrigation cycle, or both. Underwatering is irrigating too infrequently or applying insufficient amounts during an irrigation. Overwatering of some trees and underwatering of others can occur in a grove at the same time.

Figure 14 shows the average monthly water requirements for 8-year-old avocado trees at an interior southern California (Riverside) growing site. Trees' actual needs for water vary depending on considerations such as location, tree age (canopy size), stage of crop development, and weather. Construct, maintain, and operate your irrigation systems to effectively deliver water as discussed under "Irrigation Efficiency," later in this chapter. Adjust the frequency and amount of water applied during each cycle based on your monitoring of soil moisture, tree condition, weather, or a combination of methods as discussed in "Scheduling Irrigations."

Wilted, downward-hanging leaves are a common symptom of too much or too little water. However, different causes can produce the same symptoms. This unhealthy foliage was caused by avocado root rot, a water-related, lethal disease caused by *Phytophthora cinnamomi*.

Providing appropriate soil moisture is the most critical management practice for keeping trees healthy. Too much or too little water in the root zone reduces fruit quality and yield. Inappropriate irrigation contributes to avocado root rot, mite outbreaks, nutritional disorders, salt toxicity, and sunburn.

For more on irrigation, see publications such as *Determining Daily Reference Evapotranspiration* (Snyder, Pruitt, and Shaw 1987), *Evapotranspiration and Irrigation Water Requirements* (Jensen, Burman, and Allen 1990), and *Irrigation Scheduling: A Guide for Efficient On-farm Management* (Goldhamer and Snyder 1989) listed in the suggested reading. Consult World Wide Web sites, including

http://avocadosource.com
http://ceventura.ucdavis.edu
www.avocado.org
www.ucavo.ucr.edu
www.wateright.org

Check with experts at your county Cooperative Extension office, local Resource Conservation District, or the Natural Resources Conservation Service for current information on irrigating avocados.

Irrigation Methods

Avocados are watered by sprinkler or micro-irrigation (using drip emitters or microsprinklers). Elevation and slope of the land and the availability, cost, and source of water are some things to consider when you are choosing an irrigation system. Installation, operation, and maintenance costs differ for different systems and sites, especially where avocados are grown on steep terrain or where irrigation water is undesirably alkaline or saline.

Sprinkler Irrigation. In comparison with micro-irrigation, conventional sprinklers use more widely spaced emitters and each head applies water at a greater output rate (more gallons per hour) over a larger surface area. Advantages include a lower maintenance requirement (since there are fewer emitters) and the ability to supply water more quickly when the trees' moisture demands are high. However, considerable energy is required for pumping and pressurizing to distribute

sprinkler-applied water. Uniform water distribution among trees is especially difficult on slopes or where trees are irregularly spaced. Runoff, weed growth where the soil is not shaded, and diseases such as canker and crown rots that are favored by wetting crowns and trunks are greater problems with sprinklers than with micro-irrigation.

Micro-Irrigation. With drip (trickle) emitters and microsprinklers, each emitter wets a small area of the grove floor. Water system pressure and output rate from each emitter are much lower with micro-irrigation than with high-volume sprinklers.

Micro-irrigation lowers the energy costs of irrigation and generally produces more uniform tree growth and less variation in yield between trees. In comparison with sprinkler irrigation, a higher proportion of the water applied by micro-

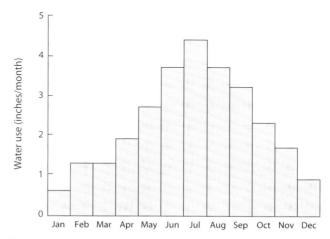

Figure 14. Average monthly water use in an 8-year-old avocado grove, Riverside, California, 1987–1990. Location, irrigation system, and weather are among the factors that cause actual water use to vary. Schedule irrigation using good methods, such as monitoring of evapotranspiration (ET). *Source:* Meyer, Yates, Stottlemyer et al. 1992.

irrigation is used by the trees, so micro-irrigation conserves water. When trees are young, micro-irrigation minimizes the application of water between trees, thus reducing weed growth. Micro-irrigation works well on heavy soils with a low infiltration rate and can be the best irrigation method for trees where soil or water is alkaline or salty.

Disadvantages of micro-irrigation include a smaller amount of reserve moisture in the soil available to trees and a high level of maintenance. Clogging is usually managed by chemical injection, filters, or both, depending on whether the clogging is due to algae and molds, chemical precipitates, or physical particulates. The soil moisture reserve is smaller because a smaller area of soil is wetted, and as a result micro-irrigated trees have a smaller root zone than sprinkler-irrigated trees. Soil moisture deficits cannot be quickly remedied with micro-irrigation, so trees must be watered more frequently to avoid water stress. To avoid tree stress under hot conditions, and the resulting yield reductions, a micro-irrigation system must be engineered and operated to meet the trees' maximum expected water use demand.

Soil and Water

Certain soil properties and the ways they influence the availability of water to plants are illustrated in Figure 15. *Soil texture* refers to the relative proportion of different sizes of soil particles, including sand (the largest soil particles), silt (intermediate sizes), and clay (the smallest particles). Loam soils are a mixture of clay, sand, and silt. *Soil structure* is the arrangement of the particles in soil. *Pore spaces* are the voids between soil particles; they can be occupied by air or water or a combination of both. *Field capacity* is the amount of water that can be held in the pore spaces by capillary action after excess water has moved down, beyond the topsoil layer due to gravity. *Capillary action* results from the natural attraction of water molecules to the surface of soil particles and the attraction of water molecules to each other. This capillary action causes *water tension* (*suction* or *negative pressure*) on moisture in soil above the underground water table. Smaller pores hold water with more tension than larger pores. As soil dries and films of water around soil separate or get thinner, water tension increases, and that makes it harder for plants to extract moisture from the soil. Water tension can be measured with tensiometer devices that are used to schedule irrigation. Because of the attraction between soil and water, only a portion of the water in the grove's soil—the *available water*—can be extracted by plants. The *wilting point* occurs when plants still require more water after having extracted all of the available water.

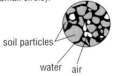

Soil is about half solid material by volume (large circle). The rest of the soil volume consists of pore spaces between soil particles. Pore spaces hold varying proportions of air and water (small circle).

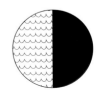

When the soil is **saturated** after irrigation or rain, pore spaces are filled with water.

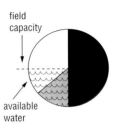

When soil has drained following irrigation, it is at **field capacity**. In most soils, about half of the pore space is filled with water. About half of this water is **available** to plants; the rest is unavailable because too much suction is needed to remove it from pore spaces. The proportion of soil water that is available is higher in clays and lower in sandy soils.

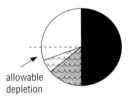

The **allowable depletion** is the proportion of the available water the crop can use before irrigation is needed.

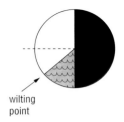

At the **wilting point**, all available water is gone. Plants die unless water is added.

Figure 15. The soil water reservoir and its relationship to moisture availability to plants and irrigation scheduling.

Table 7. Soil-Based Moisture Monitoring Devices: A Comparison of Some Accurate Tools for Scheduling Irrigation.

Method[1]	Cost	Ease of use	Accuracy	Reliability	Salt-affected
Gypsum block	L	H	H	H	L
Tensiometer	L	M	H	M	L
Portable tensiometer	M	M	H	M	L
Solid-state tensiometer	M	H	H	H	L
Neutron probe	H	L	H	H	L
Gravimetric (oven)	L	M	H	H	L

L = low
M = medium
H = high
1. Other devices are available, but many of those have less well-documented utility to growers, are more highly affected by salinity, or are otherwise less accurate. Adapted from Faber 2005.

Scheduling Irrigations

Determine how much, how often, and when to water using soil- or weather-based methods or both in combination.

Tree-Based Assessment. Watching trees for symptoms such as curled, pale, or wilted leaves is not a recommended method for scheduling irrigations. By the time plants exhibit these visible symptoms of drought stress, they have often sustained some production loss or tree damage already. Limp or discolored foliage can also be caused by overwatering—or anything else that makes roots unhealthy, including root asphyxiation and Phytophthora root rot—so visual symptoms are not diagnostic of irrigation need. Researchers quantitatively monitor plants' water status by measuring leaf transpiration, temperature differences that are affected by transpiration, and water pressure or water tension within tissue. However, the plant monitoring instruments they use are costly, the methods are labor intensive, and the actual applicability of the resulting data to commercial groves is uncertain.

Soil-Based Assessment. "Look and feel" methods allow you to judge the availability of moisture based on the degree to which soil lightens in color as it dries and the extent to which soil can be molded, rolled, or squeezed into a ball in your hand and then crumbled. Guidelines for estimating soil texture and moisture by how soil feels and molds include the table in *Water Management* (Hartin and Faber 2002), listed in the suggested reading. However, the appearance and feel of soil can vary based on the experience and qualitative judgment of whoever makes the assessment. Tensiometers, gypsum blocks, and neutron probes are accurate, reliable devices, and are the preferred means for monitoring soil moisture to schedule irrigation (Table 7).

A tensiometer is a closed tube with a porous, water-filled cup at the bottom. The tube is buried so that its bottom contacts the water film surrounding soil particles in the root zone. As soil dries, water is sucked out of the cup, creating a vacuum, which is measured by an analog pressure gauge or digital sensor. Water tension measurements indicate the availability of moisture to plants (Figure 15) based on how easily healthy roots can extract water from soil.

Solid-state tensiometers convert mechanical pressure changes to electrical signals. These devices can be wired into irrigation system controllers that will then apply water automatically according to set criteria determined by the grower. Tensiometer gauges report soil moisture in centibars (cb) or kiloPascals (kPa), which are equivalent (1 cb = 1 kPa). As tensiometer readings go further below 0, they indicate progressively drier soil and consequently greater water tension. Irrigation begins at a high water tension set point, commonly ranging from −30 to −50 kPa depending on soil type. Watering ends at a low tension set point near field capacity for holding water, perhaps about −10 kPa. Avoid under-watering (several consecutive days at −50 to −70 kPa) or overwatering (several days at 0 to −10 kPa).

Typically, several stationary, properly calibrated tensiometers are placed in various representative soil locations in the grove. For example, you could place a tensiometer's tip 6 to 12 inches (15–30 cm) deep, or preferably two instruments at 6 and 12 inches underground, near the drip line of at least one or two representative trees in each section of a grove. Certain tensiometer models are portable, allowing you to move a single unit regularly to collect readings at multiple soil locations.

Useful alternative devices include neutron probes and electrical conductance or resistance sensors such as gypsum blocks. A block of gypsum placed in soil will absorb moisture or dry out at close to the rate that soil moisture changes. Wet gypsum readily conducts electricity (i.e., it has low resistance); dry gypsum resists electricity. A pair of electrodes within the block measure the gypsum's changes in electrical conductance, and this information is calibrated to indicate soil moisture tension. Gypsum blocks are inexpensive and easy to use, they may the best choice in heavy (clay) soils where the range in soil moisture exceeds the measuring ability of many tensiometers.

Neutron probes use a radiation source and a detection tube unit inserted into the soil. The emitted neutrons slow down when they encounter hydrogen ions in water. The extent to which neutrons slow indicates soil moisture. Properly calibrated neutron probes are very accurate and

This tensiometer with a vacuum pressure gauge is one of several accurate and reliable devices for measuring soil moisture and scheduling irrigation.

reliable, but they are somewhat difficult to use, and the operator must be licensed to handle radioactive material.

Tensiometers and gypsum blocks measure moisture indirectly through porous materials that come to equilibrium with soil moisture. Their readings can be affected by discontinuities in soil such as rocks or rodent holes. Place the devices carefully to obtain accurate readings. Direct measures of soil moisture include neutron probes and oven-drying. For example, relatively speedy gravimetric ovens measure the weight change of a soil sample dried by microwave. The wetter the soil is to begin with, the greater the weight loss will be during drying.

Accuracy, cost, ease of use, portability, reliability, and the extent to which salinity effects readings are primary considerations when you choose a soil moisture monitoring device. Tensiometers, gypsum blocks, and neutron probes are well-understood tools that are quite accurate when properly calibrated and correctly used. Some other methods are less accurate or not well researched to document their accuracy and practical utility. Soil moisture monitoring devices and techniques are constantly being improved. For current information, check World Wide Web sites such as those listed at the back of this book, or consult experts at your county Cooperative Extension office, local Resource Conservation District, or the Natural Resources Conservation Service.

Evapotranspiration. You can schedule irrigations based on water evaporation from soil surfaces and transpiration from plants. Combined, these water losses are called evapotranspiration (ET), commonly expressed in inches per day. *Reference ET* (ET_o) is the amount of water used by a well-watered, cool-season turfgrass. The ET_o reading is recorded and published for many locations and used as a basis for scheduling crop irrigations. Because the evapotranspiration of mature avocado is lower than the turfgrass standard, you have to multiply ET_o by a crop-specific coefficient (K_c) to estimate the crop evapotranspiration (ET_c):

$$ET_c = ET_o \times K_c$$

The K_c for established avocado trees ranges from lows of 0.35 to 0.50 (35–50% of ET_o) during winter to highs of about 0.60 to 0.70 (60–70% of ET_o) during summer. Appropriate K_c values for an individual grove vary depending on local conditions.

Historical and current (real-time) ET_o values are available from public news outlets, the University of California Cooperative Extension, and government agencies such as the California Irrigation Management Information System (CIMIS). ET_o data from CIMIS locations and other sites throughout California are available at the UC Statewide IPM Program Web site (www.ipm.ucdavis.edu). Evaporation outdoors can also be monitored on site by regularly measuring water loss from a shallow pan or using automated evaporation pans with sensors that monitor water level and send that information to a data logger or automated irrigation control system. Some irrigation controllers and personal computer software applications either access historical ET_o data and use this as the predicted ET_o or automatically obtain current ET_o data and use it as a basis for scheduling irrigations.

For any individual irrigation system, crop evapotranspiration (ET_c) is divided by the irrigation system's distribution uniformity (DU) to determine the amount of applied water (ET_{aw}) needed:

$$ET_{aw} = ET_c \div DU$$

In addition to ET_c and DU, the specific method for operating an irrigation system to provide this ET_{aw} varies depending on the system's emitters (number, spacing, and gallons per hour of output), any leaching required to flush salts below the root zone, and rainfall. These considerations are easily incorporated if you use one of the online calculators such as those at www.avocado.org and http://avocadosource.com.

Irrigation Efficiency

Irrigation efficiency is a system's effectiveness in delivering water to improve tree health and crop yield. By maximizing efficiency, you can reduce water-related diseases and disorders and minimize water waste and the off-site movement of contaminants due to overirrigation. Irrigation efficiency is expressed as a ratio of the amount of water stored in the crop's root zone and the total amount of water applied. Efficiency is a product of the irrigation system's design, maintenance, and operation.

It is not economically feasible to supply each tree with the precise amount of water it needs for optimal growth and yield. You will overwater some trees in your effort to ensure that every tree receives sufficient water. A practical approach to improving irrigation efficiency is to focus on maximizing the system's distribution uniformity.

DU (%) = (average low quarter output ÷ overall average output) × 100

An excellent DU is 75% to 85%, while a good DU is 65% to 70%. Measure DU for each irrigation system. You can keep the differences between emitters within a system to a minimum by maintaining or replacing nozzles, adjusting system component size and water pressure, and installing flow regulators. Recalculate the DU after you modify the system.

Aeration Deficit or Root Asphyxiation

Aeration is the extent to which roots have access to adequate oxygen. The avocado tree's roots require oxygen for metabolism, respiration, and uptake of nutrients and water.

Greatly differing outputs for emitters in an irrigation system guarantees that some trees will receive too much or too little water, either of which can cause many disorders and diseases. The catchment test being performed here uses a modified 1-liter drink bottle to divert water from a running emitter for collection in a graduated cylinder. Water output during a fixed number of seconds is compared for the emitters being tested. Changes in nozzles and system pressure are used to improve irrigation distribution uniformity.

Anything from a simple rain gauge to a complex automated system for measuring precipitation within the grove is very helpful for scheduling irrigation if the equipment is regularly monitored and properly maintained. This stand also includes a minimum-maximum thermometer (in the white cover).

Distribution Uniformity. Distribution uniformity (DU) is the evenness with which water is distributed over an irrigated area; it is in large part determined by variations in output by emitters in the system. You calculate DU using a catchment test:

1. Collect water for a fixed number of seconds from each of many emitters on the same system.
2. Compare the catchment amounts (ounces [oz] or ml of water collected from each emitter during a fixed number of seconds) for the various emitters.
3. Calculate the DU by dividing the average output (measured volume) from the lowest one-quarter of emitters by the average output from all emitters, and multiplying the result by 100:

Too little oxygen in the soil causes asphyxiation of roots, a serious problem that can kill trees. Insufficient aeration, excess soil moisture, and diseases such as Phytophthora root rot often act in combination to damage or kill trees.

Asphyxiation occurs mainly in soils that are compacted, fine-textured (clay soils), or shallow with an impervious subsoil (hardpan), or that have poor drainage (slow water infiltration). When problem soils are over-irrigated or wet from prolonged rainy periods, water displaces the gas in pore spaces between the soil particles. Waterlogged soils impede the diffusion of oxygen (its movement through the soil) and leave few water-free pore spaces for oxygen to occupy.

Symptoms of aeration deficit usually are evident throughout the entire tree. Symptoms include discolored or yellow leaves, premature leaf drop, stunted growth, wilting, and gradual decline. If aeration deficit is extreme or prolonged, the leaves will suddenly collapse and turn brown. Fruit withers or softens and then usually drops. Branches typically die back from the tips, but only a few branches or one limb may die.

Diagnose aeration deficit by assessing whether site conditions and cultural practices are conducive to root asphyxiation. Look for groups of trees that exhibit similar symptoms, since damage often appears on clusters of trees that share a patch of problem soil. Examine small roots to determine whether they appear to be healthy (abundant, firm, and pale inside) or unhealthy (sparse and dark). Dig 1 to 2 inches (2.5–5 cm) below the surface and check the soil for the odor of sulfides (rotten eggs), which indicates anaerobic (oxygen-deprived) conditions. Send samples of the soil to a laboratory to determine its composition (soil aeration decreases as the percentage of clay increases). Consider measuring soil drainage (infiltration rate) by performing percolation tests to assess whether water is too slow to drain or infiltrate the soil. One drainage assessment method is illustrated in Figure 16.

Take steps to improve your site conditions and management practices to remedy any aeration deficit. Reduce the frequency or amount of water applied, where appropriate. Consider using alternate-row irrigation, applying water on only one side of the tree, then watering the other side during the next irrigation cycle. Keep any furrows or tree basins open during rainy weather to facilitate drainage. After prolonged rainy conditions, do not remove weeds until the water-logged soil has dried since weed transpiration will reduce soil moisture. Where an impervious soil layer is the cause of poor aeration, deeply rip the soil alongside each tree or auger holes 4 to 6 inches (10–15 cm) in diameter through the hardpan beneath the tree roots and then backfill the holes with coarse gravel. If the trees drop an excessive number of leaves, quickly harvest any mature fruit and whitewash the bark to minimize sunburn. Once the trees recover, prune any dead branches back to live growth about 3 to 5 months after vigorous new shoots develop.

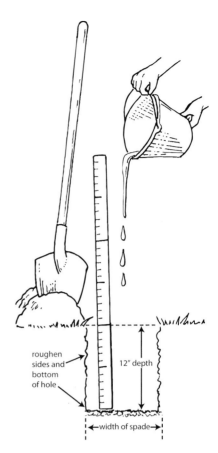

roughen sides and bottom of hole

12" depth

width of spade

Figure 16. Some soils exhibit slow water infiltration (slow drainage). Wet soil that drains slowly can damage roots due to insufficient aeration (lack of oxygen in soil). One way to assess the infiltration rate of topsoil is to conduct a percolation test. Dig a 12-inch-deep hole the width of a spade. Roughen the bottom and sides to eliminate any smeared, packed soil. Fill the hole to the top with water at least once and soak the surrounding surface so that soil around the hole becomes saturated with water. Wait 24 hours, refill the hole with water, and observe how long it takes for all the water to drain. Depending on the situation, a desirable drainage rate may be about 1 to 2 inches per hour (roughly 6 to 12 hours are required to drain a 12-inch hole).

Careful examination of avocado roots can help diagnose the specific cause of many maladies. Poor root health is often caused by insufficient soil aeration, excess soil moisture, or pathogens such as root rot that can act in combination to cause severe damage or kill trees.

Avocado trees should have numerous rootlets near the soil surface. Healthy rootlets are flexible (they will bend to some extent without breaking), firm, and tan to white in color beneath their outer epidermal layer, which has been scraped off in this photograph.

Dead shoots that retain brown leaves are symptomatic of root asphyxiation. This tree was planted during fall, then damaged by prolonged winter rains that waterlogged the soil. New leaf growth seen here during spring indicates that the tree is recovering. Weeds are being allowed to grow to help dry out the soil.

Fertilization

Seventeen elements are required for plant growth. Carbon, hydrogen, and oxygen are the most abundant elements in plants and are provided by air and water. The remaining are mineral elements, which plants absorb primarily from soil through roots (Table 8).

California avocado grove soils contain sufficient amounts of most essential mineral nutrients. Modest amounts of nitrogen and potassium and occasional phosphorus and zinc (and perhaps boron in some locations) are the primary fertilizer applications recommended for avocado.

In comparison with most fruit and nut crops, avocados exhibit low nutrient removal (the amount of nutrients that are in fruit and are removed from the grove when you

Table 8. Soil-Derived Mineral Nutrients Essential for Avocado Growth.

Macronutrients	Micronutrients
nitrogen (N)	iron (Fe)
potassium (K)	chlorine (Cl)
calcium (Ca)	manganese (Mn)
phosphorus (P)	zinc (Zn)
magnesium (Mg)	boron (B)
sulfur (S)	copper (Cu)
	molybdenum (Mo)
	nickel (Ni)

Nutrients are listed in decreasing order of their abundance as commonly found in dry-weight plant tissue. Essential elements not listed above are carbon (C), hydrogen (H), and oxygen (O), which are provided by air and water.

harvest). The correct amount and timing for fertilization to maximize avocado fruit yield are unclear, and subjects of ongoing research. Approximately 100 lb nitrogen (N), 50 lb potassium (K), and 30 lb phosphorus (P) per year per acre of mature avocado are sometimes recommended. The trees' actual need for fertilization can be very different. For example, one study found that avocado trees absorb approximately four times more potassium during on-years (alternate-bearing years with high fruit production) than during off-years. Fruit load, soil type, and tree size, and the extent to which fertigation water and soil are lost from the root zone affect the trees' need for fertilization. Certain air pollutants, composts, mulches, soil amendments, and some sources of irrigation water also supply significant amounts of nutrients, at least of nitrogen.

The trees' ability to take up nutrients depends on factors such as the type of fertilizer and method of application; the pH, moisture content, and type of soil; the stage of crop development; and temperature. Make sure that you apply the appropriate amount and type of fertilizer at the right time and that you place and retain it in the root zone. Adjust your fertilization plan according to grove conditions and need, such as fruit load. Trees with many fruit need increased nutrients. Reduce fertilization amounts when trees have few fruit; otherwise the excess nitrogen will increase the need for irrigation and pruning, produce a bigger tree, and reduce subsequent fruit production levels.

Fertilization decisions are primarily based on whether nutrient concentrations in leaves are within an optimal range as summarized in Table 9. The nutrient content of foliage is determined by proper laboratory testing. Tests of soil and irrigation water and knowledge of the amount of nutrients you remove from the grove in harvested fruit may also provide evidence of the need for fertilization.

Routinely test leaves (and perhaps soil and water) at least once a year (see Figure 13). Some nutrient deficiencies produce characteristic leaf symptoms, but you should always confirm suspected deficiencies with a laboratory analysis of leaves. Keep in mind that nutrient deficiency symptoms frequently are not due to inadequate nutrient levels in the

Table 9. General Guide to Avocado Leaf Nutrient and Mineral Concentrations as Determined by Laboratory Analysis of Foliage Samples.

Element	Symbol	Unit	Deficient if less than	Adequate	Excess if greater than
Nitrogen	N	%	1.6	1.8–2.4	2.8
Phosphorus	P	%	0.05	0.08–0.25	0.3
Potassium	K	%	0.35	0.75–2	3
Calcium	Ca	%	0.5	1.0–3.0	4
Magnesium	Mg	%	0.15	0.25–0.8	1
Sulfur	S	%	0.05	0.20–0.6	1
Boron	B	ppm	10–20	50–90	100–250
Iron	Fe	ppm	20–40	50–200	?
Manganese	Mn	ppm	10–15	30–500	1,000
Zinc	Zn	ppm	10–20	30–150	300
Copper	Cu	ppm	2–3	5–15	25
Molybdenum	Mo	ppm	0.01	0.05–1.0	?
Chloride (Chlorine)	Cl	%	?	?	0.25–0.5
Sodium	Na	%	NA	NA	0.25–0.5
Lithium	Li	ppm	NA	NA	50-75

KEY
? = unknown
NA = not applicable, not an essential nutrient but of concern at excess levels
ppm = parts per million
Adapted from Lee 1979, 1980; Jones and Embleton 1966.

To determine foliar nutrient status, collect leaves in the fall (September to October) for laboratory analysis. Sample the spring flush leaves as shown here. These are several-month-old leaves that are immediately terminal to the ring of buds marking the end of last year's growth.

soil. Routine application of nutrients simply because the foliage exhibits deficiency symptoms may actually make things worse by delaying you from finding the true cause of the unhealthy trees. You can increase the trees' ability to absorb minerals by improving soil conditions and promoting root health.

Consult with your farm advisor, PCA, or diagnostic laboratory for specific recommendations on fertilizer use and how to collect leaf, soil, and water samples for laboratory analysis. Other sources of information on fertilization include Web sites such as http://avocadosource.com and publications such as *Avocado Handbook* (Faber 2005) listed in the suggested reading.

Nutrient and Mineral Disorders

Too much or too little of essential minerals can produce a variety of symptoms (Table 10). Nutrient deficiencies can cause foliage to discolor, fade, distort, or become spotted, sometimes in a characteristic pattern that can help you identify the cause. Nutrient-deficient trees may produce fewer or smaller leaves, flowers, and fruit. These parts may develop later than normal and remain undersized. More severely deficient plants become stunted, exhibit dieback, are predisposed to other maladies, and have a poor fruit yield. Excess nutrients also commonly cause problems, such as by contributing to salinity or water contamination and favoring excess succulent foliage growth, which reduces yields and favors increased populations of certain invertebrate pests.

JACK KELLY CLARK

When applying materials in irrigation water, use good technique and proper equipment, such as this metered injection pump. Avoid applying excess amounts. For example, inject nitrogen only during the last half hour of a several-hour irrigation cycle, then flush the system with plain water for about an additional 30 minutes. This way the nutrients will be retained near the surface where most roots occur and there will be less risk of contaminating groundwater or surface water.

Table 10. Symptoms of Nutrient or Mineral Deficiency or Toxicity in Avocado.

Nutrient or mineral	Deficiency or low concentration	Toxicity or high concentration
Boron	Young leaves pale green to yellowish. Rare in California.	Leaf margins and tips chlorotic to necrotic. Foliage drops prematurely.
Chloride	—	Leaf tips and margins necrotic. Leaves drop prematurely.
Iron	Young leaves yellowish between veins. Only veins may be green. Possible tip and marginal necrosis. Leaves may drop prematurely. Resembles manganese deficiency. Fruit may be pale.	Induces manganese deficiency.
Manganese	Older leaves chlorotic between veins. Only veins may be green. Possible tip and marginal necrosis. Resembles iron deficiency, but is much less common.	Interveinal chlorosis. Possibly reddish brown to black foliar spots. Rare or does not occur in California.
Nitrogen	Leaves yellowish overall and undersized, especially new foliage. Short internodes. Leaves may drop prematurely.	Leaves dark green, brown, or gray, especially along margins. Excess succulent foliage growth.
Phosphorus	Older leaves dark, tinged brownish, possibly undersized. Shoots may die back. Rare in California avocado.	Induces copper and zinc deficiencies.
Potassium	Leaves small and narrow. Older leaves chlorotic between veins, may have necrotic patches. Foliage may be sparse. Branches may be thin or die back. Few fruit produced.	Induces calcium and magnesium deficiencies.
Salinity, high EC	—	Leaf tips and margins necrotic, especially older foliage. Leaves wilt, drop prematurely. Plant growth stunted.
Sodium	—	Leaves chlorotic or necrotic between veins and marginally. Foliage may brown, die, and drop prematurely.
Zinc	Young leaves yellowish between veins. Leaves undersized. Leaves may have marginal necrosis or drop prematurely. Shoots may be bushy, display rosetting and have short internodes. Fruit may be round.	—

— = Rarely occurs or not a reported problem in California.
Actual symptoms vary, partly due to growing conditions, cultivar, and interacting factors.

During fertilization, nutrients usually are applied as salts. These salts can be toxic to plants if present in excess amounts or if incorrectly applied. Irrigation water and soil in many areas of California also have naturally high levels of salts. Toxicity symptoms from excess nutrients or salts include leaf tip dieback, marginal leaf chlorosis or necrosis, branch dieback, and increased pest problems. If a leaf analysis reveals toxic levels of minerals such as sodium, boron, or chlorine, test the soil and irrigation water to determine the source of the toxic mineral levels so you will be able to choose the appropriate corrective measures.

When nutrient deficiency symptoms appear in trees, the cause is often not a lack of adequate nutrients in soil. In fact, nutrient disorders can be caused by any adverse soil condition or root injury that prevents the plants from absorbing adequate nutrients. Common causes of deficiency symptoms include aeration deficit, high soil pH, inappropriate irrigation, poor drainage, and root decay pathogens. Fertilization will often fail to increase yields and improve tree health unless you also take measures to improve soil conditions and promote root health.

Nitrogen

A relatively uniform yellowing of leaves is often the first symptom of nitrogen (N) deficiency. Deficient avocado leaves may be smaller than normal and may drop prematurely. Fruit may be undersized and fewer than normal. Nitrogen deficiency may increase the plants' susceptibility to other maladies, such as cold damage.

Excess nitrogen causes leaves to turn dark green, gray, or brown along the margins (fertilizer burn). Overfertilization causes excessively vigorous vegetative growth or abnormally large leaves that develop at the expense of flowers and fruit. This excess growth increases the trees' need for irrigation and pruning and can increase populations of certain sucking insects and mites. Excess nitrogen is detrimental to soil chemistry and beneficial microorganisms and can pollute groundwater and surface water. Excess nitrogen reduces the number of fruit, shortens their storage life, and increases their susceptibility to physiological problems.

If otherwise healthy, avocado trees are highly efficient at scavenging nitrogen from soil and litter. Avoid improper or excessive fertilization. Be aware that visual observation of symptoms alone cannot diagnose nitrogen deficiency. Determine whether a supplemental application of nitrogen is appropriate based on laboratory analysis of properly sampled leaves and an informed judgment of the growth rate of the tree. To determine the trees' status for nitrogen and most other nutrients, collect foliage in the fall (August to September) for laboratory analysis. Sample leaves of the spring flush, which are the leaves terminal to the ring of buds marking the end of the previous year's growth. Be aware that irrigation, soil pH, and temperature are among the factors affecting nitrogen availability to plants. If leaves are deficient in comparison to recommended levels (see Table 9), determine the actual cause of the symptoms so you will be able to apply the proper remedies.

Nitrogen is available in various organic and inorganic forms. Typically it is applied onto soil or injected through the irrigation system. If you determine that your avocado trees need an application of nitrogen, consider which amount, form, and method and timing of application is most appropriate for your situation. Products differ in the extent to which they may undesirably alter soil pH or increase salinity. Use the correct type, rate, and method of fertilization for the specific situation. Be aware that soil temperature, root health, and many other factors affect a tree's ability to absorb and use nutrients.

Phosphorus

Phosphorus (P) deficiency and its symptoms are rare in California avocado trees. Exceptions are trees growing in very sandy soil or where severe grading has removed most topsoil. Plants that are deficient in phosphorus produce

Nitrogen deficiency commonly causes a relatively uniform yellowing of leaves. The slightly greener veins here may also indicate maladies such as iron or zinc deficiency. Examination of root health and soil conditions and laboratory testing of leaves help to diagnose the actual cause of these foliage symptoms.

small, dark or brownish tinged leaves. An application of phosphorus can increase its level in leaves, but the addition of phosphorus has not actually been shown to improve fruit quality or yield. Excess phosphorus will inhibit the tree's absorption of copper and zinc and can cause symptoms of deficiency of these nutrients.

Potassium

Potassium (K) deficiency is characterized by small, narrow, yellow or pale green leaves in new growth. Potassium deficiency causes older leaves to become chlorotic between veins, develop discolored to necrotic spots, and perhaps curl at the margins. Fruit yield and size may decline. Potassium deficiency is a particular problem when roots are unhealthy and where topsoil is sandy, sparse, or excessively leached by water. Unwarranted calcium or magnesium applications can induce potassium deficiency symptoms.

You can remedy potassium deficiencies by improving soil conditions and root health, spreading organic mulch beneath plants, or both fertilizing and mulching. Although organic mulch only slowly remedies a potassium deficiency, mulching provides other benefits such as a reduction in root rot disease. Slow-release formulations include potassium silicate, potassium sulfate, and sulfur- or polymer-coated potassium materials. Potassium nitrate can be used, but this may result in the application of excess nitrogen unless you have also identified nitrogen deficiency as a problem. Do not use potassium chloride where chloride or salt toxicity is a problem. Be aware that adding excess potassium reduces the availability of calcium and magnesium and that excess magnesium makes potassium unavailable. Trees' need for potassium is positively correlated with their fruit load, so adjust applications accordingly. Most studies have found that, once you meet and maintain minimum requirements (see Table 9), there are no yield improvements from applying additional potassium.

Iron

Iron (Fe) deficiency causes new foliage to be bleached, chlorotic, or pale with green veins. Fading appears first around leaf margins, then spreads inward until only the veins are green. As severity increases, new shoots and leaves are undersized and pale, leaves become necrotic along their margins and tips, and foliage sheds. Affected fruit may be pale.

Iron deficiency is most prevalent in alkaline, calcareous (high in calcium), and coastal soils. Symptoms occur anywhere soil is too cool, poorly drained, or waterlogged. Deficiency symptoms also develop when root health is impaired, such as by asphyxiation or root decay pathogens.

Tissue analysis may not be reliable in diagnosing iron deficiency. Instead, diagnose this malady based on visual symptoms, soil tests (that, for example, show high pH or low organic matter), and your knowledge of existing cultural practices and soil conditions that favor the disorder. Certain preemergence herbicides cause similar damage symptoms, but preemergence herbicide damage occurs primarily on older leaves, while iron deficiency symptoms are most pronounced in new growth.

The main way to remedy iron deficiency is to improve cultural practices and the soil environment. For instance, improve aeration and reduce waterlogging, such as by increasing the time between irrigations to the maximum interval that still provides good growth. Allow fallen leaves to remain on the soil and regularly add composted organic matter as mulch beneath trees. Organic mulch helps prevent iron deficiency and slowly remedies the condition. As organic matter decays, it causes soil at the surface to become more acidic, allowing the tree roots to draw iron out of the soil. Mulch provides many other benefits besides increasing nutrient availability.

If you are applying inorganic fertilizers, switch from nitrate- to ammonium-based compounds; ammoniacal fertilizers such as ammonium nitrate gradually lower the soil pH. One quick method is to apply iron chelate to soil or foliage according to the product label. The healthy appearance of foliage is only temporarily restored by chelates, so if you use them, apply them in combination with other measures that improve cultural care, the growing environment, and soil conditions, such as by acidifying a high-pH soil.

The best time to prevent iron deficiency is before planting. Plant the trees on a berm or mound to improve drainage. Amend the soil to improve drainage, reduce pH, and increase organic matter. Consider incorporating well-composted organic material into the top 1 to 2 feet (0.3–0.6 m) of soil at a rate not exceeding 20% of soil volume. Be aware that amended soils will settle as organic matter decomposes, so plant on a mound or berm of soil several inches above the native soil line.

Alternatively, where soil is alkaline, add 1 to 2 pounds elemental sulfur per 100 square feet (0.5–1 kg/10 sq m) of soil surface. About 6 months before planting, till sulfur into the top 6 inches (15 cm) of soil and irrigate. Soil bacteria slowly convert sulfur to sulfuric acid, lowering the soil pH and increasing the availability of iron. This acidifying process may take several months, and the soil must be moist, warm, and well aerated. Acidification is not effective if the soil alkalinity is too high to begin with (high in lime content, such as excess calcium carbonate). See the sections on "pH" and "Alkalinity" later in this chapter for more discussion.

Potassium deficiency causes older leaves to become chlorotic between veins, develop discolored spots, and curl at the margins.

Iron deficiency causes young leaves to become chlorotic with green veins. Iron is present in sufficient amounts in most soils. Often conditions such as avocado root rot and high soil pH prevent trees from absorbing sufficient iron.

Manganese

Manganese (Mn) deficiency produces interveinal chlorosis that progresses to the point that only the smallest veins remain green. In extreme cases, leaves become yellowish overall or develop necrotic spots. Manganese deficiency symptoms occur in new foliage and are visually indistinguishable from those of iron deficiency.

Manganese deficiency is uncommon, but can occur in soils that are alkaline, cool, or poorly drained. Manganese deficiency can be induced by excess application of iron chelates. Remedy leaf symptoms by lowering the soil pH, increasing organic matter, and otherwise improving cultural care and the growing environment as discussed in the "Iron" section. Manganese chelate applied to newly emerging foliage is a quick, temporary remedy.

Zinc

Zinc (Zn) deficiency is relatively common in California avocados. Symptoms often develop where trees grow in calcareous coastal soils, where the pH of irrigation water or soil is high, and on granitic hillsides where soil pH is low. Common symptoms are interveinal chlorosis and reduced size of new leaves and shoots, including rosetting or a "feather duster" appearance. Symptoms often resemble those of glyphosate

herbicide injury, and this can lead to some confusion. Tree health and fruit yield can decline in zinc deficient trees. Fruit may be more round than normal or may develop reddish tinged skin.

You can diagnose zinc deficiency based on characteristic foliar symptoms, an assessment of whether other factors such as glyphosate application could have caused these symptoms, and consideration of how orchard soil conditions and water quality affect zinc availability. For example, high pH reduces zinc availability and low pH increases zinc leaching. Test the soil and symptomatic foliage and compare your results with the values in Table 9.

Zinc availability to plants is reduced by unhealthy roots and the same adverse soil conditions and inappropriate cultural practices as discussed for iron and nitrogen deficiencies. To remedy a zinc deficiency, modify your irrigation schedule and improve soil conditions in a way that will facilitate zinc uptake by plants. If needed, apply zinc sulfate onto soil near the drip line or apply it though the irrigation systems, following product label instructions. Trunk injection of zinc does not appear to be very effective. Foliar-applied zinc does not

Manganese deficiency produces interveinal chlorosis, progressing so that only the smallest veins remain green. Symptoms occur in new foliage and are visually indistinguishable from those of iron deficiency. A laboratory test can help to determine the actual cause of these symptoms.

Severe zinc deficiency (shown here in almond) often causes resetting or a featherduster appearance. New leaves and shoots are pale and smaller than normal, and internodes are shortened. These symptoms also resemble those of injury from glyphosate herbicide.

JACK KELLY CLARK

Zinc deficiency can cause fruit to be more round than normal. Here the suspected cause is off-season fruiting, which can also result in abnormal fruit development. The dark patches are leaf shadows.

translocate well, so although it will remedy a deficiency in leaves that are sprayed when they are succulent, it may not benefit the entire tree.

Chloride and Sodium

Avocado are highly susceptible to excess chloride (Cl compounds) and sodium (Na) in soil or water. Chloride toxicity causes necrosis of leaf margins and tips. Leaves drop prematurely during summer and fall, leading to sunburn and tree stress. Sodium toxicity symptoms include interveinal and marginal chlorosis, which develops into necrosis. If severe, this can cause entire shoots to dry and die. Chloride or sodium toxicity symptoms often occur if concentrations of either in foliage (dry weight) exceed about 0.25 to 0.5 % (see Table 9). With chloride, damaging levels develop in leaves when concentrations exceed about 3 to 4 milliequivalents (meq) /liter in irrigation water (106–142 ppm, where for chloride, 1 meq/liter = 35.4 ppm) or 5 to 6 meq/liter in the root zone.

Sodium toxicity, chloride toxicity, or both typically occur when you irrigate with low-quality (salty) groundwater. Suboptimal irrigation management practices, such as frequent, shallow watering and lack of water-conserving mulch, exacerbate salt toxicity. Excessive applications of manures or certain other amendments can increase salt toxicity. To avoid or remedy chloride or sodium toxicity, follow the steps discussed below for salinity.

Salinity

Salts are compounds that separate (disassociate) into anions and cations in water or moist soil. Anions are negatively charged compounds or elements, such as chloride and sulfate, and cations are positively charged compounds or elements, such as ammonium, calcium, and sodium. Plants normally obtain most of their nutrients from salts, but excess salinity in the soil or irrigation water causes problems. Avocado is more sensitive to salinity than most crops. Damage can occur from exposure to high concentrations of any salts, including those applied as fertilizers or contained in low-quality irrigation water.

Root exposure to high salt concentrations causes wilting, stunted plant growth, and premature leaf drop. Margins of leaves turn brown, reddish, or yellow, usually beginning with older foliage. Foliage wetted directly with salty water discolors at the end and edges and may drop prematurely. Foliar salt exposure sometimes produces a distinct pattern of damage—for instance, damage only on lower leaves that have been sprinkled with salty water or on the windward side of plants that face the ocean breeze.

Soils with high salt concentrations are called *saline* soils. Soils high in exchangeable (readily available) sodium are called *alkaline* or *sodic* soils. Sometimes you can identify a sodic soil by a white or dark crust that appears on the soil surface and an increasingly slow rate of water penetration. Salt toxicity is relatively common in many inland and coastal areas in southern California. Toxicity also occurs where plants are irrigated with water that is high in minerals. Excessive fertilization and frequent irrigation where drainage is poor can result in salt damage. Higher rainfall lessens the toxicity by leaching salts deeper into the soil, carrying the salts below the root zone.

Necrotic tips and chlorosis between the veins are typical symptoms of sodium toxicity.

Excess chlorine, sodium, and certain other minerals can cause severe leaf necrosis. Correct diagnosis of the cause may require laboratory tests on samples of foliage, irrigation water, and soil.

Monitoring Salinity. Evaluate salinity by having a professional laboratory test samples of grove soil, irrigation water, or both. Electrical conductivity (EC), sodium adsorption ratio (SAR), and (less commonly and only for water) total dissolved solids (TDS) are measures of overall salinity.

To determine a soil's EC, mix together several subsamples from the root zone. A laboratory will mix the soil with water before testing EC. Laboratories use different amounts of water to extract salt from soil, and the results considered to be acceptable values vary depending on the method. For example, when using the saturated paste extract method on soil or when testing irrigation water, EC values exceeding about 1 decisiemens per meter (dS/m) may cause damage to avocado trees. There are alternatives to the saturated paste extract method, and EC may be reported in other units, such as millimhos per centimeter (mmhos/cm; 1 dS/m = 1 mmhos/cm). The laboratory should provide you with guidelines on interpreting the test results as they relate to the specific method it used.

Sodium adsorption ratio (SAR) is the ratio of sodium to calcium plus magnesium. If the SAR exceeds about 2 in water or about 6 in soil, the sodium may be directly toxic to avocado trees. Total dissolved solids (TDS) greater than about 1,000 milligrams per liter of water may stress or damage avocado trees.

Basic tests of overall salinity (EC, TDS, and SAR) do not, however, provide information on certain specific ions that can be toxic at relatively low concentrations even when overall salt measures are within acceptable limits. Depending on what you think is causing the problems, you may need to test separately for EC, SAR, and several specific ions such as boron and chloride. You may need to make separate collections of more than one type of sample (e.g., irrigation water, leaves, and soil).

Foliage, soil, and water tests for specific ions report their results variously as percentages, ppm, or mg/L. If you are sampling salts in foliage, collect older, exposed leaves from the outer canopy, where most salts accumulate. It may be best to perform comparison testing by collecting separate samples from symptomatic foliage and from older, outer foliage on nearby plants that have apparently healthy leaves. Compare the results for symptomatic foliage against reference concentrations (see Table 9) and against the results of tests on asymptomatic plants. For more detailed information on salinity testing, consult publications such as *Western Fertilizer Handbook* (California Plant Health Association 2001) or *Water Quality for Agriculture* (Ayers and Westcot 1994).

Managing Salinity. Avocado rootstocks vary greatly in their tolerance to salt. Consider planting more salt-tolerant rootstocks where salinity will be a problem. For example, Dusa, Evstro, and VC 801 grafted to Hass scions and irrigated with salty water have been shown to develop greater canopy volume and accumulate less chloride and sodium than other rootstocks planted in the same conditions. Consult Table 2 for the relative salinity tolerances of various rootstocks. Seek the latest information on rootstock tolerances before planting.

Apply water that is low in minerals, such as captured rainwater, if you need to leach salts away from roots. Leaching is not effective unless the leaching water is low in salts. The cost of purchasing low-salt surface water for irrigation rather than using low-quality groundwater can be more than covered by the increase in crop quality, yield, and revenue that results from using high-quality irrigation water.

Improve soil drainage so that salts can be leached below the root zone. Increase the length of each irrigation and apply a greater volume of low-salt water during each irrigation so minerals will leach deeper into the soil and below the roots. At the same time, increase the interval between irrigations to avoid overwatering. Apply mulch beneath trees to reduce evaporation, which concentrates minerals near the soil surface where most of the roots occur.

Saline soils cannot be remedied with chemical amendments or fertilizers. A fertilizer adds salts to the soil, so you should minimize fertilization if salinity is a problem. If you do apply fertilizers, use formulations with a low salt hazard (salt index). If you use animal manures, composts, or sewage sludge, obtain an analysis of the material or test its salinity before you decide whether to apply it.

Boron

Boron (B) occurs naturally at high concentrations in the soils and water of certain Southern California and Central Coast locations. Boron toxicity can be a problem anywhere when you irrigate with low-quality groundwater or reclaimed wastewater. Boron toxicity usually is not a problem in inland San Diego County areas with decomposed granitic soils where boron levels are commonly low.

Where excessive, boron accumulates primarily in older avocado foliage, causing the margins or tips of leaves to turn yellow then brown and necrotic. Discolored foliage may die and drop prematurely. You can diagnose boron toxicity based on visible symptoms on plants, a knowledge of locations where boron is typically a problem, and ion-specific laboratory tests of leaves (see Table 9), soil, or water. Avocado trees are very sensitive to boron. Toxicity occurs when the soil or irrigation water exceeds about 0.5 ppm (0.5 mg/L) of boron.

Tiny amounts of boron are essential for plant growth, but there is a narrow "acceptable" range between sufficient and excessive concentrations. A well-timed foliar boron application during bloom may improve your trees' fruit yield and quality where boron levels are low. Boron should not, however, be applied in areas where excess boron is a problem.

Manage high boron levels with the methods described above for salinity, especially by modifying the frequency and amount of irrigation and by applying water that is low in boron. Improved drainage may gradually help to leach soil boron down below the root zone, but only if the water you use for irrigation is low in boron. Boron salts are not very soluble. Excess boron can be leached from soil only slowly over the long term.

pH

Hydrogen ion concentration (pH) affects the form and availability of nutrients and the ability of roots to absorb nutrients and water (Figure 17). Except for San Diego County growing areas, high pH is common in most of coastal and inland Southern California where soils are alkaline (calcareous, typically fine-textured, light-colored) or highly alkaline (sodic, high in sodium, often crusty and poorly drained). Chlorotic, necrotic, and undersized foliage develop when avocado trees grow in high-pH soil. Damage is often due to the resulting reduced availability of iron, manganese, and zinc. Any of the symptoms described earlier for those deficiencies can occur in alkaline soils due to high pH.

Chlorotic or necrotic foliage, slow growth, and distorted tissue can also develop if soil is too acidic. However, too low a pH is rarely a problem in California soils. A major exception is found in exposed subsoils from soil cuts and severe grading in the Coast Range, where plants are grown in what were formerly subsoils. Low pH can also become a problem when acidifying ammoniacal or urea nitrogen is applied repeatedly to slightly acidic granitic soils, such as in inland San Diego County.

A substance's pH value is expressed on a scale of 0 to 14, where low numbers represent acidic conditions and high numbers represent alkaline (also called basic) conditions. Neutral pH is rated as 7. Because pH values follow a negative logarithmic scale, ten times as many positively charged hydrogen ions are available at pH 6 as at pH 7. The pH of California water and soils is commonly higher than 7. Avocado grows best in acidic soils; a pH of about 6.2 to 6.5 is generally recommended.

You can diagnose pH problems based on your knowledge of local soil conditions and on tests of soil from the root zone. If you suspect you have alkaline soil, obtain a separate test of alkalinity to measure the soil's buffering capacity (its resistance to pH change), as discussed for alkalinity, below.

To lower a soil's pH before planting, mix elemental sulfur or iron sulfate into the topsoil several months before you plant or amend the soil with organic matter as discussed earlier in the "Iron" section. After planting, fertilizing with acidifying fertilizers such as ammonium sulfate or urea helps to lower pH.

If acidic soils have a pH lower than about 5, raise the pH by spreading agricultural lime beneath the tree canopy and slowly watering it in. When applying nitrogen to overly acidic soils, use a form of fertilizer that raises pH, such as calcium nitrate.

Alkalinity

The term *alkaline* (meaning basic or high pH) is often confused with *alkalinity*. High alkalinity results in high pH, but high pH does not always mean high alkalinity. A pH test by itself is not an indication of alkalinity. Alkalinity is a measure of the soil or water's ability to neutralize or buffer acids. When alkalinity is low, the pH of soil or water readily changes to more closely resemble the acidity of fertilizers and other amendments that are added. If alkalinity is high, the pH tends to stay high (and becomes even higher after repeated irrigations), even when acidic chemicals are added. Bicarbonates and carbonates such as calcium carbonate ($CaCO_3$) are usually the major contributors to alkalinity.

Tests of alkalinity indicate the amount of acidifying amendments or fertilizers it will take to lower the pH of the soil or water (Figure 18), and how feasible it is to remedy that

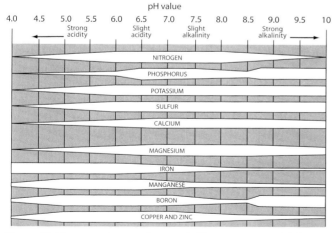

Figure 17. The approximate influence of pH on nutrient availability in mineral soils. Wider bars indicate the nutrient is more available at that pH. Adapted from Truog 1948.

high alkalinity. If soil or water has a high pH (are alkaline) but have relatively low alkalinity, the addition of acidifying amendments or fertilizers can help remedy the pH problem. If both pH and alkalinity are too high in soil or water, it generally is not feasible to lower the pH. In that case, the grower should find an alternative, less-alkaline water source for the avocado grove.

Phytotoxicity

Phytotoxicity is plant injury caused by the application of materials such as fertilizers and pesticides. Certain herbicides present the greatest risk of phytotoxicity, but fungicides, insecticides, and other materials can also damage plants. Pesticides can cause foliage or shoots to become discolored, distorted, spotted, and twisted, and to die. Affected foliage may be undersized and may drop prematurely, stunting plant growth. Plants exposed to certain herbicides may not exhibit damage until months later, such as when new growth occurs. Phytotoxicity is most likely to occur when the chemical applicator applies excessive rates or otherwise fails to follow label

directions. Adverse environmental conditions and treatment of trees when they are stressed also increase the likelihood of a phytotoxic reaction.

Common herbicide damage symptoms include chlorosis, necrosis, or spotting of leaves, and distortion or stunting of leaves, shoots, and roots. Each kind of herbicide causes characteristic damage symptoms, as illustrated in resources such as the UC Davis Weed Research and Information Center Web site (http://wric.ucdavis.edu).

Nonselective postemergence herbicides such as glyphosate and herbicides that selectively target broadleaf plants, such as 2,4-D, should only be used where you are able to completely avoid exposure to trees. Preemergence herbicides generally do not cause significant damage to established trees that have healthy, well-developed root systems, but an avocado tree's shallow root system may make it more susceptible to injury by preemergents, especially if the trees are young or poorly rooted.

A phytotoxic reaction can be difficult to diagnose. Symptoms can resemble those of many other maladies, including inappropriate irrigation, nutritional disorders, an unfavorable soil environment (compaction, pH, or salinity), certain foliar or root pathogens, and virtually anything that contributes to unhealthy roots.

A thorough knowledge of the grove's chemical application history and of characteristic symptoms for various types of injury can help you diagnose phytotoxicity. A laboratory may be able to test your soil for preemergence herbicides or test your foliage for systemic herbicides or spray residues. Samples should be tested soon after the suspected exposure, and you should tell the laboratory which specific pesticides you want them to test for.

If you suspect phytotoxicity, reevaluate your chemical application methods and materials, looking for ways to avoid causing future problems. Be diligent about providing affected trees with proper cultural care, especially appropriate irrigation. Avoid fertilization and do not overirrigate. If you amend the soil around small trees with activated charcoal or organic compost and then keep the soil moist when temperatures are warm, you can reduce the activity of certain preemergence herbicides, but incorporating the charcoal into the soil will injure tree roots. You can remove soluble herbicides by leaching the soil with water, but injury to the trees may increase after you irrigate. Do not leach the soil unless you are sure you can prevent offsite movement of herbicide-contaminated soil and water. Usually, you just have to wait for chemical residues to completely degrade and for the trees to outgrow their injuries.

A good way to avoid phytotoxicity is to employ alternative control methods whenever feasible, such as mulching to suppress weeds. Apply any pesticides carefully and as directed on the label.

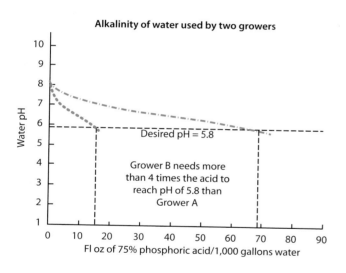

Alkalinity of water used by two growers

Fl oz of 75% phosphoric acid/1,000 gallons water

Desired pH = 5.8

Grower B needs more than 4 times the acid to reach pH of 5.8 than Grower A

●●●● Grower A (1.42 meq/L alkalinity)

─ ∙ ─ Grower B (6.20 meq/L alkalinity)

Figure 18. Do not confuse the terms "alkaline" (meaning pH higher than 7.0) and "alkalinity" (water's capacity to neutralize acids). For example, Grower A and Grower B illustrated here both have alkaline (pH 8) irrigation water. However, it takes more than four times as much phosphoric acid (68.6 fl oz/1,000 gal, compared to 15.8 fl oz/1,000 gal for Grower A water) to drop Grower B's water to pH 5.8, due to the greater alkalinity (more bicarbonates and carbonates, typically reported as milliequivalents per liter of water, or meq/L, where 1 meq/L = 50 ppm) of Grower B's water. Adapted from Bailey and Bilderback 1998.

Pesticides sometimes injure plants, most commonly because of careless use or application contrary to the label. Glyphosate (Roundup) exposure (shown here on pear) can cause shoots to develop undersized, puckered, and almost needlelike leaves, resembling the symptoms of severe zinc deficiency.

Injuries

Avocado fruit and trees are susceptible to injury from a variety of adverse environmental conditions, including fire, frost, heat, sunburn, and wind. Orchard management practices can cause physical or mechanical injury to any part of the tree, including the fruit, leaves, roots, and trunk. Pruning injures trees and operating tractors and other equipment in orchards can compact soil, crush roots, or injure bark. Symptoms of mechanical injury include bleeding or cankered bark, disfigured fruit, limb dieback, or tattered leaves. For example, where trunks are injected with nutrients or pesticides, application wounds can ooze profusely or develop cankers.

Exercise caution when operating heavy equipment near trees to avoid impacting trunks or crushing roots. Keep equipment and workers out of the groves when the soil is wet. Use good technique and appropriate equipment and materials and minimize the number and size of wounds when you are pruning or injecting trees. Avoid or minimize tree injections by using alternative application methods where feasible, such as foliar sprays or soil drenches.

Profuse bark bleeding developed after this trunk was wounded during phosphorus injection. This mechanical injury symptom superficially resembles some canker diseases.

This elongated canker developed due to mechanical injury from phosphorus injection. If you are injecting trunks, use good technique and minimize the number and size of wounds.

These brown gouges are old wounds caused during tree pruning with a chain saw.

This elongated fruit scar was caused by abrasion with the adjacent twig during movement by the wind.

Tattered leaves are generally harmless to trees, but they indicate a windy site prone to mechanical fruit damage. Plant windbreaks at exposed sites to reduce wind damage to fruit.

Carapace spot is the name for angular, cracked or corky blemishes that develop from rubbing of tender young fruit by leaves or stems. Scarring on the fruit on the right resembles damage from scab fungus (*Sphaceloma perseae*). Scab occurs in Florida, Mexico, and elsewhere but not in California. Mechanical scarring of the fruit on the left could be confused with avocado thrips feeding.

Carapace Spot

Rubbing or brushing of tender young fruit by leaves or stems causes corky or cracked blemishes that may form somewhat regular, angular divisions on the fruit skin. This mechanical injury damage is called *carapace spot* because the skin markings often resemble the markings on a turtle's shell. The flesh under the abraded skin is undamaged, but because of its exterior appearance the fruit is culled or downgraded at the packinghouse. Fruit are more prone to abrasion injury when exposed to strong winds. Plant tall, dense windbreaks to reduce mechanical injury in windy areas.

Sunburn

Bark, fruit, and leaves that are exposed to direct sunlight can be injured by heating and drying of tissue. Damage typically is most severe on the south and southwest sides of trees. Sunburn initially causes a pale yellowish area on the exposed side of the fruit. The center of the discolored area may turn black, brown, or red, and then become necrotic or withered. Sunburned leaves develop chlorotic, then necrotic blotches, which initially form between the veins. Sunburned twigs become cracked, discolored, purplish, or roughened on the exposed (usually upper) side. When sunburn is severe, affected trunk and limb bark and the cambium underneath can discolor and die, causing cankers that can girdle and possibly kill limbs.

Sunburn, sometimes called sunscald, typically occurs when trees defoliate, exposing fruit or previously shaded bark. Newly planted trees that have been grown in the nursery with their bark shaded and trees that are unable to take up enough water because of unhealthy roots or inappropriate irrigation are highly susceptible to sunburn.

Prevent sunburn by providing the trees with good growing conditions and proper cultural care, with particular attention to irrigation amounts and frequency of irrigation. Where feasible, prevent conditions that cause foliage to drop prematurely, including Phytophthora root rot and high persea mite populations. Do not irrigate defoliated trees until the soil in their root zone approaches dryness. By reducing the tree's transpiration rate, defoliation reduces its use of water, so the soil will remain wet longer beneath a defoliated tree than beneath an unaffected tree. Examine the soil carefully and frequently and modify your irrigation program to prevent the accumulation of excess moisture in the root zone.

Whitewash young trees routinely at planting. Whitewash the trunk and major limbs of older trees if they develop sparse canopies or are severely pruned. Special whitewash products are available, but you can use white interior latex paint diluted 50% with water. An inexpensive whitewash formula is 50 pounds (23 kg) of hydrated lime and 4 pounds (1.8 kg) of zinc sulfate to each 100 gallons (380 L) of water. Certain white film kaolin clay particle products can be sprayed onto the foliage to reduce sunburn and tree heat stress, apparently without interfering with leaf photosynthesis.

Sunburned leaves develop chlorotic, then necrotic blotches, initially between the veins. The brown to purplish, roughened bark on upper side of small branches is also from sunburn.

This elongated sunburn canker developed on an outer canopy branch exposed to direct afternoon sunlight. Mechanical injury and certain pathogens also cause cankers, but sunburn usually occurs in the south or west portion of trees.

The exposed side of sunburned fruit initially develops a pale yellowish discoloration that can darken in the center.

Advanced sunburn symptoms include extensive black, brown, or red discoloration. Sunburned areas are often circular and may become withered or necrotic. Similar damage is caused by fruit rot fungi and exposure to fire.

Whitewash trunks if older trees have been severely pruned or topworked, as shown here. Apply whitewash to the trunk and main limbs of all young trees at planting time and to any older tree with a sparse canopy, as can occur after defoliation due to Phytophthora root rot or abundant persea mites.

Heat Damage

High temperature and dry winds can cause fruit to drop, usually when the fruit are small. Less-severely affected fruit may develop normally, but the area around the stem may not properly mature and soften. Heat also causes *ringneck*, discussed below.

Heat damage usually is not widespread in a grove. It occurs after sudden high temperatures, perhaps due to water deficit. Provide good growing conditions and appropriate cultural care. Plant windbreaks in areas that are subject to hot, windy conditions, and apply sufficient irrigation water to trees when hot, windy conditions are expected.

Ringneck

A dry, corky, reddish brown to black lesion on the pedicle (stem) just above its attachment to the fruit is called ringneck. This lesion characteristically is $\frac{1}{12}$ to $\frac{4}{5}$ inch (2–20 mm) long and partially or completely encircles the fruit stalk. Ringneck may be a shallow lesion on the surface or it may extend deep into the stalk. Discolored tissue may peel from the pedicle. The skin of affected fruit may crack or darken. The seed coat may darken and leave a skinlike layer attached to the fruit's flesh. Affected fruit often stops growing, drops prematurely, or dries and mummifies.

Ringneck is believed to result from water deficiency during flowering and fruit set, although the cause is not definitely known. The malady develops when trees are underirrigated, if soil is overly dry, or when foliage dries rapidly because of hot, dry winds. Ringneck also occurs in trees that have suffered root damage, especially from Phytophthora root rot. Carefully monitor your trees' water needs and irrigate appropriately, especially during critical development periods such as flowering and fruit set. Apply and maintain adequate mulch to conserve soil moisture and improve root health. Control other stresses and injuries, such as root diseases.

Fire

Avocado trees planted near wildlands are susceptible to wildfires. If the tree canopies are singed without injury to major limbs or trunks, prune away the dead branches after foliage regrows. Provide proper cultural care to restore tree vigor and yield. Apply mulch to bare soil beneath the trees. Protect recovering trees from any further injury.

If a tree's trunk is burned and sap boils through bark, the tree will die. Rootstock suckers from below the graft will grow, but the fruit from the rootstock cultivar will not be marketable. Remove the dead trees and replant. Alternatively, if the old rootstock is healthy and free of root rot, you can graft new budwood to a vigorous sucker. The grafted scion will grow faster and come into production sooner than an entirely new tree, but grafting requires more maintenance to control rootstock suckers and train the budwood into a well-structured tree.

It can be difficult to keep your trees from burning during a wildfire. Advance preparation is a good approach. Control brush and weeds near your trees. Consider creating firebreaks (areas of little or no vegetation) around your groves to help keep fire from moving in. If fire threatens, irrigate the groves to increase their resistance to burning.

Frost and Freeze

Frost and freezing reduce bloom, fruit quality, and yield, and stunt tree growth. Frozen blossoms, leaves, and twigs turn brown or black within a few days. A tree may completely recover from cold damage, or it may die. Whether the tree will live or die may not be apparent for months after the damage occurs. Larger frozen wood may never blacken. You cannot accurately evaluate the severity of cold injury until new growth appears during spring and summer.

Wildland fire burned these trees, causing leaves to turn brown and drop. If canopies are singed without injury to major limbs or trunks, whitewash the trunks and main limbs and apply proper cultural practices. Wait until foliage regrows (it can sometimes take months), then prune off dead limbs.

The pale patches on this avocado trunk are from sap that boiled from the cambium during a wildfire. Unlike some causes of defoliation, from which trees may recover, this dry sap residue demonstrates that the tree was burned so severely that the trunk is dead.

Fruit damage and marketability can be difficult to assess after cold conditions. Affected fruit may develop no external symptoms or symptoms may be slow to appear. For example,

These suckers indicate that the scion may be dead. In most cases, rootstock suckers will produce unmarketable fruit unless grafted. If further investigation reveals that fire has killed the trunk, cut the tree down. You can then graft budwood to a vigorous sucker or plant a new tree.

Avocado fruit with a black lesion caused by wildfire. Sunburn and certain fruit rots are other maladies that cause similar damage.

stem browning a few days after cold weather is common in Fuerte avocados. Sometimes frozen fruit will discolor, crack, split, or drop. Severely frozen fruit may develop brown, water-soaked spots on the skin. The most common internal symptom is darkened xylem tissue resembling dark strings extending from the stem into the flesh. The flesh may turn black or gray overall. Consult your marketing organization and agricultural inspector to help determine whether fruit exposed to cold can be marketed.

Frost and freezing produce the same symptoms but occur under different conditions. Freezing occurs when air temperatures fall below 32°F (0°C) because a cold air mass has moved in. Frost or local radiation frost occurs during clear nights when plants radiate heat to the sky. During radiation cooling, plant tissue temperatures drop below 32°F (0°C) even though the air temperature may be warmer.

Non-Mexican cultivars, poor tree health, water stress, and young age all increase an avocado tree's susceptibility to cold damage (Tables 11, 12). The risk of injury to fruit and trees is influenced by how low temperatures go and for how long. For example, three or four hours of 29°F (–2°C) may injure fruit and trees more than a brief drop to 25°F (–4°C).

Managing Cold Damage. In areas where freezing or frost is a possibility, monitor temperatures throughout the grove. Several minimum thermometers can be mounted in standard shelters and then inspected regularly during threatening conditions. Electronic sensors in the grove are more convenient and can automatically and remotely warn of damaging temperatures. Various services monitor temperatures and can warn growers of crop-damaging weather.

Some management methods for freezing do not apply to frost, and vice versa. During a freeze, air must be heated to protect trees. Historically, growers have used special orchard burners (e.g., smudge pots or orchard heaters). The cost of fuel, risk of accidentally setting leaf mulch on fire, and more

rigorous air quality regulations have greatly reduced the use of heaters. Running irrigation throughout a cold night provides some heat to groves, as irrigation water temperatures are usually well above freezing and water must release heat before it can change from liquid form to ice.

Table 12. Some Factors That Increase Fruit and Tree Susceptibility to Frost and Freeze Damage.

Trees are:
- Young, up to about 3 years of age.
- Severely pruned or recently topworked, regardless of cultivar.
- Heavily shading most ground so soil absorbs less of the sun's heat and has less warmth to radiate at night.
- Crowded, so air flow is restricted, reducing downhill drainage of cold air, blocking air mixing by fans, and limiting effect of grove heating.
- Weak or unhealthy.
- Water stressed; withholding irrigation water in the fall to "harden up" foliage can make trees more susceptible.
- Growing in dry soil, moist soil can absorb and retain more heat, which radiates to trees at night.
- Cultivars more sensitive to cold.

This reddish brown discoloration or scorched appearance on the underside of leaves commonly develops after frost damage.

Table 11. Critical Temperatures Below Which Fruit and Trees Are Highly Subject to Cold Damage.

Race	Typical cultivars	Critical temperature
Mexican	Bacon, Duke, Mexicola, Topa Topa, Zutano	25°F
Hybrids	Fuerte, Hass, Puebla	28°F
Guatemalan (tender)	Endranol, MacArthur, Nabal, Rincon, Ryan	29°F
Guatemalan (very tender)	Anaheim, Carlsbad, Challenge, Dickinson, Hellen	30°F
West Indian	Rarely grown in California; the least cold-tolerant cultivars.	

This table provides only a general guideline. Many factors affect actual susceptibility to cold. See Table 12.

During radiation cooling (frost), there is often a temperature inversion where the air a short distance above the ground is warmer than the air nearest to the ground. In a frost situation, fans may protect trees by mixing the colder, ground-level air with warmer, upper-level air.

Choose a good growing location to minimize the chances of cold damage. Cold air is heavier than warmer air, so planting on a slope allows cold air to flow down and out of your groves. Select rootstocks and scions that are less susceptible to cold (Table 11). For example, Mexican avocados are more cold tolerant than Guatemalan cultivars. Provide your trees with good cultural care, and especially with appropriate irrigation. The practice of withholding irrigation water in the fall to "harden up" foliage can actually weaken trees and make them more susceptible to cold. Dry soil absorbs and retains less heat than wet soil, reducing the soil's capacity to warm trees at night. Providing your trees with good cultural care earlier in the season may also reduce their susceptibility to freezing.

Consider thinning dense groves to increase the amount of sunshine that reaches the soil surface and to improve air flow. Delay pruning until early spring whenever possible to minimize the likelihood that succulent, new flush induced by pruning will emerge during cold temperatures. The risk of frost is somewhat less if some soil is kept bare, so mow or otherwise keep low any cover crop or other vegetation near trees during late fall and winter.

Protect trees from sunburn if any foliage freezes and dies. Do not prune freeze-damaged plants until after you are certain about which tissues are dead. It is best to wait until after the next spring, when new shoots are at least 2 or 3 feet long, and then remove the dead wood. This will usually be in midsummer, 6 to 8 months following the cold damage.

If young trees freeze to below the bud union, you can bud or graft the desired cultivar onto strong suckers the following spring. If sucker growth is weak, replace the whole tree. Continual irrigation, grove heaters (if located safely away from mulch), wind machines, or a combination of these are the most effective methods for preventing damage when cold temperatures are imminent. Certain foliar sprays can modestly increase avocado trees' tolerance to cold, but some materials advertised as such do not actually work. Young trees can be wrapped with paper, mounded with dirt, or surrounded with corn stalks to reduce radiation heat loss.

Heaters. Heaters usually provide more effective protection than wind machines, but they can be unpleasant and expensive to operate. A large number of small fires scattered throughout the grove provide better protection than a few large fires. Light only enough heaters to maintain a safe temperature, keeping additional heaters and fuel distributed in the groves for use if needed. Disadvantages include the smokiness of certain fuels, costs (investment, maintenance, and operation), fire hazards around dry leaves, and labor

Leaves curl and turn brown or black within a few days of frost or freezing, as shown here on citrus. Cold-damaged, necrotic leaves drop prematurely.

JACK KELLY CLARK

requirements. Smoke ordinances regulate the use of heaters in some communities. Permanently installed pipeline heaters that burn oil or natural gas are efficient but very expensive. Propane heaters are clean-burning and easy to maintain. Nine-gallon bowl heaters with improved stack designs, burning low-grade diesel oil, have been widely used.

Wind Machines. Fans are useful for groves on flat land, but they are not very useful for groves on slopes because the slanting orchard floor already provides good air movement. Large fans mix the air so the coldest air near the ground is diluted with somewhat warmer air from above the grove. Fans typically are installed on permanent wind towers. Growers can also use helicopters, hovering and slowly flying low over the avocado groves. Fans alone can be sufficient to prevent damage from local radiation frosts when temperatures go only 2 or 3 degrees Fahrenheit below the damaging point, and they are more economical and require less labor than heaters. A helicopter can be expensive and may not be available, depending on when, where, and how often you need it. Fans are not effective, however, during freezing conditions, when temperatures go 4 or 5 degrees Fahrenheit or more below the damaging point, or when there is not a layer of somewhat warmer air above the grove. Fans provide unequal protection through the grove and are less effective in young plantings.

Genetic Disorders

Various genetic disorders and maladies of unknown cause damage avocado fruit. See other publications such as *Avocado Fruit Abnormalities and Defects Revisited* (Hofshi and Arpaia 2002) for more extensive discussion and photographs.

Cuke

Certain trees (usually Fuertes) sometimes produce unusually elongated fruit. This disorder is called *cuke* because these oblong, green fruit resemble cucumbers. When sliced, the fruit are seedless or contain only a degenerated ovule. Cukes are believed to result from incomplete fertilization of the ovule during pollination. Avoid propagating from trees that are affected by this disorder and consider culling affected trees.

Wind machines can help protect trees from frost or radiation frost. Fans mix the colder, ground-level air with warmer, upper-layer air.

Avocado trees need protection from cold, especially when grown on flat land. Because of the fire hazard, fuel-burning smudge pots are best used when they can be placed on bare soil near trees as shown here, away from mulch or dry weeds.

These Fuerte fruit are abnormally elongated and lack a seed pit. The cause is a genetic mutation called "cuke" because affected fruit resemble cucumbers.

Embossment

Occasionally, a section of fruit surface will be raised slightly or be a darker color, most often on Fuerte. This is *sectional chimera* or genetic mutation called *embossment*. This problem is of only minor importance. The only known management technique is to cull affected fruit.

Disorders of Unknown Cause

A deep, dark indentation in fruit (crick-side), split fruit, warty fruit, and woody avocados occasionally develop due to unknown causes.

Crick-Side

Crick-side has also been called *kink-neck* or *kink-side*. Crick-side is a distinct depression or distortion on one side of fruit near the stem end. Sometimes the depressed area turns black. Affected fruit may drop or they may grow and mature, still remaining distorted. Crick-side is usually found on trees that are carrying a heavy load of fruit.

The cause is unknown. It may develop as a result of high temperatures or temporary water stress. Provide the trees with good growing conditions and proper cultural care to maximize fruit quality and yield.

Split Fruit

Split fruit are relatively uncommon in avocados. Fruit occasionally break open laterally or longitudinally, particularly on thin-skinned cultivars such as Bacon and Zutano. If overmature, both cultivars are prone to split laterally around their base, where a dark, sunken depression will develop in the fruit (sometimes called "blossom-end rot").

This embossment or sectional chimera is a genetic mutation. It causes a raised ridge or dark distortion on avocado fruit.

"Crick" or "crick-side" refers to avocados with a depressed, dark indentation near the stem end of fruit. The cause is unknown—possibly high temperatures or water stress.

This dark discoloration and cracking around the bottom of fruit is sometimes called blossom-end rot. Affected fruit may split and drop. This damage is to Bacon avocados, which are relatively thin-skinned. The fruit were overmature, and exposed to prolonged rainy conditions, which caused water to collect at the bottom of the fruit.

Warty Fruit

Very young fruit occasionally develop a small or large number of small, wartlike protuberances on their skin. These blemishes become less conspicuous as the fruit mature, and typically are no longer evident by harvest time. Insect or mite feeding or *Botrytis*-infected floral parts coming into contact with young fruit may be the cause. This malady can be more common during wet, rainy springs.

Woody Avocados

Avocado fruit sometimes develop into a grotesque, woody structure that only superficially resembles an avocado. The structure is hard and dark brown, and may have cauliflower-shaped protrusions. Fuerte and Hass varieties have been found to exhibit this rare malady. No management is known except to cull affected fruit.

Avocado fruit sometimes develops into a gnarled, hard, brown structure. The cause of woody avocado is unknown, so the only management is to cull affected "fruit."

Diseases

Avocado diseases are caused by pathogenic microorganisms and noninfectious disorders (environmental stress). Noninfectious diseases caused by adverse growing conditions such as inadequate water management are discussed in the fourth chapter, "Cultural Practices and Abiotic Disorders." Some of the most devastating but avoidable diseases are caused by fungi and other pathogens, as discussed below.

Disease symptoms differ depending on a number of factors, such as the rootstock cultivar, growing location, and time of year. The severity of both the disease and its damage depends on three basic factors, known together as the disease triangle (Figure 19): the virulence of the pathogen, the susceptibility and age of the host plant, and environmental conditions (such as moisture, soil characteristics, and temperature). How the disease is expressed in symptoms and how the pathogens impact the tree also depend on where the infection occurs on the tree.

Most root and crown diseases cause similar aboveground symptoms. Unhealthy aerial plant parts are usually the first clue to the presence of these pathogens. Damage to the roots and root crown inhibits the uptake of nutrients and water and their transport to and from the roots. Affected trees typically have fewer leaves than normal, leaves that are chlorotic and undersized, necrotic leaf tips, premature leaf drop, terminal dieback, and reduced fruit yield. Root and root crown diseases usually cause premature death of the tree, either suddenly or after a slow decline.

Limb and trunk cankers injure bark and the cambium under the bark. The cambium produces food-conducting phloem in the inner bark and water-conducting xylem in

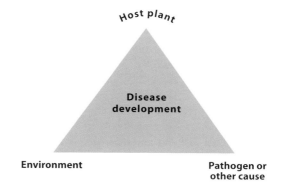

Figure 19. The disease triangle. Disease results from interactions among a susceptible host plant, an environment favorable for disease development, and virulent pathogens. Time (such as season or duration of disease-favoring conditions) is also a factor, so this disease-development interaction is sometimes illustrated as a pyramid with time as a fourth axis.

the outer wood. Damage to cambium inhibits its production of new vascular tissue, thereby reducing the tree's capacity to transport plant food (such as carbohydrates), minerals, and water; this results in reduced growth and causes many of the symptoms described above for root and crown decays. If cankers kill the cambium around the entire circumference of a trunk or branch (a condition called girdling), the portion of the tree above the cankers will die.

Vascular pathogens such as *Verticillium dahliae* fungus in avocado invade and plug the xylem, stopping the transport of water up from the roots. This causes aboveground plant parts to wilt and show symptoms that look like those of root and crown decay. Certain other pathogens sometimes spread within plants via vascular fluids, including the sunblotch viroid (ASBV) and *Xanthomonas campestris*, the cause of bacterial canker. *Xylella fastidiosa* is a vascular pathogen of grapes and certain other crops and is spread by the glassy-winged sharpshooter and other leafhoppers. Glassy-winged sharpshooters can be abundant in avocado groves that grow near citrus. No *Xylella* diseases affecting avocado have been found in California, although a strain of *X. fastidiosa* that is pathogenic to avocado has been reported in Central America.

Several pathogens infect fruit, leaves, small branches, or twigs. Lesions on fruit are the effects of greatest concern resulting from these pathogens, and those symptoms include anthracnose, Dothiorella fruit rot, Phytophthora fruit rot, and stem end rot. Sometimes the same organism can cause a variety of different diseases depending on which plant part it infects. For example, Dothiorella fruit rot is caused by the same group of fungal species that cause Dothiorella canker and Dothiorella leaf and stem blight. *Phytophthora citricola* causes Phytophthora fruit rot and Phytophthora canker. For more information, consult the latest update of *Avocado: UC IPM Pest Management Guidelines: Diseases* (online at www.ipm.ucdavis.edu) and other publications listed in the suggested reading.

Monitoring and Diagnosis

Learn which diseases are most likely to affect avocado, and then regularly inspect your groves for disease signs (actual structures of pathogens, such as *Armillaria* and *Ganoderma* mushrooms or other fruiting bodies) and symptoms (outward expressions of poor plant health, such as pale, wilted leaves). Be especially alert for conditions that favor pathogen infection and disease development, such as a significantly higher-than-normal level of rain or drainage from nearby, unhealthy groves. Regular monitoring will allow you to take early, prompt action that can minimize tree damage and preserve fruit quality and yield.

Concentrate periodic scouting on locations where your grove has a history of disease and where growing conditions are less favorable, such as low-lying areas with prolonged waterlogging of soil and contaminated runoff water. Also inspect trees near the top of slopes, where they may be subject to stress from less-efficient irrigation, shallower (eroded) soils, and more exposure to drying winds. Examine trees near where harvest bins are brought in and stored, as these sometimes are contaminated with pathogens from other groves.

Where a tree looks unhealthy, examine as many of its parts as possible to help get an accurate diagnosis of the cause. Brush away mulch to inspect the appearance of feeder roots. Remove soil from around the root crown and cut beneath discolored bark to expose cankers or fungal mycelium. A chisel, a hatchet, a hand lens, a pocket knife, and a shovel are important monitoring tools.

Keep accurate records of your grove inspections, and repeat the inspections at regular intervals to document the progress or seasonal nature of symptoms and to assess whether management actions are having the desired effect. Carry photocopies of maps of the grove to help you accurately record specific locations, and note the date of your observations. Use a notebook or record-keeping form, perhaps a form copied onto the back of each map. Use fluorescent spray paint and colored plastic flagging to mark trees with symbols or color codes that are keyed to symptoms or the suspected cause of disease and make a note of what each color or symbol means.

Be aware that similar symptoms can have very different causes and that plants are often affected by more than one stress or malady at a time. When you find a symptom on a tree, inspect several nearby trees for earlier, subtler, or more characteristic symptoms. Patterns in symptoms among several trees can give you a clue as to the cause. Do not base your diagnosis on only one symptom. You will often need to observe several symptoms and growing conditions in combination before you can reliably diagnose a particular disease. Compare your field observations with the descriptions and photographs in this book to help identify the causes of damage. Be aware, though, that certain diseases can be confirmed only by an expert or through laboratory tests on properly collected samples. Accurate disease diagnosis requires a combination of experience, knowledge, observation skills, and information resources.

Prevention and Management

The best way to achieve disease control is through an integrated approach of prevention and management. Most diseases are effectively managed only by means of prevention or action during an early stage of development. Once symptoms become apparent or severe, your treatment options become more limited, diseased trees may no longer be salvageable, and a larger portion of the grove may be damaged. Consider the pathogen, the age and condition of your trees, and the trees' environment when you are looking for ways to manage

Unhealthy aerial parts are often the first obvious symptom that trees are diseased. Phytophthora root rot infects the left tree, but this leaf yellowing can result from any of a number of causes, including Armillaria root rot and too much or too little irrigation.

Several species of fungi, inappropriate soil conditions, and poor water management are primary causes of most diseases in avocado. The shoot dieback and paucity of leaves shown here were caused by Phytophthora root rot.

Virtually any injury to limbs or trunks can cause bark to discolor and exude liquid, which often dries to a whitish powder. Dothiorella canker (shown here), bacterial canker, avocado black streak, and Citricola or Phytophthora canker are common causes of these disease symptoms.

disease (Figure 19). Most actions that are feasible involve manipulating the tree and its care and environment, since many pathogens are difficult to control directly. Prevention is the most effective strategy and often the only approach that will avoid losses of yield and damage to trees. Consult the latest update of *Avocado: UC IPM Pest Management Guidelines: Diseases* (online at www.ipm.ucdavis.edu) for more information on avocado disease management. See Table 1 and the third chapter, "Managing Pests in Avocados," for a summary of practices that growers use to manage many different pests.

Plant Wisely. Choose a good growing site. Well-drained soil is especially important for avocado production. A grove planted on upper slopes or hillsides will generally have good drainage. Prepare the soil well before planting, especially if you are planting on lower slopes or valley floors, which often have subsurface soil layers that inhibit good drainage. Install subsurface drains and backhoe or rip through any impervious subsoils before planting, if warranted. Properly grade your grove site and plant the trees on a broad, raised mound or soil berm to improve drainage. If planting on raised soil, loosen and otherwise properly prepare subsoil layers so roots will be able to penetrate the soil beneath mounds and anchor the trees well to avoid tipping trunks.

Install an efficient irrigation system that is carefully designed and maintained to suit the climatic and physical conditions at the site. Obtain certified, disease-free nursery stock where possible. Diseased nursery stock historically has been a major source of diseases such as avocado root rot, bacterial canker, and Dothiorella canker. Plant rootstocks that are resistant to or tolerant of key diseases such as Phytophthora root rot. Because rootstock cultivars that are resistant to one disease may be more susceptible to another, consider planting a mixture of the recommended rootstock cultivars (see Table 2).

Use Good Sanitation. Prevent the movement of soil and water from pathogen-infested areas, as this can spread microorganisms that cause Phytophthora root rot and other diseases. Clean bins, ladders, vehicles, and other plant- and soil-contaminated equipment before bringing it into your groves. Stay out of groves when the soil surface is wet. Prune to develop tree structure, limit tree height, improve air circulation and spray penetration, and remove dead and dying wood. Dispose of dead wood and (where practical) old fruit away from your groves. Sterilize tools before you begin to work on a new tree so you will not mechanically spread pathogens. To sterilize and eliminate most pathogens, scrub tools clean and then soak them in a 1.5% sodium hypochlorite solution for several minutes. Rotate among several tools as you work so some can soak in the disinfectant while you are using others. Be sure to use a registered disinfectant and follow label directions.

Provide Good Cultural Care. Proper irrigation is critical for improving and maintaining tree health and managing disease. Schedule the frequency and amount of irrigation using reliable methods, such as monitoring local evapotranspiration or using devices such as soil tensiometers (described in the fourth chapter, "Cultural Practices and Abiotic Disorders"). Avoid sprinkling water onto the trunks and minimize waterlogging of soil near the root crown, especially in groves with a history of Phytophthora canker and crown rot. Use high-quality irrigation water without high overall salinity or an excess of specific minerals such as boron, chloride, and sodium. The extra cost of purchasing high-quality water is usually more than justified by the reduced incidence of disease and increased crop quality and yield.

Improve soil conditions with appropriate amendments, including gypsum applications and maintenance of a thick organic mulch beneath trees. Provide the trees with appropriate nutrition, primarily modest amounts of nitrogen and occasional applications of potassium, phosphorus, and zinc (and perhaps boron in some locations) to maintain good growth. Avoid overfertilization, which can itself induce deficiency symptoms, pollute water, and reduce yields. If you plan to apply a fungicide, choose and apply that material carefully. Use fungicides only in combination with other recommended practices.

Regularly monitor groves to detect problems. Concentrate your scouting in locations with a history of disease and where growing conditions are less favorable. For example, the avocado tree in the foreground is growing near the top of a rocky ridge. The drying winds and relatively shallower topsoil at this site likely promote stress- and drought-aggravated diseases such as Dothiorella canker.

Nursery stock can be a source of diseases such as Phytophthora root rot, bacterial canker, and Dothiorella canker. Especially when planting in new areas, use trees that are certified to be free of diseases—especially avocado root rot and sunblotch. Inspect new stock and determine the cause of any questionable appearance before you plant the trees.

PATHOGENS THAT INFECT THROUGH ROOTS

Avocado root rot, Armillaria root rot, and several other fungal diseases discussed here infect avocado trees through their root systems. Sunblotch viroid can also infect via the roots, but it will be discussed later. Most root-infecting fungal pathogens cause similar aboveground symptoms, and unhealthy aerial plant parts are usually the first indicators of these pathogens' presence.

Avocado Root Rot or Phytophthora Root Rot

Phytophthora cinnamomi

Phytophthora root rot is the most serious avocado disease in California and most other avocado-producing areas of the world. The causal agent, *Phytophthora cinnamomi*, has more than 1,000 host species, including many annual flower crops, berries, deciduous fruit trees, ornamentals, and vegetables. Although they are not true fungi (technically, they are oomycetes or water molds related to brown algae), *Phytophthora* species have many fungus-like attributes.

Preventing soil and water movement from infested areas is a key strategy for managing certain pathogens. This culvert will divert runoff that may be contaminated with *Phytophthora* propagules, preventing infested soil and water from draining into the adjacent grove.

Symptoms and Damage

Foliar symptoms of avocado root rot include small, pale green or yellowish leaves. Often, the leaves wilt and have brown necrotic tips. Foliage is sparse and new growth is rare, or new leaves may be small and pale. There may be little mulch under infected trees. Small branches die back in the tree canopy, exposing other branches to sunburn because of the lack of shading foliage. Fruit yield declines, but diseased trees will in many cases set a heavy crop of small fruit.

Roots that are pencil-sized or larger are seldom attacked by *Phytophthora cinnamomi*. The pathogen infects the smaller (feeder) roots, and small brownish lesions encircling feeder roots are an early symptom of infection. In advanced stages of this disease, the small, fibrous feeder roots are scarce. Where present, the small roots are black, brittle, and dead from infection. The paucity of healthy feeder roots prevents nutrient and water uptake, and the soil under diseased trees stays wet even though foliage is wilted. Affected trees will decline and die, some rapidly and others more slowly.

Seasonal Development

Root rot thrives in areas of excess soil moisture and poor drainage. Trees of any size and age may be affected. The pathogen is easily spread and growers and workers can move it unawares from a few trees to the entire orchard (Figure 20). *Phytophthora cinnamomi* spreads through the movement of contaminated nursery stock (avocado and other plants), on equipment and shoes, in seed from fruit that have lain on infested soil, or through any human or animal activity that moves moist soil from one place to another. *Phytophthora* produces spores that are specialized to spread from tree to tree easily and rapidly in water as it moves over or through the soil.

These chlorotic or pale, wilted leaves with brown necrotic tips are advanced foliar symptoms of avocado root rot.

The center avocado tree has a sparse canopy, as evidenced by its large limbs being visible from a distance. Infection by *Phytophthora cinnamomi* was promoted by the tree's location in a gully down slope from infested areas. *Phytophthora* readily spreads as spores in surface water, subsurface drainage, or by any means that moves moist soil.

These unusually abundant, small fruit are characteristic of trees infected with avocado root rot. A sparse canopy of drooping older leaves and new shoots of small, pale leaves are other typical symptoms.

Management Guidelines

You will achieve the best control of Phytophthora root rot if you use an integrated approach that emphasizes prevention. Use certified disease-free nursery stock (if available) and root-rot-resistant cultivars. Inspect the roots, and if their health seems questionable, seek advice from a farm advisor or private consultant before you plant the trees. Employ stringent sanitation measures, good cultural practices, and

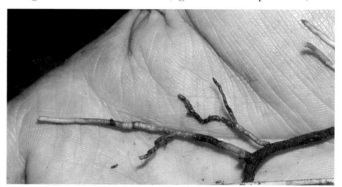

When trees are infected with avocado root rot, small rootlets turn black as shown here. The black roots are brittle and readily break when bent. Healthy rootlets flex without breaking.

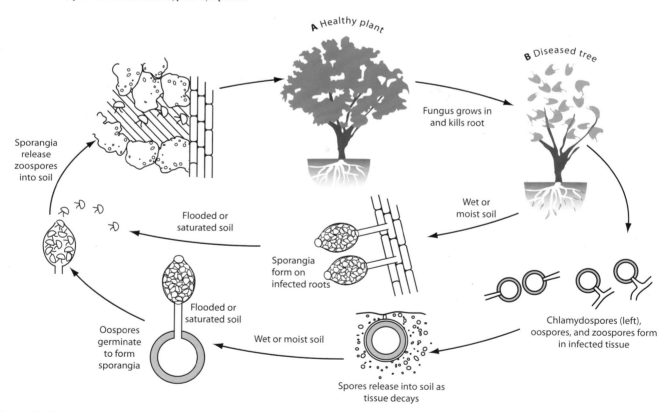

Figure 20. The avocado root rot disease cycle due to spread and infection by *Phytophthora cinnamomi*. Infected root tissue develops spore-forming structures (sporangia) and produces spores (chlamydospores, oospores, zoospores). *Phytophthora* spores move or persist in soil and water and infect healthy trees. A. To protect healthy avocado trees: prevent the spread of pathogen-contaminated soil and water to uninfested areas, apply gypsum, mulch beneath trees using coarse organic material, and provide optimal irrigation and other cultural care. B. To prolong the life of infected trees: improve irrigation and other cultural practices and apply an effective fungicide if appropriate. Adapted from Wilcox 1992.

appropriate chemical controls. The most important control of this disease is good irrigation management. For example, where new trees are interplanted among older trees, separate irrigation lines are needed to ensure appropriate irrigation frequency and amounts for the different-aged trees. Consult the latest update of *Avocado: UC IPM Pest Management Guidelines: Diseases* (online at www.ipm.ucdavis.edu) for more information on fungicides and avocado disease management.

Provide Favorable Soil Conditions. In new plantings, avoid soil conditions that are favorable to root rot development, including poor drainage, salinity, or pathogen infestations. Plant on well-drained soil or improve the soil's drainage characteristics before planting. Methods include planting on a soil berm, deep-ripping impervious subsoils, and installing subsurface drains. Root rot develops in soils that have poor internal drainage. Accumulated moisture increases the ability of *Phytophthora* to form spores and infect roots. In established plantings, manage the soil carefully to keep excess moisture from accumulating in the soil.

Use Certified, Disease-Free Nursery Stock. Historically, diseased nursery stock has been a major source of the spread of avocado root rot in California. Nurseries should use disinfested propagation material (such as seed immersed in water at 120° to 122°F (49° to 50°C) for 30 minutes, and then quickly cooled), pasteurized soil mix, clean irrigation water from deep wells or disinfested surface water, and stringent sanitation practices to prevent introduction or spread of the pathogen. Nurseries that rely only on fungicides can promote fungicide resistance and produce symptomless plants that nonetheless have infections that will develop later, after planting. Request certified, disease-free plants, especially when planting new areas, since the disease is especially damaging to young trees.

Plant Resistant Rootstocks. Certain rootstock cultivars are resistant to or tolerant of root rot, including Dusa, Latas, and others listed in Table 2. Newer recommended cultivars may also be available, such as Uzi and Zentmyer. Barr Duke, Duke 7, and Duke 9 can also be good rootstocks, but lack the *Phytophthora* resistance of some newer cultivars. Clonal cultivars are available, and rootstocks produced in nurseries using the clonal method are recommended because clonally produced cultivars are more reliably resistant than rootstocks from seedlings. Be aware that resistant rootstocks are not immune to root rot. If you plant or maintain them under adverse conditions, they may be killed by a combination of the adverse conditions and the pathogen.

Prevent Soil or Water Movement from Infested Areas. Excluding *P. cinnamomi* from an uninfested grove is the most economical control method. The pathogen can move by any means by which moist soil is moved and it can also be spread downhill from an infested area, traveling in surface or subsurface drainage water. Install watertight drains to divert surface runoff if a diseased area lies uphill from a healthy grove. Control gophers, as their burrows can provide a channel for the waterborne pathogen. Do not work in infested groves when the soil surface is wet; *Phytophthora* is readily spread by activities such as walking or driving on wet, infested soil. Bring only clean bins and equipment into your groves. Begin harvesting and other activities in healthy areas of the grove and work last of all in diseased areas to minimize pathogen movement.

Establish a Barrier. If the pathogen occurs in only one area of the grove and cannot spread downhill in surface runoff or drainage water, erect a physical barrier to prevent people and activities from spreading it into protected areas. Establish the barrier at least two tree rows beyond where tests indicate the pathogen is present. The barrier should be a fence with warning signs to inhibit movement between the affected area and healthy sections of the grove.

Irrigate Carefully. Appropriate irrigation is the single most critical element in improving the health of affected trees and managing root rot. Schedule the frequency and amount of irrigations based on sophisticated methods, such as according to local evapotranspiration rates or according to soil moisture data from monitoring devices such as tensiometers installed in your grove. Good irrigation management is especially important where trees are diseased, near the margins of diseased areas of groves, or growing in thick mulch. Because high soil moisture favors root rot development, careful irrigation can retard the spread of the disease and often prolong the life of affected trees. Diseased trees have fewer roots to take up water, so avoid watering soil that is already wet since it could become waterlogged and increase the severity of the disease.

Use High-Quality Irrigation Water. Irrigation water with high overall salinity or an excess of boron, chloride, or sodium promotes *Phytophthora* infection of roots. Water from some sources, such as surface water runoff from infested soil, can itself be contaminated with *Phytophthora*. The extra cost of purchasing high-quality water is generally justified by the benefits it brings: less incidence of disease and increased crop quality and yields.

Apply Gypsum and Mulch. Create soil conditions that suppress Phytophthora root rot by applying gypsum under the canopy of each tree, perhaps 25 pounds (11 kg) beneath a medium-sized tree. Apply at least 4 to 6 inches (10–15 cm) of coarse organic mulch onto the soil beneath the tree canopies, but keep the mulch several inches away from the trunk itself. Use organic mulch such as avocado trimmings, composted green waste (yard trimmings), or hardwood chips. Mulching promotes the development of beneficial microorganisms antagonistic to *Phytophthora cinnamomi* and reduces the adverse effects of saline soil and water. Gypsum supplies calcium, which suppresses the formation of *Phytophthora* spores. For best results, apply mulch and gypsum when the orchard is being established. As the trees grow they will produce their own mulch, but by applying additional mulch containing mostly ground wood you provide better *Phytophthora* control. Apply additional gypsum as the old material dissolves from view.

Provide Appropriate Nutrition. Moderate amounts of nitrogen promote good growth that helps make avocado trees more tolerant to root rot, but avoid applying excessive amounts of fertilizer. In particular, avoid applying large amounts of animal manures or other products high in ammonia or salts. Avocado roots are sensitive to ammonia and salts.

Rotate Crops. Replanting infested soil to resistant crops for at least a few years is one way to manage avocado root rot. *Phytophthora* has a wide range of hosts, but there are plants that are not susceptible. For example, cherimoya, citrus, and persimmon are highly resistant to the *Phytophthora* species that cause Phytophthora root rot in avocado.

Chemical Control. Certain fungicides help to control root rot when applied to soil, in irrigation water, or (by injection) directly into trees. Remember, though, that good control requires that you use fungicides in combination with other recommended practices, such as careful irrigation and

application of wood chip mulch. Fungicide efficacy varies greatly depending on the method and timing of application and the specific situation in your grove, such as disease severity and tree age. For fungicide recommendations, see the latest update of *Avocado: UC IPM Pest Management Guidelines: Diseases* (online at www.ipm.ucdavis.edu).

If only a few trees are affected and the disease is detected early, you may be able to cut the trees off at ground level and fumigate the soil. However, eradication of *P. cinnamomi* from infested field soil is extremely difficult. In many cases, *P. cinnamomi* will re-invade fumigated soil and the resulting avocado root rot will be worse than it was in the first place because populations of the rest of the soil's microbial community and competing microorganisms have been reduced by the fumigation.

Good sanitation practices are needed so that avocado trees bordering a nursery are not a source of pathogens. For example, drainage from uphill should be diverted to avoid spreading *Phytophthora* propagules into the grove.

Brush away mulch and carefully inspect root health if you suspect avocado root rot. If roots are sparse or black, this strongly indicates root rot. Roots larger than pencil size are seldom attacked by *Phytophthora cinnamomi,* so examine the small feeder roots.

Planting these young avocado trees on a soil berm to improve drainage and applying mulch and gypsum greatly help to control root rot. When planting on raised soil, properly prepare subsurface layers so the roots will penetrate well and anchor the trees.

Water puddling under this trunk indicates excessively wet soil, which favors development of *Phytophthora cinnamomi* spores and promotes their infection of roots. Poor aeration or a lack of oxygen in excessively wet soil can also directly injure or kill trees by asphyxiating their roots.

Muddy tire ruts are an alarming indication that workers may be spreading propagules of root rot, the most serious avocado disease. Stay out of groves when the soil surface is wet from recent irrigation or rain.

Bird's nest fungus (*Cyathus olla*) produced these small, tan, cup-shaped structures, which contain egglike fruiting bodies (peridioles) full of spores. Water splashing into the cups flings the fruiting bodies up into nearby plants where they stick and release their spores into the air several feet above the ground. Bird's nest fungus is one of many microorganisms that are antagonistic to Phytophthora root rot. This and other beneficial fungi are favored by thick organic mulch beneath trees.

JACK KELLY CLARK

Armillaria Root Rot

Armillaria mellea

Armillaria root rot infects many crops and native and ornamental plants. Common hosts include avocado, cherimoya, citrus, and oak trees. The fungus persists in infested roots and wood in soil, infecting new plantings and spreading to infect nearby plants (Figure 21).

Symptoms and Damage

The *Armillaria* fungus can become well established in roots and the root crown before any symptoms are visible above ground. Infected trees usually die prematurely, and if they are young trees they often die quickly after infection. Mature trees may die quickly or slowly, or they may recover at least temporarily if conditions become good for tree growth and poor for disease development.

Wilted, downward-hanging foliage is often the first obvious symptom of Armillaria root rot. Other symptoms include yellowing of the foliage, leaf drop, and dieback of upper limbs. During rainy fall and winter periods, short-lived mushrooms often appear around the base of *Armillaria*-infected trees. The mushroom caps vary in color from off-white to honey-yellow to almost black. Each cap is about 1 to 10 inches (2.5–25 cm) in diameter. The mushrooms always occur in groups, never singly. Mushrooms have a ring on the stalk just under the cap

This wilted, downward-hanging foliage is a symptom of infection by *Armillaria mellea.* Other symptoms of Armillaria root rot include yellowing of foliage, leaf drop, and dieback of upper limbs.

JACK KELLY CLARK

During the rainy fall and winter, short-lived mushrooms often grow around the base of *Armillaria*-infected trees such as this almond. Scout your groves for these mushrooms after rains. Mark any trees where mushrooms occur, confirm whether the cause is Armillaria root rot, and then develop and implement a management plan.

The most reliable sign of Armillaria root rot is white, cottony fungal mycelial growth in cambial tissue. If trees exhibit aboveground symptoms of infection, expose the root crown and cut under the crown's bark to look for *Armillaria* mycelium.

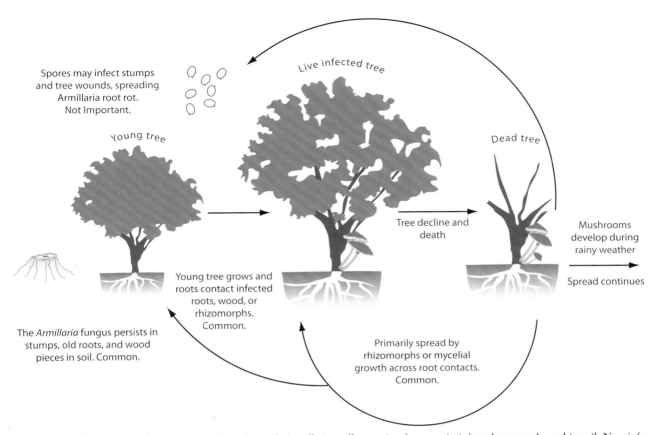

Spores may infect stumps and tree wounds, spreading Armillaria root rot. Not Important.

Live infected tree

Young tree

Dead tree

Tree decline and death

Mushrooms develop during rainy weather

Spread continues

Young tree grows and roots contact infected roots, wood, or rhizomorphs. Common.

The *Armillaria* fungus persists in stumps, old roots, and wood pieces in soil. Common.

Primarily spread by rhizomorphs or mycelial growth across root contacts. Common.

Figure 21. Armillaria root rot development cycle and spread. *Armillaria mellea* persists for years in infected roots and wood in soil. New infections occur when roots grow and contact infected roots or wood or when fungal rhizomorphs grow short distances in soil to contact nearby plants. *Armillaria* spores can infect stumps and tree wounds, but spores apparently are not an important source of Armillaria root rot in California. Eliminating infected trees and removing old stumps, large roots, and wood pieces from soil can break the disease cycle.

These scattered, small, white patches are *Armillaria mellea* mycelium growing beneath bark on the root crown of an avocado tree.

and shed numerous minuscule, white spores. Spores do not appear to be an important source of infection in California avocados.

The most reliable sign of Armillaria root rot is a white growth of fungal mycelium in the cambial tissue. If trees exhibit aboveground symptoms of infection, cut under the bark of the root crown and major roots to check for mycelium, which are whitish and have a strong mushroom odor. Growth typically occurs in patches in the cambium and inner bark.

Seasonal Development

Armillaria mycelium persists for years under the bark of a tree's diseased roots or root crown. The fungus spreads from tree to tree mainly by means of natural root-to-root grafts and by cordlike rhizomorphs, which resemble small, dark roots. In contrast, healthy avocado roots are lighter colored, usually light brown to whitish. When pulled apart, rhizomorphs have a cottony interior, while the center of a healthy root is solid and woody. Rhizomorphs grow along or out from diseased roots, eventually contacting and infecting the healthy roots of adjacent trees. *Armillaria* also spreads when any activity moves soil containing infested wood fragments, such as during cultivation.

Long after the aerial parts of a tree have been removed, *Armillaria* can remain alive in the remaining roots and stumps. Then, when new avocado trees are planted, the new roots grow into contact with *Armillaria*-infected roots or infested wood pieces and the new tree becomes infected. *Armillaria* can also be introduced on infected nursery stock.

Management Guidelines

Provide a good growing environment and proper cultural practices and use good sanitation to manage Armillaria root rot. Good drainage is important, as is not irrigating excessively. *Armillaria* fungus is very susceptible to drying. Citrus growers sometimes excavate the soil around the trunk to temporarily air-dry the root crown to prolong the life of an infected citrus tree. This excavation may also be effective on avocado trees, but apparently it has not been tested. If you do expose any root crowns, shade them to protect them from sunburn. When an infected tree dies, remove it and any immediately adjacent trees, which may also be infected. Remove the stumps also, and as many root pieces as possible from the soil. Thoroughly clean all soil from the equipment that you use, and leave the soil on-site before you remove the equipment. Consider replanting the ground with crops that are not susceptible to *Armillaria*.

Soil fumigation with chemicals has successfully controlled Armillaria root rot under favorable soil conditions by preventing spread of the fungus and permitting growers to replant fumigated areas. Fumigation is expensive and potentially hazardous, however, and often it is only partially effective. Consult the latest update of *Avocado: UC IPM Pest Management Guidelines: Diseases* (online at www.ipm. ucdavis.edu) for more information on fungicides and disease management.

Dematophora or Rosellinia Root Rot

Dematophora necatrix

Dematophora root rot is not common in avocado groves in the United States. When present, however, Dematophora root rot is a very serious disease of avocado and requires prompt action to prevent its spread to more trees.

Yellow foliage, shriveled fruit, and little or no new growth are symptoms of Dematophora root rot. Cottony, white mycelia cover small feeder roots, and the roots decay. Mycelia grow into the soil and upward into the tree, forming small, pale patches under or in the bark of major roots, the root crown, and lower trunk, which eventually decay. Older mycelia turn gray or black. The fungus can also cause a purple canker in wood at the root crown of young trees. Diseased trees will defoliate and they always die prematurely, usually within 1 to 3 years of initial infection.

Armillaria mycelia can develop as large, white, fan-shaped plaques beneath the bark. After the aerial parts of a tree are gone, *Armillaria* can remain alive for years in roots and on pieces of wood in the soil.

Armillaria can spread by cordlike rhizomorphs (see arrows, top of photo), which resemble small dark roots. Healthy roots (bottom) are lighter-colored, usually light brown to whitish.

Dematophora root rot is also called "white root rot" in reference to its pale mycelium, or "Rosellinia root rot" because the causal fungus is named *Rosellinia necatrix* during the sexual stage of its development. The fungus persists for years in buried wood and organic matter in soil. It spreads to nearby trees through root grafts and moves longer distances in infested soil or wood that is moved. Spores apparently are not important in spreading the disease. The whitish mycelial patches of the *Rosellinia* stage resemble those of *Armillaria*, but *Rosellinia* mycelia lack the characteristic mushroomlike odor produced by *Armillaria*. One way to help diagnose *Rosellinia* is to moisten and then seal infected wood, roots, or soil in a container, and watch for the growth of extensive white mycelium, which should appear within a few days. Because of its severity and persistence, however, you

Armillaria fungus is very susceptible to drying. Temporary excavation of the soil around the root crown to promote drying can prolong the life of infected citrus. The efficacy of this practice has not been demonstrated in avocado, but excavation is being tried in this grove.

should seek expert assistance if you suspect the presence of Dematophora root rot.

Management for Dematophora root rot is much the same as for *Armillaria*, described above: uproot and dispose of infected trees, remove immediately adjacent trees that may also be infected, remove as many root pieces from the soil as possible, trench around the infected site to break root grafts, establish a "dry zone" and prevent all movement of soil or runoff of water from that site, and fumigate or solarize the ground before replanting.

Root, Crown, and Wood Rots

Chlorotic, undersized, sparse leaves and branch dieback are common symptoms when roots, the basal trunk (also called the root crown or butt), or limbs are unhealthy. When decay or rot fungi are the cause, major roots, the root crown, or wood in the trunk and limbs can decay and the trunk may become hollow near its base. There may be dark or whitish fungal mycelium growing on or in the decayed roots or trunk wood. Fungal fruiting bodies often grow from the bark, root crown, or stump, or from soil near the trunk. These fruiting bodies may be mushroom-shaped like those of *Armillaria*, bracket- or seashell-shaped, or they may simply appear as a discolored crust on decayed wood. Root, crown, and wood rots primarily affect old trees.

Various decay fungi cause root, crown, and wood decay. These include *Ganoderma*, *Polyporus*, and *Trames* spp. *Ganoderma applanatum* produces large, elliptical fruiting bodies, or "conks." Conks usually have a brownish upper surface with concentric rings and ridges and a pale underside. *Polyporus* and *Trames* spp. commonly produce bracket- or seashell-shaped fruiting bodies or toadstool- or umbrella-shaped mushrooms that grow from bark. Root, crown, and

wood rot fruiting bodies produce copious amounts of tiny spores that spread in wind or splashing water and infect other trees through existing wounds. Some rots can colonize stumps or dead limbs; others may already have been present in wood before the tree was cut, and may then spread to nearby trees through natural root grafts or through mycelium growing in soil. Most of these fungi are saprophytes that can only grow on a severely stressed or injured host or that must develop substantial inoculum on dead wood before they can infect healthy trees.

Avoid root, crown, and wood decay by providing your trees with good growing conditions and optimal cultural care, especially appropriate irrigation as discussed under "Avocado Root Rot" earlier in this chapter. Prune out dead limbs and dispose of the dead wood away from avocado trees. Slope the surface of any large pruning cut so water will drain away from any pruning wounds on stumps and limbs. Keep other wounding of limbs, trunks, and roots to a minimum. When a tree is cut down, remove the entire tree—including the stump and major roots—especially if you plan to replant with avocado.

When trees are infected with Dematophora or Rosellinia root rot, this cottony, white mycelium may be visible on the soil near the trunk, as with this apple tree. Mycelium can also occur on feeder roots or under the bark of major roots, the root crown, or the lower trunk.

Verticillium Wilt

Verticillium dahliae

Verticillium dahliae fungus infects many hosts, including various berry and flower crops, cotton, eggplant, olive, pepper, stone fruit trees, strawberry, and tomato. Verticillium wilt is present throughout California, but is a less common problem in avocado groves than are root rot and canker diseases.

Symptoms and Damage

The entire tree or only one or a few branches wilt suddenly when infected with *Verticillium*. Leaves turn brown and die, but the dead leaves usually remain on the tree for several months. Brown to gray-brown streaks are visible in the xylem of the branches or roots when the bark is removed. Trees with Verticillium wilt often send out new, vigorous shoots within a few months after the initial wilting. If well cared for, affected trees often recover completely with no reoccurrence of the disease, but not all trees survive an infection, and disease symptoms sometimes show up again after an apparent recovery.

Seasonal Development

Verticillium dahliae persists for years as microsclerotia in soil. Microsclerotia and spores move in water and wind and spread in infested organic matter and soil that is moved. The fungus infects through feeder roots, then moves up via the water-conducting xylem, retarding or preventing the movement of water from the roots to the foliage.

Ganoderma spp. are common root and crown rot fungi. *Ganoderma* produce large, elliptical conks, usually near the root crown. Conks often have a brownish upper surface with concentric rings and ridges and a pale underside.

Management Guidelines

No management methods have been found to be effective in curing infected trees. Trees often recover completely and display no further symptoms, even though they still remain infected. After dieback ceases and new growth begins, however, you should prune off dead branches. Provide optimal irrigation and modest fertilization to promote new growth. If a tree dies from *Verticillium*, remove it and replant with a nonhost crop or fumigate the planting hole and surrounding soil before you replant with avocado. In areas where *V. dahliae* is known to occur, plant Mexican rootstocks instead of the more *Verticillium*-susceptible Guatemalan rootstocks. Do not plant avocados on land where crops susceptible to Verticillium wilt have previously grown. Do not interplant avocados with other *Verticillium* hosts. You can find lists of plants to avoid in several publications, including *Plants Resistant or Susceptible to Verticillium Wilt* (McCain, Raabe, and Wilhelm 1981) in the suggested reading. Even if they have recovered, do not use trees that have been affected with Verticillium wilt as a source of budwood or seed. Consult the latest update of *Avocado: UC IPM Pest Management Guidelines: Diseases* (online at www.ipm.ucdavis.edu) for more information on fungicides and avocado disease management.

One method of diagnosing Verticillium wilt is to remove a strip of bark and look for discolored streaks. Vascular tissue and wood infected with *Verticillium* are commonly brown, gray, or reddish.

JACK KELLY CLARK

CANKERS ON LIMBS AND TRUNKS

Cankers are dead tissue or necrotic lesions on bark and in cambium, xylem, and wood underneath bark. A canker is a discolored area that oozes liquid, and its surface may be sunken or cracked. Serious canker damage to trunks and limbs inhibits a plant's ability to transport nutrients and water, causing overall symptoms of decline including discolored and wilted foliage. Phytophthora canker is the most important canker disease. Avocado black streak, bacterial canker, and Dothiorella canker are also discussed in this section. *Dematophora necatrix*, discussed earlier in this chapter, can also cause limb cankers. All canker diseases display similar types of damage; in the field, pay close attention to the location and appearance of damage as described and illustrated below and then submit samples to a diagnostic laboratory for help in distinguishing the cankers' cause.

Phytophthora Canker or Citricola Canker

Phytophthora citricola

Phytophthora citricola infects the root crown and lower trunk and limbs of older trees. The resulting disease is called Phytophthora canker, Citricola, Citricola canker, Phytophthora canker and collar rot, or Phytophthora canker and crown rot. Previously uncommon, Phytophthora canker has become widespread in California and is now second only to root rot in severity among diseases of avocado. *Phytophthora citricola* has a wide host range, including cherimoya, cherry, fir, and walnut. *Phytophthora citricola* also damages fruit, as discussed later, under Phytophthora Fruit Rot.

Symptoms and Damage

Phytophthora cankers usually originate at or below ground level, but can occur higher above ground, especially where trunks or lower limbs have been wounded. The canker appears as a region of dark bark, often exuding red resin that becomes brownish to white and powdery as it dries. Cutting away the superficial canker reveals an orange-tan to brown lesion instead of the normal white or cream-colored tissues. The lesion may have a fruity odor when exposed. The lesion infects the inner bark and outer layer of wood, killing cambium and phloem. Lesions can spread in the crown roots and proceed up into the bark of the trunk, but discoloring rarely extends deeper into wood than the outer woody layer. Depending on the local conditions and rootstock, the avocado tree may ward off the disease and its lesions may heal.

Affected trees show a gradual loss of vigor and decline of the top. Foliar symptoms of trees with an advanced case of the disease resemble the symptoms caused by avocado root rot (*Phytophthora cinnamomi*), including fewer leaves than normal and pale, wilted leaves with brown, necrotic tips. Unlike root rot, however, canker and collar rot affects the major tree roots, while the smaller feeder roots usually remain present. Occasionally, in advanced stages, a tree will die suddenly, its leaves turning brown within a short period of time. Confirmation of *P. citricola* infection is made through laboratory tissue tests.

Seasonal Development

Phytophthora citricola occurs innocuously on the feeder roots of many or most avocados, but disease only occurs on some of these trees. Disease develops after crowns, limbs, or trunks become infected through wounds, such as injuries from equipment, pruning, vertebrate chewing, and wind damage. The spread of spores and disease development are favored by excess soil moisture and overall wet conditions. Cankers often occur on the side of trunks that have been repeatedly wetted by irrigation sprinklers. *Phytophthora citricola* produces

HOWARD OHR

This reddish brown resin and white powder on bark were caused by Phytophthora canker and collar rot, also called Citricola. Avocado black streak and Dothiorella canker are common diseases that also cause symptoms such as this, but cankers from those diseases often occur higher on the trunk and on limbs.

microscopic oospores (sexual spores), often in abundance in the exudate from wounds. Spores readily spread in splashing water or anything else that contacts the ooze, such as equipment and tools that then go on to wound healthy trees, causing a new infection. The seasonal development described above for *Phytophthora cinnamomi* applies to *P. citricola* as well, with the notable difference that *P. citricola* damages trunks and limbs and only the larger roots, while *P. cinnamomi* damages small roots.

Management Guidelines

In California, the diseases caused by *Phytophthora* spp. (root rot and canker) are increasingly found together. Hence, growers need to follow integrated approaches to the control of both, including sanitation, selection of tolerant rootstocks, good water management, and wound prevention.

Phytophthora citricola can easily be spread in contaminated nursery stock and on irrigation equipment, vehicles, and people. Follow the same sanitation procedures as described above for avocado root rot.

Consider planting more than one rootstock in your grove if the grove has a history of Phytophthora canker or Phytophthora root rot. Seedling rootstocks are much more sensitive to trunk cankers than are most of the clonal cultivars. In University of California field trials, Toro Canyon, Duke 7, Duke 9, and Barr Duke have shown moderate tolerance, as compared to other, more-susceptible rootstocks (see Table 2). Thomas rootstock, which is tolerant to root rot, is quite susceptible to canker and collar rot.

Do not keep the avocado trees' lower trunk wet for long periods, since this would increase the chances of infection. Place drippers away from trunks, aim sprinklers to avoid wetting the trunks, or switch from sprinkler to drip irrigation where feasible. Avoid wounding major roots and trunks, and especially avoid pulling suckers since that can easily damage the belowground bark. Do not stack cut wood against a tree trunk. Rake mulch several inches back from the trunk.

Consider promptly treating fresh wounds, such as wounds from pruning, with a fungicide. Remove suckers only by cutting them off above ground, and then treat the wound. Disinfect your pruning tools periodically, for instance after you finish working on each tree. If you detect cankers at an early stage before they invade a large part of the trunk, you may be able to control the disease by cutting out the infected tissue and spraying the wound with an effective fungicide. Where cankers extend below ground level, a combination of aboveground applications and a soil drench with fungicide may be warranted. Consult the latest update of *Avocado: UC IPM Pest Management Guidelines: Diseases* (online at www.ipm.ucdavis.edu) for more information on fungicides and avocado disease management.

This rough, dark-stained bark near the soil is a result of Phytophthora canker.

This brownish orange discolored cambium and wood beneath the bark is a symptom of Phytophthora canker. Other canker diseases cause virtually identical damage. Inspect plants for multiple signs and symptoms, send samples to a laboratory, or consult an expert to help you confidently diagnose the cause of a disease.

Dothiorella Canker

Botryosphaeria and *Fusicoccum* spp.

Several pathogens cause Dothiorella canker on trunks and large limbs. Small branches or twigs and their leaves killed by these fungi are discussed under "Dothiorella Leaf and Stem Blight," later in this chapter. Fruit decay caused by these pathogens is discussed under "Dothiorella Fruit Rot."

Symptoms and Damage

Dothiorella cankers exude reddish sap that dries to a brown and white powder. Bark may be cracked, darkly discolored, or slightly sunken. With older cankers, bark may shed from the damaged area or it may be easily removed. Under the canker, the inner bark and wood is brown, orangish, or red, instead of the normal, pale color. Brown, dead leaves remain attached if much of the xylem becomes infected, rapidly killing the entire limb.

Dothiorella canker can be a serious problem in new plantings; stock sometimes arrives from the nursery with latent infections in the graft union. Where infection kills the graft union, the dead scion retains a dry, brown canopy, while shoots and green leaves sprout up from the rootstock. The graft union may be unusually swollen and rough prior to the young tree's death. Cutting inside at the graft union reveals dark, discolored wood that can extend through the entire width of the small trunk.

In contrast, Dothiorella canker is usually of minor importance in established, older trees. Scattered small branches and sometimes large limbs can die back. Usually, Dothiorella will not affect an entire, older tree, and the tree as a whole will remain productive. In unusually severe cases, the main trunk becomes girdled, killing the tree.

Seasonal Development

This disease was formerly attributed to *Dothiorella gregaria*, hence the name Dothiorella canker. *Fusicoccum luteum* is now known to be the most common cause of Dothiorella canker disease on avocados in California. *Botryosphaeria dothidea* (also named *Fusicoccum aesculi* during another stage of its development) also causes Dothiorella canker in California avocados. Several other *Botryosphaeria, Diplodia,* or *Fusicoccum* spp. cause Dothiorella canker, fruit rot, or leaf and stem blight in avocado, and these fungi can not reliably be distinguished from one another during certain stages of their growth except by means of molecular tests such as PCR (polymerase chain reaction).

Dothiorella cankers closely resemble Phytophthora cankers. Dothiorella cankers usually occur higher above the ground, beginning around the first main branch crotch or higher. Dothiorella can infect much smaller limbs, such as twigs and small branches, as well as the upper trunk and large limbs. When cut into with a knife, Dothiorella cankers are sometimes found to extend deep into wood, while Phytophthora cankers discolor only a shallow layer

This dark, discolored bark exuding white powder around branch crotches and the upper trunk is caused by Dothiorella canker. Dothiorella diseases can also affect fruit, leaves, and branches.

This single dead limb in a green canopy is a source of pathogen spores. Prune out dead limbs during dry weather.

This shallow, brown discoloration under bark was caused by Dothiorella canker. Because other maladies such as avocado black streak and Phytophthora canker cause similar symptoms, you should have tissue samples tested by a laboratory to help you diagnose the actual cause.

This young tree was killed from a graft infection that occurred in the nursery. The root stock suckers indicate that the scion is completely dead and the tree should be replaced.

of outer wood. Except when trees are young, Dothiorella canker usually is not as serious as diseases caused by *Phytophthora* spp.

The fungi that cause Dothiorella canker can infect only through wounds. Heavy rainfall causes increased spore production and infection, and the spores spread in air and water. Stress makes trees much more susceptible to this disease. Common causes of stress are poor irrigation, low-quality irrigation water, nutritional deficiencies, or severe insect and mite feeding. Drought stress in particular promotes disease and symptom development in infected trees. Mexican rootstocks in general are much more resistant to this disease than are Guatemalan cultivars.

Management

Consider planting rootstock cultivars that are more resistant to this disease (Table 2). Where Dothiorella canker is a problem, rely primarily on sanitation and good cultural practices to control it. Prune out dead limbs and twigs. Dispose of dead wood and old fruit well away from avocado trees. Prune and harvest only when the weather is dry and leaf, wood, and soil surfaces are dry. Correct the causes of any environmental or nutritional stresses and keep other pest problems to a minimum. Maintaining an appropriate amount and frequency of irrigation is especially important. Leach the soil periodically and use low-salinity water if salt toxicity is a problem. Nurseries should use especially stringent sanitation measures, disinfest their propagative material, and consider treating all graft unions with fungicide.

Bacterial Canker

Xanthomonas campestris

Bacterial canker is widespread but is a relatively unimportant disease in California avocados. In some groves the bacterium infects more than 60% of the trees, but most of these trees

Leaves that are mostly green with necrotic patches are typical of infection by the fungi that cause various Dothiorella diseases.

will perform well if they are otherwise well cared for. The pathogen can also be introduced into groves on new trees obtained from nurseries using poor practices.

Symptoms and Damage

Cankers appear as slightly sunken, dark areas on the bark. They vary from about 1 to 4 inches (2.5–10 cm) in diameter. Bark around cankers may crack. Fluid often oozes from the cankers and dries, leaving a white powder over or around the lesion. Cankers usually appear first near the base of the tree and often spread in an upward line on one side of the trunk or branch. A cut under the bark surface will reveal a decayed, reddish brown necrotic pocket that may contain liquid. Dark streaks in the wood radiate outward both above and below the lesions. These necrotic streaks are usually in the bark cortex or xylem, but they sometimes extend deeper into the center of the branch or trunk.

Severely affected trees may have pale, sparse foliage and low fruit yields on one branch or on the entire tree, but this is rare. Sometimes a newly planted tree will become stunted from many lesions. New branches may grow from buds below the affected part.

Seasonal Development

Xanthomonas campestris is a common bacterium on avocado leaves and green twigs, where it appears to be harmless. Its reproduction and spread are favored by wet plants and humid conditions. It can infect through wounds and branch stubs. It can systemically colonize the vascular system. Drought stress and boron deficiency may promote the development of disease symptoms.

Management Guidelines

This disease is a minor problem. Established trees usually require no control measures. If the disease is severe and fruit yield is affected, however, remove the tree. Keep all of your trees healthy and provide good cultural care. Provide the appropriate amount and frequency of irrigation, and maintain distribution uniformity of water among your trees. Use certified, disease-free nursery stock if available. Regularly inspect young trees and remove and dispose of any that are infected. Nurseries should follow stringent sanitation practices, regularly screen their stock for disease, and dispose of affected trees.

When small, roundish, liquidy or pale dry patches occur in a row and cutting into cankers reveals necrotic pockets or oozing liquid under bark, the cause is usually bacterial canker.

Cutting under the bark surface of roundish patches caused by bacterial canker will reveal unhealthy tissue. Infected cambium is often discolored reddish or brown and there may be necrotic, sunken pockets containing liquid.

Avocado Black Streak

Black streak develops under adverse growing conditions and is a serious disease that can kill avocado trees. The disease's cause has in the past been attributed to a viroid, but that does not appear to be the case. The specific cause is unknown.

Symptoms and Damage

Black streak appears as an elongated, dark canker or discoloration on the tree's bark. Small cankers can run parallel to the direction of limb or trunk growth, but in some cases cankers will encircle limbs or the trunk. On green shoots and young trees, lesions look like black blotches with distinct margins. Cankered bark develops shallow cracks that ooze sap, which dries as a brownish or white powder on the bark surface. This exudate is readily washed off by rain or sprinklers, and in the absence of the powder the canker can be difficult to see externally from the bark surface. Black streak lesions can be very small or they can encompass the greater part of the trunk. Cankers often appear first on the lower trunk and the underside of lower limbs and later appear higher in the tree.

When you scrape off the bark over the canker, you reveal shallow, reddish brown to black areas. This discoloration forms mottled areas of dead and live tissue or can merge into one large necrotic area. This shallow discoloration rarely extends into the cambium and can be removed easily if you insert a knife blade under the canker and pry upward. Because a tree can die from only a very few lesions, it appears that the lesions are a symptom of the disease and not the actual cause of tree death. Other symptoms of black streak include chlorosis, early bloom, branch dieback, leaf blotching, zinc deficiency, bunchy terminal leaf growth due to shortened internodes, wilting of foliage, poor yield, and death of new growth, which may die rapidly.

Seasonal Development

Many symptoms of avocado black streak are similar to those of other diseases. The specific appearance of the cankers, the disease's pattern of development in the grove, and laboratory

Black streak caused this dark staining and the powdery white exudate on the trunk bark. This avocado tree is stressed by insufficient irrigation and excess salt in the irrigation water.

Scraping away a thin layer of bark to reveal the canker underneath helps to diagnose the cause of disease. With avocado black streak, the reddish brown cankered tissue is often very shallow. Scraping slightly deeper beneath the discoloration will expose lighter-colored, apparently healthy wood underneath.

tests to detect whether other potential causes are present help to diagnose avocado black streak. Black streak can spread in the grove, and a microorganism may be involved. Avocado black streak appears after prolonged periods of environmental or cultural stress, especially conditions of high salinity and insufficient water. An affected tree can decline gradually and may eventually die, or it may collapse and die rapidly. Conversely, improved cultural practices can cause trees to recover and symptoms to virtually disappear.

Avocado black streak may occur wherever Guatemalan cultivars are grown in California. All ages of trees are affected and symptoms have been observed on trees ranging from 1 year old to more than 35 years old. Many groves appear to be free of the disease, and disease incidence varies considerably even within an affected grove. Avocado black streak symptoms typically are most severe on those trees that appear to be the most stressed.

Management Guidelines

Manage avocado black streak by maintaining plant health with good fertilization and irrigation practices and otherwise preventing stress. Adequate irrigation with high-quality water is believed to be especially important.

SYMPTOMS ON FRUIT, LEAVES, AND TWIGS

Many fungi, several bacteria, and at least one viroid can directly damage avocado fruit. Many fruit diseases caused by pathogens are overlooked by growers because damage from fruit diseases frequently does not become apparent until after harvest.

Sunblotch

Avocado Sunblotch Viroid (ASBVD)

Sunblotch is caused by submicroscopic particles of genetic material (viroids) that alter the development and growth of infected plants. It causes a wide variety of symptoms, and no visible symptoms at all in some hosts.

Symptoms and Damage

Symptoms of sunblotch include necrotic tissue that appears as black, brown, red, yellow, or white discolorations on fruit, often in depressions or scars in the fruit surface. Twigs can develop narrow black, brown, red, or yellow necrotic streaks on their surface or in shallow lengthwise indentations along the twig. Leaves may have white or yellowish variegated areas and may deform, but leaf symptoms are uncommon in the field. Rectangular cracking and checking of the bark, called "alligator bark," often occurs on the trunk and larger branches. Infected trees may be stunted and may have a

disproportionate amount of horizontal growth or sprawling, lateral, low limbs. Trees with visible sunblotch symptoms often have a reduced fruit yield. Infected trees can also be symptomless, although a large reduction in yield from previously vigorous trees may indicate the presence of the viroid in otherwise symptomless carriers.

Careful propagation of nursery stock to eliminate viroids has greatly reduced sunblotch to the point that it is now a relatively minor disease, although ongoing monitoring and management are required both in nurseries and in established groves. Sunblotch is easily overlooked and a tree can become infected in many different ways (Figure 22).

Sunblotch causes narrow sunken streaks on fruit, which can be black, red, yellow, or whitish. Because fruit infected via pollen can occur on otherwise healthy trees, any tree with symptomatic fruit and those near it should be tested to determine which trees are systemically infected, and should therefore be removed.

Bushy shoots are one symptom of trees that are systemically infected with sunblotch. The left shoot with short internodes and small leaves is from a tree that should be tested to determine if it is infected.

Seasonal Development

Sunblotch is the only known viroid disease of avocado, but it has dozens of variants. Symptoms vary depending on environmental conditions, the host cultivar, and the viroid strain. Sunblotch viroid can move systemically within an avocado tree. Once infected, a tree remains infected for the rest of its life. Trees that show no symptoms even though the viroid is present are known as "symptomless carriers." Nearly all cuttings and seed from symptomless carriers are infected with the viroid. Although seedlings from symptomless carriers do not show sunblotch symptoms when they are used as rootstocks, the disease will often appear on the scions grafted onto them. Conversely, most seed produced by trees with symptoms are not infected, and budwood and shoot cuttings from symptomatic trees often do not contain the viroid. The viroid transmits in the trees' pollen, but pollen only infects the fruit and seed produced from that infected flower. Unless a tree is infected through grafting or through some other means than pollen, there will be no viroid in budwood, root grafts, and shoot cuttings from that tree.

Transmission of the viroid most often occurs during grafting when the propagator uses infected budwood or rootstock seedlings from infected trees (Figure 22). Natural root-to-root grafts are important in transmitting sunblotch within a grove. Mechanical transmission through wounds caused by contaminated harvest clippers, pruning tools, and injection equipment can also be important if some trees in the grove are infected. When the viroid spreads via pollen from an infected tree to a flower ovule on an uninfected tree and results in an infected seed, that individual fruit may be culled, but the viroid will not spread any further unless that seed is propagated. There is no evidence of transmission by insects.

Rectangular cracking or checking on limb or trunk bark, called alligator bark, is one symptom of sunblotch infection.

Management Guidelines

In the nursery, carefully select viroid-free scions and seed sources. Follow stringent sanitation protocols and practice frequent disinfection to avoid spreading pathogens. Periodically perform tests to confirm that your propagation sources are disease-free (this is called indexing). Certain laboratories index plants by performing a genetic test to detect whether a tree is infected. Another indexing method involves grafting propagative source material to young Mexican seedlings and then observing leaves and twigs for sunblotch symptoms. Grow your propagation sources away from commercial groves and periodically index all of the trees in your propagation source groves.

Growers should plant only indexed nursery stock that is registered as disease-free. Promptly remove symptomatic trees from the grove and chemically kill the stumps. If only fruit and seed are infected (from infected pollen), it may not be necessary to remove the tree if indexing indicates the rest of the tree is uninfected. When a tree has only fruit and seed

infections, that probably means that other infected (and possibly symptomless) trees are nearby and need to be indexed or removed. Do not retain infected, symptomless trees just because their yield does not seem to be affected. Symptomless carriers constitute a highly infective source that can dramatically reduce yields on other trees. Index any suspect orchards to positively identify infected, symptomless trees.

The danger of spreading the viroid increases in established orchards where mature trees are pruned to reduce tree size and restimulate or maintain fruit production. Severe pruning of symptomless carriers, and perhaps other severe causes of tree stress, may cause the viroid to become active in new growth, inducing previously symptomless trees to exhibit symptoms. Disinfect all pruning tools, harvest clippers, and injection equipment before you begin work on a new tree. Scrubbing tools clean and then soaking them in a 1.5% sodium hypochlorite solution is effective. Growers must use a registered disinfectant and follow label directions.

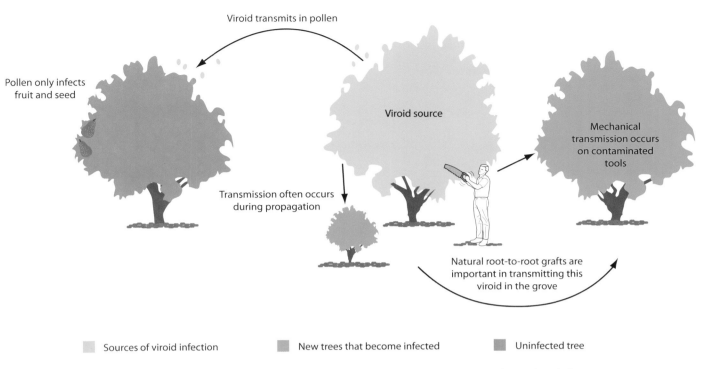

Figure 22. How avocado sunblotch viroid is transmitted. This pathogen is easily spread during propagation from infected plants, in root-to-root grafts, mechanically (such as through wounds caused by contaminated pruning tools), and in pollen. Some infected hosts can be symptomless but still be sources of new infections.

Anthracnose
Colletotrichum gloeosporioides

Anthracnose normally is a minor problem in California avocados. Low humidity and a lack of rain during much of the growing season limit disease development.

Symptoms and Damage

Anthracnose symptoms can develop on flowers, fruit, leaves, or twigs (Figure 23). Infected fruit is the most serious concern, but most fruit damage does not develop until after harvest. Unhealthy or dead leaves are the most obvious symptoms in groves. Spots form on leaves, beginning as yellow discolorations, then turning brown and coalescing into large, dead areas. Necrosis occurs across or between leaf veins, on leaf margins, and most often at leaf tips. If the disease is severe, affected trees will drop many leaves prematurely. New shoots can develop brown or purplish lesions, and shoots may die back. Infected flower heads can turn dark and die without producing fruit or young fruit may form then drop.

Prior to harvest, brown to black lesions less than ⅕ inch (5 mm) in diameter develop around the lenticels on infected fruit. These small discolorations are easy to overlook while fruit are still on the tree, and the lesions usually do not enlarge until the fruit ripens after harvest. Large lesions sometimes appear on avocado fruit on the tree, usually after

infected fruit are injured by insects or mechanically by wind rubbing.

After harvest, the lesions become blacker, larger, and increasingly sunken. Eventually, the lesions spread over the entire fruit surface and throughout pulp. When you cut the fruit in half through one of the lesions, the rot that

Anthracnose infection caused the black lesion spots and specks on these fruit. Usually this is a problem only after prolonged rains. As with most diseases of fruit, damage often is not obvious until after harvest, but control measures must be applied in the grove.

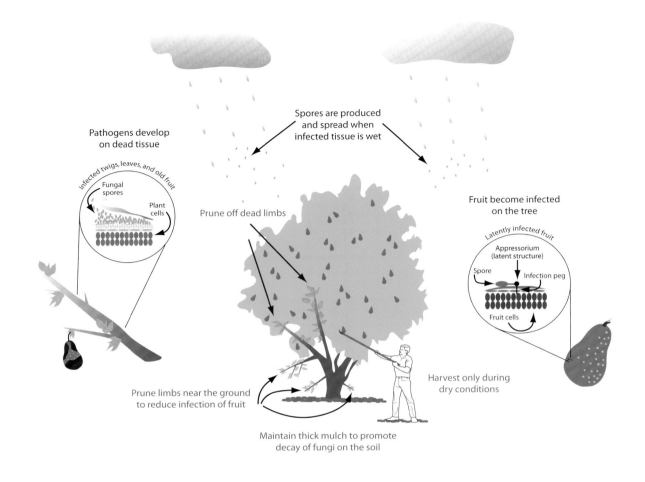

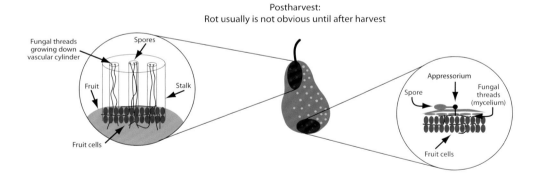

Figure 23. Disease cycle for fruit rots and *(labeled in blue)* methods for preventing fruit rots. Anthracnose, Dothiorella fruit rot, Phytophthora fruit rot, and stem end rot fungi develop in cankers and decaying plant tissue. During wet conditions, pathogens produce spores that spread to infect fruit on the tree. Fruit rot sometimes becomes apparent on the tree, such as on fruit near soil where water splashes or after prolong rains. Rot usually is not obvious until after harvest. As fruit ripen, infections develop into dark decay. Mulching, pruning out dead limbs, working in groves only when conditions are dry, and good cultural practices such as appropriate irrigation can minimize fruit rots. Adapted from Cutting and Dixon 2001.

extends into the flesh often exhibits a hemispherical pattern. Decayed pulp is firm at first, but becomes soft and putrid as decay advances. Pink spore masses may form on the fruit surface and, under wet conditions, a slimy mass of pink spores will erupt through the fruit's skin.

Otherwise healthy trees recover from foliar infections and defoliation once the weather conditions become dry again. Anthracnose becomes a postharvest problem if the grove has been excessively wet for extended periods. Poor growing practices and mishandling of fruit during or after harvest will greatly increase the potential for significant fruit loss.

Seasonal Development

Colletotrichum gloeosporioides is widespread in avocado and citrus groves. It is normally of little importance because it takes unusually large numbers of spores to produce a damaging infection. When a grove is subject to extended foggy or rainy conditions and mild winter temperatures and where many dead leaves and twigs and mummified fruit accumulate in the trees, the fungus can produce enough spores to cause a disease problem. Spores spread in splashing water and can cause infection at any time from fruit set to harvest. Once infected the fruit start to ripen, temperatures of 75°F (24°C) and above will accelerate anthracnose development, while temperatures below 59°F (15°C) retard disease development.

Management Guidelines

Fuerte, Rincon, and Wurtz scion cultivars are more susceptible to anthracnose than Hass. Because of cultivar differences in natural antifungal compounds called dienes, rootstocks also influence the development of anthracnose aboveground. However, anthracnose is not important enough in California for the degree of susceptibility to anthracnose to be an important cultivar selection criteria for avocado propagators or growers. To control anthracnose, follow good cultural practices in the grove and proper preharvest and postharvest fruit handling practices.

Prune out dead limbs and twigs where the fungi sporulate. If many dead leaves are entwined in the canopy, knock them down. Prune low limbs to leave at least 2 feet (60 cm) between the ground and the lowest limbs in order to improve air circulation and thus reduce humidity within the canopy. Dispose of dead wood and old fruit away from avocado trees before they flower. Prune and harvest only under dry conditions. Use fruit handling Best Management Practices to minimize fruit contamination and injury.

Postharvest treatments should not be needed if the fruit are properly handled. Keep fruit dry and cool until they are sold. The postharvest temperature is especially critical to anthracnose development. Cool the fruit to 41°F (5°C) as soon as possible after harvest. Delays of longer than 6 hours after harvest before cooling result in increased postharvest

fruit decay. Prompt cooling of fruit is of increasing importance as the season progresses because fruit ripens faster as its maturity increases. Avoid storage temperatures below 41°F (5°C) because chilling injury may occur. Bring harvested fruit quickly to market.

Stem End Rot

Decay at the stem end of an avocado fruit is caused by any of several species of bacteria and fungi. Infection typically occurs during harvest and develops into decay after the fruit are shipped to the packinghouse.

Symptoms and Damage

Decay begins as slight shriveling around the stem button. Fungal mycelium is often visible on these fruit if the button is removed. Conspicuous dark decay with a well-defined margin develops at the stem end. As fruit ripens, decay spreads and rots the entire fruit, which becomes dark and shriveled. Depending on the causal organisms, the fruit's flesh may be watery and soft, or initially dry and corky, becoming watery later as secondary organisms colonize its tissue.

Seasonal Development

Many different microorganisms can cause stem end rot (see Figure 23). Causal agents include the fungus *Botryodiplodia theobromae* and other fungi, discussed under "Anthracnose" and "Dothiorella Fruit Rot," as well as *Alternaria* and *Phomopsis* species. These stem end-rotting species are saprophytes (decay organisms) or weak pathogens that are present in soil and most any dead or dying avocado tissue, including senescing flowers and injured bark, fruit, and leaves. Spores

This decay was caused by one or more species of stem end rot pathogen, which infected the fruit before or during harvest. If the cause had been Phytophthora fruit rot, the decay would likely have developed at the bottom end of the fruit (which is at the top of this photo).

Do not handle fruit or harvest it when foliage or fruit is wet. Picking wet fruit greatly reduces its quality during storage and increases the incidence of postharvest diseases.

spread in wind and splashing water. Stem end rot begins as infections in the grove, but does not develop into disease until after harvest. Harvesting injures fruit around the button and the microorganisms, already present, move into the freshly cut stem, causing decay as the fruit ripens.

Management Guidelines

Use good sanitation and optimal cultural practices to minimize fruit rots. Prune out dead limbs and twigs. Dispose of dead wood and old fruit away from trees. Prune and harvest only under dry conditions. Correct environmental and nutritional stresses. Minimize other diseases and disorders that injure bark, fruit, or leaves. Provide sufficient irrigation with high-quality water appropriately applied. Maintain a thick layer of mulch under the canopies to hasten the decomposition of pathogen propagules. Do not harvest during or soon after a rain; allow trees and fruit to dry before harvesting. Minimize the time between harvest and placement of fruit into cold storage at the packinghouse, since prompt cold

storage reduces the incidence of disease. Follow the same postharvest handling instructions discussed earlier under "Anthracnose."

Phytophthora Fruit Rot
Phytophthora citricola

Fruit rot develops after pathogen infection under wet conditions. Phytophthora fruit rot is usually of only minor importance in California.

Symptoms and Damage

Affected fruit are often found touching the soil or hanging on low branches. Most damage occurs within 3 feet (90 cm) of the ground. Diseased fruit have a distinct, black, circular area that usually occurs near the bottom or lowest spot on the fruit. Internally, the rot extends into the flesh, darkening it in the same pattern as appears on the affected surface.

Seasonal Development

Phytophthora fruit rot is caused by *Phytophthora* spp., usually *P. citricola*, the same pathogen that causes Phytophthora canker or collar rot. Phytophthora fruit rot is most damaging after prolonged wet conditions, the same conditions that favor anthracnose (see Figure 23). In contrast to anthracnose, which is primarily a postharvest problem, Phytophthora fruit rot infections often become obvious while the fruit are still hanging on the tree, besides causing decay after harvest.

Management Guidelines

The most common cause of infection is believed to be the splashing of *Phytophthora* propagules from the soil surface to the fruit during heavy rain or sprinkler irrigation. Prune the

Phytophthora fruit rot caused the black, circular decay near the bottom of these fruit. Damage is easily overlooked on the Hass avocado at left because its skin normally darkens as the fruit ripens.

A thick layer of mulch beneath avocado trees hastens fungal decomposition and reduces spore splash, helping to reduce the incidence of fruit rot diseases.

lower limbs so they are no closer than 2 to 3 feet (60–90 cm) from the ground. Maintain a thick layer of mulch to hasten the decomposition of fungi on the soil. Prune out dead limbs and twigs and dispose of dead wood and old fruit away from the avocado trees. Consider removing and disposing of any fruit lying on the ground since the pathogen sporulates on dropped fruit.

Dothiorella Fruit Rot

Botryosphaeria and *Fusicoccum* spp.

Dothiorella fruit rot is caused by several *Botryosphaeria* and *Fusicoccum* species. These fungi can infect all aboveground plant parts and also cause other diseases, as discussed under "Dothiorella Canker" and "Dothiorella Leaf and Stem Blight."

Symptoms and Damage

Dothiorella fruit rot usually is not visibly present while fruit is on the tree. Small, superficial lesions can develop on fruit in the grove, but the disease usually becomes apparent only on fruit that is very overmature, is hanging on dead limbs, or has fallen onto the ground.

Infections usually become active after the fruit is picked and starts to soften (see Figure 23). Initially lesions are small, irregular brown to reddish discolorations on the peel. Under the peel, brown streaks may be seen running lengthwise in the flesh as the decay initially spreads along vascular bundles in the fruit. Small, purplish brown spots may appear on any part of the fruit, most often at the stem end. As the fruit ages, the surface lesions gradually enlarge and become sunken and black. The fruit shrivels and the black surface can become covered with grayish brown fungal mycelia and spores. At this point, decay has spread throughout the entire fruit and its flesh is a discolored brown from watery decay and has an offensive odor.

Postharvest rots are a relatively minor problem for California avocados, but the prevalence of Dothiorella fruit rot may be underestimated. Damage from Dothiorella fruit rot closely resembles that caused by anthracnose and stemend rot, and fruit damaged by these pathogens usually are culled and lumped together in the packinghouse. During early stages, Dothiorella fruit rot lesions can occur anywhere on the avocado's skin, while stem end rot initially occurs only near the narrow end of fruit where the decay begins under the button. Anthracnose produces pink sporulation on the fruit surface, in contrast with the grayish mycelium produced by Dothiorella fruit rot.

Seasonal Development

Fusicoccum luteum and *Botryosphaeria dothidea* (the latter is also called *Fusicoccum aesculi* during its sexual stage of growth) are common causes of this disease. The disease used to be attributed to *Dothiorella gregaria*, hence the name

This shrunken, decayed fruit is the result of Dothiorella fruit rot. Dothiorella fungal spores occur as brown patches (shown here) or purplish discoloration on the skin. If anthracnose were the cause of this decay, any spores on the surface would be pinkish.

Dothiorella fruit rot. Several *Botryosphaeria, Diplodia,* and *Fusicoccum* species of fungi can cause fruit rot, Dothiorella canker, or leaf and stem blight.

These pathogens spread as windblown ascospores and water-splashed spores (conidia). Spores are produced in or on cankers, dead twigs, and dying fruit and leaves. Spores infect through wounds and through lenticels, tiny natural openings on fruit. Infection itself occurs in the grove, but the disease usually is not obvious until after the fruit are picked and start to ripen.

Management Guidelines

Use good sanitation and optimal cultural practices to minimize fruit rots. Prune out dead limbs and twigs. Dispose of dead wood and old fruit away from avocado trees. Prune and harvest only under dry conditions. Correct environmental and nutritional stresses and minimize other diseases and disorders that injure bark, fruit, or leaves. For example, anything that causes a large number of leaves to develop necrosis will cause fruit decay spores to become abundant on those leaves and spread to contaminate nearby fruit. Provide sufficient, properly applied irrigation with high-quality water to minimize this and many other avocado problems. Follow the same postharvest handling instructions for fruit as were discussed under "Anthracnose," earlier in this chapter.

Dothiorella Leaf and Stem Blight
Botryosphaeria and *Fusicoccum* spp.

Small branches and leaves can be killed by several similar fungal species named under "Dothiorella Canker," earlier in this chapter. Entirely brown, dry leaves usually remain on dead limbs for months after the branches are killed by Dothiorella disease. Dead branches may retain fruit, which

These dark, shriveled avocados on the ground harbor Dothiorella fruit rot and will produce spores that will spread to fruit on the tree. Dispose of old fruit away from trees and prune lower limbs to reduce the number of spores that can splash from soil onto trees and you will reduce the incidence of most types of fruit rot.

These dead stems and old fruit hanging from the tree should be pruned out and disposed of away from avocado trees to help control Dothiorella fruit rot and stem blight.

will blacken and shrivel. When leaves are infected but are attached to healthy stems, the leaves are in many cases mostly green with necrosis only in brown patches along the leaf margins and at the tips. When stems are healthy, typically only some of the leaves on a stem will have necrotic patches. Within a tree, usually only one or a few scattered stems have necrotic leaves, and all leaves on most branches will show no symptoms of infection.

Dothiorella leaf and stem blight is a common disease of minor importance to the health of established trees. Otherwise healthy trees tolerate scattered necrotic leaves and a few branches killed by Dothiorella disease. The primary concern is over the health of fruit and nursery stock. Copious amounts of spores are produced on dead limbs and leaves and these spores inoculate fruit on the tree, sometimes causing significant fruit rot and stem end rot problems after harvest. If plant parts used for propagation become contaminated, the young trees can die as a result of infection of the graft between the rootstock and scion.

Prune off dead limbs and twigs during dry conditions and dispose of the dead wood and old fruit away from avocado trees. Knock down groups of dead leaves that are stuck in the trees. Maintain a thick layer of mulch to hasten the decomposition of fungi on the ground. Stem and leaf blight commonly develops during hot weather and where irrigation is not adequately managed. Use optimal cultural practices and good sanitation to minimize disease, as discussed above under "Dothiorella Canker" and "Dothiorella Fruit Rot."

Sooty Mold

Sooty mold is a black, somewhat feltlike fungal growth on the surface of affected fruit, leaves, or stems. Sooty molds grow on honeydew that has been excreted by juice-sucking insects, including soft scales and whiteflies. Sooty molds do not infect avocado trees or fruit and generally cause no damage to the crop unless leaves become so heavily covered that photosynthesis is significantly reduced, causing chlorosis and

This distant view of partly necrotic leaves adjacent to shoots with all green leaves shows the patchy nature of Dothiorella infections in leaves.

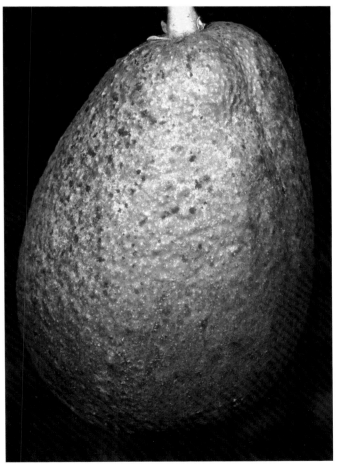

Blackish sooty mold fungal growth on an avocado fruit. The cause is honeydew excreted by plant juice-sucking insects (Homoptera) infesting the tree's leaves or stems.

possible premature leaf drop. If fruit is noticeably fouled by sooty mold, it may be downgraded at the packinghouse.

Sooty mold consists of hyphae and spores of *Capnodium* spp. and related fungi. Manage it by controlling the insects that produce honeydew. Honeydew-producing insects in avocado trees can usually be controlled well by natural enemies. To conserve these beneficial parasites and predators you need to control ants, minimize dust, and avoid using broad-spectrum insecticides. If an insect requires direct control, use selective insecticides whenever possible.

Insects, Mites, and Other Invertebrates

Many species of insects and mites occur in avocado. Some are pests, but most invertebrate species cause little or no economic damage. Certain species are highly beneficial, including pollinators as well as parasites and predators of pests. Until the 1990s, when avocado thrips and persea mite were inadvertently introduced into California, invertebrates caused only occasional problems in mature avocado groves.

Key Pests. Avocado thrips and persea mite are key pests because they often cause substantial economic losses and they are not controlled well by natural enemies. Fruit quality is downgraded when avocado skins are scarred by thrips feeding on fruit. Trees are severely stressed and subject to sunburn and potential yield reductions due to premature leaf drop caused by persea mite. Growers can apply pesticides to reduce this damage, but the applications can cause problems, such as poisoning the natural enemies of other invertebrates, thereby increasing the populations of certain secondary and occasional pest species.

Feeding by avocado thrips damaged this fruit. Avocado thrips and persea mite are key pests because they commonly cause substantial economic loss and are not well controlled by natural enemies.

Secondary and Occasional Pests. Many potential pests rarely cause economic damage in avocado because they are suppressed by natural enemies. When outbreaks do occur, it is usually because their natural enemies have been killed or disrupted. Secondary pests outbreaks are caused when natural enemies are poisoned or killed by pesticides applied to control other pests (see Figure 10). Abundant ants, excessive dust, and certain adverse environmental conditions can also disrupt biological controls.

Avocado brown mite, caterpillars, greenhouse thrips, and sixspotted mite are not problems in avocado groves in most years. Selective treatments or spot applications of pesticides are sometimes applied, but effective natural enemies usually keep any outbreaks localized and brief.

Homoptera (plant juice-sucking species) such as mealybugs, scale insects, and whiteflies are especially well controlled by parasites and predators, except when this biological control is disrupted. Ants, excessive dust in the grove, and broad-spectrum pesticides applied for other pests are the common causes of outbreaks.

Young Tree Pests. Some species that are innocuous in mature groves are pests when trees are young. Branch and twig borer, brown garden snail, earwigs, false chinch bug, Fuller rose beetle, grasshoppers, and June beetles (scarabs) are occasional pests, but only when trees are young. New plantings are also susceptible to the same invertebrates as damage older trees, but fruit-damaging species such as thrips are of little consequence on young trees that are not yet producing significant amounts of harvestable fruit.

New and Exotic Pests. Recently introduced pests have caused major problems for avocado growers, and more new pests are likely to be introduced. Introductions may accelerate with increases in trade and travel. The Caribbean, Central America, Florida, and Mexico have many avocado pests that do not occur in California. If they arrive in California, new pests may require changes in the management practices presented in this book.

For example, avocado lace bug has been a pest in the Caribbean and Florida for many years. Avocado lace bug became established in San Diego in 2004. *Neohydatothrips burungae*, a thrips species closely resembling avocado thrips, was discovered in southern California avocados in 2005. Exotic fruit flies are discovered in California from time to time and have been eradicated many times. These include the Mexican fruit fly, which is established in Mexico, and the Mediterranean fruit fly, which occurs in Central America, Hawaii, and many other regions and countries.

Beneficial Invertebrates. Many beneficial species are important in groves. Pollinating insects increase avocado fruit yields and quality. Many growers place hives of domesticated honey bees in their groves on a seasonal basis during peak flowering. Trees are also pollinated by naturally occurring insects, including native bees and the adults of predatory syrphid flies or flower flies. Parasites (mostly small wasps and certain flies) and predators (many groups, including lacewings, lady beetles, and predaceous mites and thrips) are major biological control agents for pest insects and mites. Certain invertebrates, including many soil-dwelling species, help to recycle organic matter and improve soil quality, thereby increasing crop growth.

Black scale (mature females shown here) and many other potential pests rarely cause economic damage in avocado because they normally are suppressed by natural enemies.

JACK KELLY CLARK

Most invertebrates in avocado groves are innocuous, and many are highly beneficial. This adult syrphid, also called a flower fly or hover fly, resembles a honey bee. Syrphids are among the many native insects that increase crop yield by pollinating flowers. Syrphid larvae are predators of soft-bodied insects.

Monitoring Insects and Mites

Regular monitoring for potential pests is an essential part of effective integrated pest management. Monitor for important pests at regular intervals during the appropriate times of the year as summarized earlier in this book in Figures 8 and 9. Compare your written records from quantitative monitoring on several dates to determine whether pests, natural enemies, or damage are on the increase or decrease. Compare your monitoring results to suggested action thresholds for pests such as avocado thrips and persea mite. Compare your monitoring records from before and after any control action to assess the treatment's efficacy. Determine the need for management actions by considering your monitoring results in combination with other information, such as grove history, inspection of fruit in harvest bins, and quality grading from the packinghouse.

Correctly identify pests and the cause of any damage. Even closely related species or types of damage may require different control actions. The photos in this manual and those available in the latest version of *Avocado: UC IPM Pest Management Guidelines: Insects and Mites* (online at www.ipm.ucdavis.edu) can help you identify the most common insects and mites found in avocado groves. Consult your Cooperative Extension farm advisor, agricultural commissioner, or PCA for additional help.

Begin monitoring before you expect pests to become abundant and cause any significant damage. Continue monitoring at regular intervals through the period when each pest typically causes economic damage. Keep written records of all monitoring results. Consult the *Avocado Year-Round IPM Program* (online at www.ipm.ucdavis.edu) for suggested recordkeeping forms and current recommendations on monitoring frequency and methods.

Decisions of when and where to monitor are guided by factors such as feeding preferences for certain parts of the tree or the grove that differ among species and sometimes among life stages of the same species. The location and pest stage that you monitor may not be the same as the plant part where damage would eventually occur or the life stage that would cause damage. For example, avocado thrips strongly prefer to eat succulent, young leaves, and their feeding there is usually harmless. Most avocado thrips only move on to the fruit, scarring avocado skins, after the foliage hardens. When you monitor for avocado thrips on young leaves, beginning before fruit set, you can make early population density estimates for comparison with suggested treatment thresholds. By monitoring these succulent leaves, growers are able to assess treatment needs before the avocado thrips begin to damage fruit.

Look for important natural enemies, preferably by using a quantitative method such as recording the number of predators or the percentage of parasitized or pathogen-killed pests. Abundant natural enemies can sometimes reduce pest

Visual inspection is the primary monitoring method. Examine plants regularly for damage, pests, and natural enemies. Look at the plant parts where pests are expected to occur. Monitor during the time of year when problems are likely. Record the results. A handheld global positioning system (GPS) is useful for marking the location of problems for later management or follow-up monitoring.

Inspect foliage with a hand lens when the presence of mites or other tiny creatures is suspected. Hold the lens close to your eye and move the leaf being viewed until it is in focus.

JACK KELLY CLARK

populations rapidly, so monitoring beneficials may help you to decide whether treatment can be delayed or even avoided altogether.

Monitoring Units. Divide large or varied groves into several sections. Monitor each section separately and record the results for each on a separate copy of your monitoring forms. Conditions that favor pest development can vary within a grove and between neighboring groves due to differences such as tree age, rootstock variety, and environmental conditions.

Mark the boundaries of each monitoring unit on a map and in the field, using colored flagging or spray paint on trunks. For most invertebrates, you should choose several trees at random for inspection and then monitor for pests and damage at several locations within each of those trees. Certain other pests typically first show up as problems in characteristic "hot spots." An example is avocado brown mite, which occurs in outbreaks along grove edges bordering dirt roads. Consult the individual pests sections in this chapter and the latest revision of *Avocado: UC IPM Pest Management Guidelines: Insects and Mites* or *Avocado Year-Round IPM Program* (online at www.ipm.ucdavis.edu) for current monitoring methods, suggested thresholds, and recordkeeping forms.

Visual Inspection. For most problems, look at the plant parts where damage, pests, and natural enemies are most likely to occur. Make a record of what you do or do not find. In general, the number of individuals of the species you are monitoring should be counted on each sample unit or plant part that you inspect. Presence/absence or binomial sampling is sometimes used (for instance, with persea mite) to save time by simply recording whether or not any pests of that type are in that sample.

Traps. Traps help you detect the presence and activity peaks of certain pests. Trapping information can help you determine the need for and timing of pest control actions. Various traps attract pests by scent, color, shape, or ultraviolet light. Examples include pheromone- (sex attractant-) baited bucket or sticky traps for pest moths and yellow sticky traps for glassy-winged sharpshooter. Trapping generally has to be used in combination with inspection of plant parts for damage or pests, partly because certain traps capture only flying adults and not the flightless immatures that actually cause damage. Traps are discussed under "Caterpillars," "European Earwig," "Glassy-Winged Sharpshooter," "June Beetles," "Armored Scales," and "Soft Scales," later in this chapter.

Pest Prevention and Management

Keep insect and mite populations below economically damaging levels by following good cultural practices and preserving natural enemy populations. Make careful applications of

A continuous, dense canopy with adjacent trees touching provides harborage that favors populations of caterpillars, greenhouse thrips, and mealybugs. Pruning dense canopies can reduce problems with these pests.

pesticides only when monitoring indicates that treatment is warranted. Choose materials and methods that are least disruptive to beneficial insects and predatory mites.

Cultural Practices. Irrigate adequately to reduce populations of mites and, perhaps, certain insects. Avoid excessive nitrogen applications as an increase in foliar nitrogen increases populations of phloem-sucking insects, including mealybugs, soft scales, and whiteflies. Minimize dust to conserve natural enemies. Manage bordering vegetation to control pests such as chinch bugs and grasshoppers, which cause damage only when they migrate in to feed on young trees. Caterpillars (during their moth stage), Fuller rose beetle, glassy-winged sharpshooter, and whiteflies can migrate from crop to crop, so by managing nearby crops such as citrus you can influence the likelihood that certain pests will cause problems in your avocado grove. By thinning clustered avocado fruit and pruning dense canopies to eliminate harborage, you can reduce the density of caterpillars, greenhouse thrips, and mealybugs. Where greenhouse thrips have caused damage, harvest early to reduce crop overlap and remove greenhouse thrips with the old fruit before the pests have a chance to migrate to young fruit.

Biological Control. Natural enemies constitute the primary control factor for many potential pests of avocado. Some natural enemies are indigenous to California growing areas; others have been introduced and established by University of California and government scientists during classical biological control programs to control exotic pests (see Table 3). Some growers purchase and release natural enemies to augment existing populations. These include periodic introductions of green lacewings (Figure 24), predaceous mites, or *Trichogramma* wasps.

Conservation of pathogens, parasites, and predators is the primary method used in biological control. Many natural enemies' populations are easily disrupted by pesticide

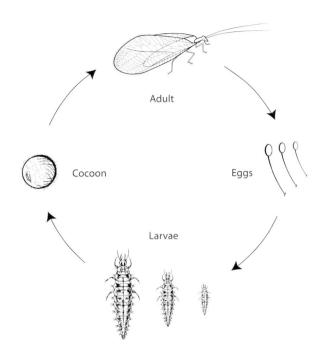

Figure 24. Green lacewing life cycle and stages. The female lays oblong eggs attached to plants by a silken stalk. Larvae develop through three instars while feeding on mites and various soft-bodied insects, including caterpillars, thrips, and Homoptera. Larvae pupate in loosely woven, spherical, silken cocoons attached to plants. The nocturnal adults emerge and mate. *Source:* larvae by Celeste Green from Smith and Hagen 1956.

applications, resulting in outbreaks of caterpillar, mealybug, mite, scale, and whitefly pests (see Figure 10). Make only limited, thoughtful use of pesticides, as discussed below. Carefully select the location, material, method, rate, and timing when applying any insecticide or miticide to ensure that treatment causes the least possible disruption to natural enemies.

Minimize dust in the orchard. Dusty conditions reduce the reproduction and host-finding ability of many natural enemies, thereby causing outbreaks of pests such as mites and scales. Control ants if Homoptera (plant juice-sucking pests) are a problem. Ants tend Homoptera and they will attack any natural enemies they encounter.

Pathogens. Pathogens are microorganisms that infect and kill the host. Naturally occurring pathogens such as viruses often cause high caterpillar populations to crash. The bacterium *Bacillus thuringiensis* (Bt) is produced commercially and sprayed to kill caterpillars that eat treated foliage. Certain microorganism by-products discussed below are available as biological pesticides.

Parasites. A parasite lives and feeds in or on a larger host. Insect parasites (more precisely called "parasitoids") are smaller than their hosts and develop either inside or attached to the outside of the host's body. In some species, only the immature stage of the parasite feeds on the host, and it kills only one host individual during its development. Adult females of certain parasites (such as many wasps that attack scales and whiteflies) also feed on their hosts. Pest mortality resulting from this host feeding by adults is easy to overlook, but it is an important aspect of biological control, adding to the host mortality caused by parasitism.

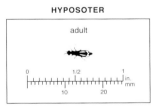

Parasites are flies and wasps that, during their larval stage, feed in or on their host. This female *Hyposoter exiguae* lays one egg in each host as shown here. This wasp parasitizes and kills caterpillars of many different species.

Lacewings are general predators that feed on mites and most any small, soft-bodied insect. Larvae, like this third-instar *Chrysoperla carnea*, are flattened and tapered at the tail. They have long, curved, mandibles for puncturing prey and sucking their body fluids.

Most parasitic insects are flies (Diptera) or wasps (Hymenoptera). Parasitic Hymenoptera occur in more than three dozen families, including Aphelinidae, Braconidae, Encyrtidae, Eulophidae, Ichneumonidae, and Trichogrammatidae. Many of these wasps are tiny species, as described and illustrated in the individual pest sections that follow. The most common parasitic flies are in the family Tachinidae. Many adult tachinids resemble house flies. Their larvae are maggots that feed inside their host.

Predators. Predators kill and feed on many individual prey during their lifetime. Some predators are specialized and feed on only one species or a few closely related species. Other, more general predators feed on a variety of organisms, and many feed on most any species that is abundant at the time. Some species are predaceous only during their immature stage, while others are predaceous as both adults and as immatures. Depending on the species, adult predators also (or only) feed on honeydew, nectar, pollen, and plant juices.

Predators that are important in pest biological control include beetles (in the insect order Coleoptera), true bugs (Hemiptera), flies (Diptera), lacewings (Neuroptera), predatory thrips (Thysanoptera), and wasps (Hymenoptera). Spiders (class Araneae, order Arachnida) are also important predators of insects. Mites in the family Phytoseiidae are very important in controlling pest mites and certain insects.

Pesticides. Relatively few insecticides and miticides are registered for application in avocado groves. Biological control is a key pest management tactic and controls most invertebrates that can become avocado pests.

For pests that are not well controlled by natural enemies (especially avocado thrips and persea mite), correct application of a needed pesticide is essential to a successful integrated pest management program. To achieve effective control, choose the correct application time, rate, ground or air speed, gallonage, and type of application equipment. Achieve good spray coverage. For information on the type and rate of pesticide to use, see the latest version of *Avocado: UC IPM Pest Management Guidelines: Insects and Mites* (online at www.ipm.ucdavis.edu).

To improve the overall success of your IPM program, choose pesticides that have the least impact on natural enemies (see Table 4). Use selective and short-residual materials when possible. Make spot applications if feasible to minimize the potential for harm to nontarget species and to provide unsprayed reservoirs from which beneficials can recolonize the trees. An occasional, single application of a broad-spectrum pesticide is less harmful to natural enemies than multiple broad-spectrum treatments.

Selectivity. Broad-spectrum pesticides include most organophosphates (e.g., malathion), carbamates, and pyrethroids. These broad-spectrum insecticides are highly toxic to natural enemies and are often more toxic to natural enemies than to pests.

Selective pesticides and those with little or no persistence are less toxic to natural enemies. Many pests can be controlled by either selective or broad-spectrum pesticides. Thrips can be controlled with the broad-spectrum organophosphates or with more selective insecticides such as abamectin, sabadilla, and spinosad.

Sabadilla is a botanical substance derived from the seeds of a lily-like plant. It has little contact toxicity and acts primarily as an insect stomach poison. Abamectin is a mixture of several avermectins, which are compounds derived from the soil bacterium *Streptomyces avermitilis*. Abamectin is an insecticide and miticide that affects the nervous system of invertebrates, paralyzing them. Spinosad is a fermentation by-product from the bacterium *Saccharopolyspora spinosa*. Spinosad is quick-acting, both on external contact and when eaten by insects. Abamectin and spinosad have translaminar activity; that is, they are absorbed short distances into leaves, especially when they are applied with oil or a surfactant. Both chemicals break down quickly in sunlight, so their movement into leaves is critical for good control.

Some insecticides are selective or safe for one group of natural enemies but not another. For example, abamectin and spinosad have low toxicity to most parasitic and predatory insects but can reduce populations of predatory *Franklinothrips* because this key predator of avocado thrips also periodically punctures avocado leaves to feed on their fluids, which can contain these insecticides.

When making a treatment decision, carefully consider the effect the pesticide may have on nontarget species and its persistence in the environment, as summarized earlier in Table 4. For example, the range of activity for malathion is expressed as "broad (insects and beneficial mites)" because malathion affects most groups of insects and beneficial mites. Conversely, the microbial *Bacillus thuringiensis* is listed as "narrow (caterpillars)" because it kills only caterpillars.

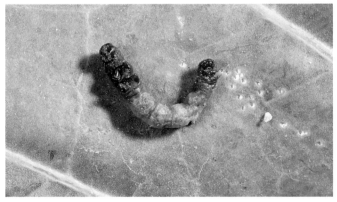

This caterpillar died from infection by *Bacillus thuringiensis* (Bt). This naturally occurring insect pathogen is commercially available as a highly selective insecticide that kills only caterpillars. Bt can be applied to control omnivorous looper and western avocado leafroller without disrupting natural enemies of other pests.

Persistence. The word "persistence" refers to the length of time a pesticide remains effective, a period that can range from a few hours or days (short) to several months (long). Certain broad-spectrum materials (including botanicals, oils, and insecticidal soap) have very short persistence. These materials have little or no toxicity to natural enemies that colonize treated surfaces after the spray has dried, so they do not disrupt most natural enemies' populations.

Once a persistent broad-spectrum pesticide has been applied, residues on the plant may remain harmful to natural enemies for weeks or months. For example, adult *Trichogramma* wasps that are placed in a jar with leaves that have been sprayed in the field with a broad-spectrum insecticide such as malathion can be killed by residues on the leaves, even when the leaves were collected many weeks after an application. Long after pesticides no longer affect their target pests, persistent residues can continue to kill natural enemies or intoxicate them such that they will reproduce poorly or be unable to locate their prey. Table 4 includes information on the persistence of various pesticides.

Resistance. Repeated use of a pesticide can cause target pests to develop resistance, selecting for pest individuals that are less susceptible to the pesticide (see Figure 11). Resistance renders subsequent treatments ineffective if you reapply that same material or some other pesticide with a similar mode of action. The development of resistance is an acute problem when only a limited number of pesticides are available for the crop, as is the case with avocados.

To slow the development of resistance, only apply pesticides when absolutely necessary. For multiple treatments, alternate between a number of pesticides with different modes of action. Leave some areas unsprayed to allow survival of beneficials and of still-susceptible pests that can then breed with any resistant pests, thereby reducing the rate of resistance development.

MITES

Spider mites (family Tetranychidae) and predatory mites (Phytoseiidae) are tiny, 8-legged arthropods. Unlike insects, mites do not have antennae or wings. Spider mites and predatory mites develop through an egg stage, a six-legged larval stage, and two eight-legged nymphal stages before becoming eight-legged adults (Figure 25). All stages of avocado bud mite (Eriophyidae) have only four legs.

Persea mite is a key pest of California avocados. Avocado brown mite and sixspotted mite are sporadic pests. Avocado bud mite has very rarely been a problem. Several beneficial mites are important predators of pest mites and certain pest insects. Natural enemies and certain management strategies vary for different pest mites. Identify the pest and natural enemy species that are present in your grove and learn their biology so you will be able to manage them as needed.

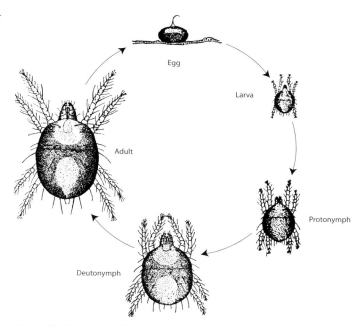

Figure 25. Spider mite life cycle and stages. Spider mites and predatory phytoseiid mites have two main body parts, their abdomen and head, and they develop through five life stages. Eggs hatch, producing six-legged larvae. The two nymphal stages and adults have eight legs. Illustrated here is a female avocado brown mite, with a leaf side view of the egg, which has a projecting stalk. *Adapted from:* Moznette 1922.

Persea Mite
Oligonychus perseae

Persea mite was discovered in California in 1990. It has become a key foliar pest in avocado. High populations cause premature leaf drop and defoliation. Defoliation leads to sunburned bark and fruit, aborted or dropped fruit, and severely stressed trees, all of which later lead to reduced yields.

Damage
A heavy persea mite infestation can often be recognized by the numerous brown-spotted, green leaves that can be found hanging from the trees and lying on the ground beneath infested trees. The canopy of a heavily infested tree can appear lighter-colored overall than that of a healthy tree when viewed from a distance. Persea mite damage early in the season can be confused with sixspotted mite damage. Persea mite also sometimes feeds on the upper leaf surface, but usually mite feeding on the upper leaf surface is by avocado brown mite. Avocado brown mite feeding causes the upper leaf surface to appear bronzed or scorched and the damage does not appear in discrete, circular spots.

Persea mite feeding on the underside of leaves causes discrete, circular, chlorotic to brown spots that initially are visible only on the lower surface of leaves. These spots later become visible on the upper leaf surface. Persea mite

This premature drop of green leaves with brown and yellow circular spots is characteristic of persea mite infestation.

These sparse avocado canopies were caused by high persea mite populations. Bark and fruit may become sunburned and future yields will be greatly reduced.

Persea mite feeds on the underside of leaves, causing distinct roundish brown to yellow blotches visible from the top leaf surface (left). Mites feed under (and are visible through) silken patches, with little obvious necrosis early in an infestation (right). Older infestations (center) produce many necrotic spots and silken patches. Many of these older discolored patches no longer contain any live mites.

Persea mite usually feeds only on leaves, but extremely high populations can also feed on fruit, causing the necrotic spotting shown here.

JACK KELLY CLARK

Persea mites are somewhat oblong and yellowish to green, with dark blotches. The similar-looking sixspotted mite produces much less webbing.

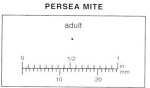

PERSEA MITE

adult

.

Adult females have an oval-shaped body that is slightly flattened and elongated. Females and immatures are yellowish or greenish with two or more small, dark blotches on the abdomen. Old females that have ceased oviposition turn darker green and become somewhat smaller and inactive. Males are smaller than reproductive females. Males are somewhat pear-shaped, slightly flattened, and yellowish, with or without small, dark spots. Persea mites feed and reproduce mostly beneath webbed patches. When occupied, these silk-covered "nests" typically contain eggs, immatures (larvae and nymphs), and adults.

Each female lays about two to four dozen eggs during her life. Eggs are round and pale yellow, and develop red "eye" spots as they mature. Egg-to-adult female development time is about 2 to 3 weeks when temperatures average 63° to 77°F (17° to 25°C). You can use degree-days to accurately estimate the number of days in a generation (Table 14).

Cool winter temperatures slow persea mite population growth. Mite densities are lowest in March and gradually increase through spring feeding on new leaf flush. Populations generally peak in July and August.

colonies are small and can be very numerous. Each colony can produce dense webbing that resembles a silvery spot on the underside of the leaf. Sixspotted mite webbing is less dense and usually does not occur in small, circular patches. Sixspotted mite feeding causes brown to purplish, irregularly shaped blotches that are often relatively contiguous along the veins, in comparison to the roundish, mostly scattered spots created by persea mite. Table 13 summarizes characteristics that distinguish the three mite pests of avocado.

Description and Seasonal Development

Persea mite occurs in most avocado-growing areas of California, with the exception of the Central Valley. It is most damaging to Hass and Gwen avocados and a few other varieties. Esther, Pinkerton, and Reed are of intermediate susceptibility. The Bacon, Fuerte, Lamb Hass, and Zutano varieties are much less susceptible. Persea mite attacks other plant species, including bamboo. Weed hosts include cheeseweeds or mallows (*Malva* spp.), lambsquarters (*Chenopodium album*), milkweed (*Asclepias fascicularis*), and sowthistle (*Sonchus oleraceus*).

Monitoring Guidelines

Monitor leaves for mites, mite damage, and natural enemies about every 7 to 10 days from mid-March through at least August, and perhaps through October. Use the methods recommended in the latest *Avocado: UC IPM Pest Management Guidelines: Insects and Mites* (online at www.ipm.ucdavis.edu). Coordinate your monitoring and treatment decision-making for mites and thrips. Persea mite and avocado thrips are usually the key invertebrate pests feeding on leaves. Certain materials applied for thrips (often earlier in the season) can also control or suppress late-season mite populations, but they may also have an adverse impact on natural enemies. The frequency with which you monitor for mites and the need for treatment and choice of treatment material can be affected by your decisions on thrips management.

Also, consider the effect of weather on your treatment decision-making. Heavy winter rains and much wind can substantially reduce subsequent mite populations and damage. Persea mite populations are suppressed or may even

Table 13. Pest Mites and Their Distinguishing Characteristics in Avocado.

Characteristic	Avocado brown mite	Persea mite	Sixspotted mite
Feeding damage and location on leaves	bronzing on upper surface, underside browning when mites are abundant	distinct circular yellow or brown spots on underside, may be yellowish spots on upper side	underside with brown to purplish irregular blotches, or relatively continuous discoloring along veins
Webbing	not obvious	dense silvery silken patches, especially along veins	light webbing not in distinct roundish patches
Female body color	dark to brown	yellow to green with two or more dark blotches	yellowish with six dark blotches
Egg color	amber to brown	pale yellow	translucent to white

Several beneficial predaceous mites also occur in avocado, as described in photographs and text.

Table 14. Persea Mite Egg-to-Adult Development Time (Days) at Several Constant Temperatures.

Temperature	59°F (15°C)	68°F (20°C)	77°F (25°C)	86°F (30°C)
Days	35	17	14	10

One generation (egg to adult female) requires 363 degree-days F (200 DD C) above a threshold of 46°F (7.8°C). *Source:* Aponte and McMurtry 1997.

crash when humidity is low and the daily high temperature is 100°F (38°C) or higher on several consecutive days.

Management Guidelines

Minimize tree stress to reduce the effect of persea mites feeding on trees. Appropriate irrigation frequency and amounts, good management of avocado root rot and other key pathogens, and early harvesting of fruit will reduce the adverse impacts of mite feeding. If you do treat for mites, whenever possible choose a pesticide that has low residual toxicity or is nontoxic to natural enemies.

In the early stages of a significant infestation, highly refined petroleum oils or certain other materials can be applied. Treat only where necessary and leave some areas unsprayed to conserve beneficials and provide refuges from which natural enemies and pesticide-susceptible pests can recolonize the treated trees. Maximize the interval between treatments and alternate your applications among pesticides with different modes of action to reduce the rate at which the pests develop resistance.

Biological Control. Numerous predators feed on persea mite. Predaceous mites include *Amblyseius* (=*Neoseiulus*) *californicus*, *Euseius hibisci*, *Galendromus annectens*, and *G. helveolus*. Black hunter thrips (*Leptothrips mali*), sixspotted thrips (*Scolothrips sexmaculatus*), brown lacewings (*Hemerobius* spp.) and green lacewings (*Chrysopa* and *Chrysoperla* spp.), dustywings (family Coniopterygidae), a predatory midge (*Feltiella* sp., Cecidomyiidae), a rove beetle (*Oligota oviformis*, Staphylinidae), and the spider mite destroyer lady beetle (*Stethorus picipes*) are other common predators. Most predators

This adult *Euseius hibisci* is a common predator of pest mites and tiny insects. This shiny predator moves quickly when exposed to bright light. It can survive when prey are scare because it also feeds on pollen and leaf sap.

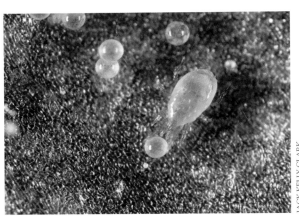

Neoseiulus (*Amblyseius*) *californicus* is one of several naturally occurring species that also are available for purchase and release. This adult is consuming spider mite eggs.

This *Galendromus annectens* predaceous mite occurs naturally at low densities in coastal avocado groves.

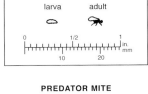

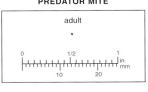

Galendromus helveolus is a specialized predator of spider mites. It prefers eggs and nymphs of avocado brown mite and sixspotted mite, but also feeds and reproduces in nests of persea mite. *Galendromus* helps to control persea mite if sufficient numbers of predators are released and releases are well-timed.

are not highly effective because of persea mites' protective, webbed nests. You should, however, conserve natural enemies, because they can reduce persea mite populations, especially when the mites are moving outside their nests, and predators often provide good biological control of avocado brown mite and sixspotted mite.

Commercially available predators include several mite species (*Amblyseius californicus, Galendromus annectens,* and *G. helveolus*) and green lacewing larvae (*Chrysoperla* spp.). *Galendromus helveolus* helps to control persea mite if the predators are introduced in sufficient numbers and those releases are well timed. To check the viability of purchased predaceous mites, gently pour some mites and any shipping substrate into a clear jar and look for an abundance of fast-moving mites, which would indicate that the predators have arrived in good condition. Consult the latest *Avocado: UC*

IPM Pest Management Guidelines: Insects and Mites (online at www.ipm.ucdavis.edu) for specific release recommendations.

Cultural Control. Eliminate or reduce alternate host plants for persea mite that are growing near your avocados, including mite-susceptible ornamentals, noncommercial fruit trees, and weeds. Provide trees with appropriate irrigation and other good cultural care to maintain the flush of new growth and compensate for mite-induced leaf drop. Be careful, though, that you do not overfertilize. Excessive fertilization, especially with quick-release formulations, may increase persea mite populations and damage during late spring and summer due to increased foliar nitrogen. Spraying the underside of leaves with a forceful stream of water can reduce mite populations on a few small trees, where this is feasible. Whitewash trunks and major limbs to protect bark and wood from sunburn after any premature leaf drop.

Eggs of most predaceous mites are oblong. A *Galendromus annectens* egg is shown here between two round spider mite eggs.

This sixspotted thrips (*Scolothrips sexmaculatus*) adult feeds almost entirely on mites. It can become common in persea mite nests during late summer.

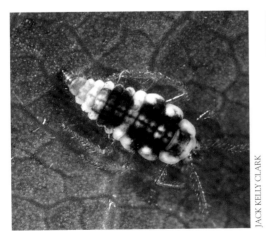

This larval dustywing (*Conwentzia barretti*) is mostly black and whitish with a strongly tapered body. It eats mites and various tiny soft-bodied insects.

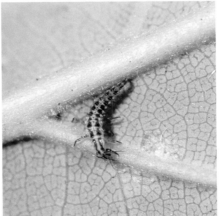

Green lacewing (*Chrysoperla comanche*) larva feeding on persea mites. Lacewings are common generalist predators of many pests, including thrips and Homoptera such as mealybugs and scales.

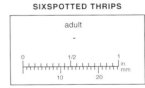

SIXSPOTTED THRIPS

adult

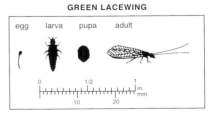

GREEN LACEWING

egg   larva   pupa   adult

Avocado Brown Mite

Oligonychus punicae

Avocado brown mite is occasionally prevalent in groves, mostly in coastal growing areas. From about July to September, avocado brown mite sometimes causes noticeable bronzing of leaves and partial defoliation of some trees. Natural enemies and temperature (hot or cold weather) usually keep populations of this mite to low, innocuous levels.

Damage

Avocado brown mite damage is most pronounced in late summer and fall, when leaf browning and the mites' whitish egg shells and cast skins become obvious to the eye. Severe infestations tend to occur on border-row trees, where road dust is detrimental to mite predator populations. Ash deposited on leaves from wildfires also reportedly causes brown mite outbreaks.

Avocado brown mite feeds almost entirely on the upper leaf surfaces. It causes no significant damage when population densities are low to moderate (about 10 to 20 adult females per leaf). If the spider mite destroyer lady beetle (*Stethorus picipes*) is present and reproducing well at this time, brown mite does not become a problem. Damage occurs if avocado brown mites average about 50 to 70 adult females per leaf (about 100–200 motile stages [adults and nymphs combined]). At these higher densities, mites also colonize the lower leaf surface and sometimes the fruit, and partial defoliation can occur. These higher populations cause leaf bronzing along the midrib, then along smaller veins, and finally the entire leaf turns brown.

Description and Seasonal Development

Avocado brown mite is a dark brown, oval mite about $\frac{1}{75}$ inch (0.3 mm) long. Its tiny amber-colored eggs have a short, projecting stalk (see Figure 25). At low populations, most eggs are laid singly along the midrib. Eggs are increasingly found throughout the upper leaf surface as populations increase. In summer there may be two complete generations per month. Temperatures of 90° to 95°F (32° to 35°C) or higher kill many of these mites and their eggs, as does the first cold weather in fall or early winter.

Monitoring and Management Guidelines

Look for bronzed leaves and brown mites during summer monitoring for other pests such as caterpillars and persea mite, especially when monitoring in coastal groves. Consider monitoring specifically for brown mite during summer in places where the trees are dusty, where they were sprayed earlier in the season with a broad-spectrum insecticide, and after wildfires. Major outbreaks have occurred after application of a broad-spectrum insecticide to control greenhouse thrips or omnivorous looper. To locate avocado brown mite and its webbing, use a hand lens to inspect along the midrib on the upper leaf surface.

Maintain good biological control by conserving natural enemies. Control the amount of dust and avoid applying broad-spectrum pesticides for any pests. When treating any pests (including avocado brown mite), spot treat individual trees where possible. Consult the latest *Avocado: UC IPM Pest Management Guidelines: Insects and Mites* (online at www.ipm.ucdavis.edu) for specific recommendations.

Biological Control. Naturally occurring populations of the spider mite destroyer (*Stethorus picipes*) provide the majority of biocontrol for avocado brown mite. Predaceous mites (especially *Euseius hibisci* and *Galendromus helveolus*) are also helpful, but predatory mites are primarily effective against sixspotted mite. Most other natural enemies mentioned for persea mite also feed on avocado brown mite.

Cultural Control. Keeping dust levels to a minimum improves the activity and effectiveness of predators, and so is critical for good biological control. Oil or pave the main orchard roads to reduce dust drift onto trees. When you use dirt roads, drive slowly. Use a water truck or trailer to wet unpaved roads and prevent airborne dust, especially during summer months when heat convection currents carry dust well up into tree canopies.

Avocado brown mite damage begins as relatively faint browning along veins on the upper side of leaves. Recognition of this initial symptom allows early actions such as controlling dust to improve the effectiveness of predators, which can then prevent mites from adversely affecting tree health.

This severe leaf bronzing can occur when avocado brown mite exceeds about 100 to 200 motile stages per leaf.

Avocado brown mites are mostly dark to brownish. Most occur on the upper leaf surface, especially along the midvein.

Avocado brown mite eggs are amber to brown. At low populations, most eggs are laid singly near the midrib. Eggs increasingly occur throughout the upper leaf surface as populations increase.

Avocado brown mite and certain other pests are often most abundant at dusty sites, such as on grove edge trees such as this one along a dirt road.

The spider mite destroyer (*Stethorus picipes*) usually provides good biological control of avocado brown mite. This adult lady beetle is shiny black with a very finely punctured surface covered with minute hairs. It feeds on all stages of spider mites.

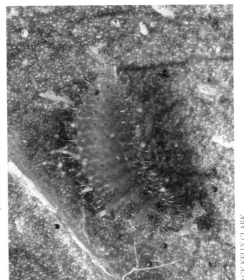

AVOCADO BROWN MITE

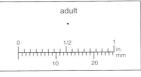

STETHORUS

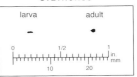

The spider mite destroyer larva is dark gray to brownish and is covered with numerous fine hairs.

Sixspotted Mite

Eotetranychus sexmaculatus

Sixspotted mites are generally under good control in avocados in the interior growing areas (Riverside and San Diego Counties) due to predators and warm weather. Locations near the coast, such as foggy areas in San Luis Obispo and Santa Barbara Counties, are more likely to experience damage. Sixspotted mite can become a problem anywhere if the trees are drought stressed or if pesticides used to control other pests disrupt natural biological control of mites.

Damage

Sixspotted mite in avocado feeds only on the lower leaf surface. It causes irregular brown to purplish discoloration, mostly along the midrib and larger veins. Sixspotted mite produces webbing, but not the dense silk patches formed by persea mite. See Table 13 for ways to distinguish pest mites in avocado.

Sixspotted spider mite can severely stress trees at relatively low densities by causing premature leaf drop, but populations rarely exceed an even lower average density of two to three mites per leaf. At this low abundance sixspotted mite is not damaging, and is easily overlooked.

Description and Seasonal Development

The oval adults are about $\frac{1}{75}$ inch (0.3 mm) long. The body is lemon yellow, often with about six dark blotches on the abdomen, although some individuals have no distinct spots. Females lay tiny, globular, pale greenish yellow to translucent or pearly white eggs, which have a slender projecting stalk. About 25 to 40 eggs are laid over 10 to 20 days. Eggs hatch in 5 days to 3 weeks, depending on temperature. In summer, mites reach maturity in 8 to 12 days. Populations are heaviest in spring and early summer.

Monitoring and Management Guidelines

Look for sixspotted mite when monitoring for persea mite. Make sure to accurately distinguish the mite species present (see Table 13). When you are monitoring specifically for sixspotted mite, select trees in dustier and more humid locations of groves. Use a hand lens to examine along the midrib and lateral veins on the underside of interior canopy leaves. Look for brown to purplish discoloring, mite webbing, and mites.

Enhance biological control of sixspotted mite and other invertebrate pests by conserving natural enemies. Minimize dust. Avoid applying nonselective pesticides that are toxic to predaceous insects and beneficial mites that control plant-feeding mites and pest insects. If you must apply nonselective pesticides, limit their application to those spots where the pests are most abundant. If control action is warranted, follow recommendations in the latest *Avocado: UC IPM Pest Management Guidelines: Insects and Mites* (online at www.ipm.ucdavis.edu).

Biological Control. Sixspotted mite is controlled primarily by predatory phytoseiid mites. These include *Amblyseius* (=*Typhlodromalus*) *limonicus* and *Galendromus helveolus*. *Euseius hibisci*, a shiny pear-shaped predator, is important in part because it can maintain and increase its populations on avocado pollen when pest mites are scarce. *Typhlodromus rickeri* also preys on sixspotted mite around Santa Barbara County. The spider mite destroyer lady beetle (*Stethorus picipes*) and sixspotted thrips (*Scolothrips sexmaculatus*) are other important natural enemies.

Sixspotted mite feeding causes brown to purplish, irregular blotches that can be relatively continuous along veins on the underside of the leaf. This mite produces webbing that is light in comparison with the dense silk patches made by persea mite.

Sixspotted mites are yellowish with dark blotches. Their egg (lower left) is translucent to pearly white.

Cultural Control. Encourage predators by oiling or paving main orchard roads to control road dust. Drive slowly when it is necessary to use dirt roads. Consider using a water truck or trailer to wet dirt roads, especially before travel during summer months, when heat convection currents carry dust well up into the tree canopies. Individual backyard trees can be hosed down in early to midsummer to remove dust and enhance biological controls.

Avocado Bud Mite

Tegolophus myersi

Avocado bud mite has very rarely been a problem in California. When it does cause problems, they can include excessive bud abortion, young fruit drop, and distorted, elongated fruit growth. Damage to commercial groves has been reported only in Orange County during the 1930s and in Ventura County in the 1990s. A related species, *Tegolophus perseaflorae*, occasionally damages buds and fruit in Florida. Bud mites (family Eriophyidae) are much smaller than spider mites. Infested buds must be dissected and examined under a binocular dissecting microscope to definitively determine that mites are present. Submerging infested buds in concentrated alcohol, such as 95% ethanol, and shaking them vigorously for 20 to 30 seconds can dislodge any eriophyids, which can then be decanted with the alcohol into a shallow dish for easier observation. The pale mites are elongated (carrot- or wedge-shaped) with all appendages protruding from one end (the wider end) of the body.

THRIPS

Thrips (spelled the same for singular or plural) are tiny, slender, insects. Thrips (order Thysanoptera) develop through five or six life stages (Figure 26) and have fringe-tipped wings as adults. Avocado thrips are pests in avocado, and (less frequently) greenhouse thrips can be pests as well. Citrus thrips (*Scirtothrips citri*) occasionally occur in avocado, especially in groves near citrus. Western flower thrips (*Frankliniella occidentalis*) commonly occur in avocado blossoms. Citrus and flower thrips do not damage avocado. Another thrips, *Neohydatothrips burungae*, has recently been discovered in avocados in southern California. It closely resembles avocado thrips but is of unknown importance. Several predatory thrips are important natural enemies of mites, plant-feeding thrips, and other pests.

Avocado Thrips

Scirtothrips perseae

Avocado thrips has become a key pest since its discovery in California in 1996. Although they have little affect on tree health, avocado thrips feed directly on immature fruit.

The internal quality of the fruit is not affected, but obvious exterior feeding scars cause severe downgrading or culling of damaged fruit. Severe scarring when fruit are young can slow or stunt the fruit's growth.

Damage

Avocado thrips feed on succulent leaves and young fruit. Feeding on young leaves causes irregular bronzing or scarring on both upper and lower sides of the leaf. Discoloration is typically concentrated along the midrib and lateral leaf veins, and also appears in scattered patches between veins as populations increase. Foliar feeding is usually unimportant, except when very high populations cause premature leaf drop.

As fruit grow, this early feeding becomes apparent as scabby or leathery brown scars expand across the skin. Thrips scarring is sometimes called "alligator skin." Mechanical injury or abrasion, such as from strong winds, also causes fruit scarring that can be confused with thrips injury.

Avocado thrips prefer to feed and lay eggs in succulent leaves. They move to young fruit when leaves harden. Almost all damage occurs when fruit are 0.2 to 0.6 inch (5–15 mm) long. Although Hass fruit are susceptible to thrips feeding until they reach about 2 inches (5 cm) in length, the feeding only causes scars on fruit when they are less than about ¾ inch (19 mm) long.

Description and Seasonal Development

Adult avocado thrips can be confused with adults of non-pest species, including citrus thrips and western flower thrips. Avocado thrips larvae resemble those of many other thrips species, including certain beneficial predaceous thrips. However, predatory thrips are seldom seen at high levels as can be common with avocado thrips. Make sure to distinguish correctly among the species, using Table 15 and the photographs in this chapter.

Avocado thrips lay yellow to whitish, kidney-shaped eggs in the underside of leaves, in young fruit, and in fruit petioles. Avocado thrips then develop through two larval and two pupal stages (Figure 26). The first instar is white to pale yellow. The second instar is larger, more robust, and bright yellow. Larvae are typically found along major veins on the underside of younger leaves and anywhere on the surface of young fruit. Although some pupation occurs on the tree in cracks and in crevices, about three-fourths of avocado thrips drop from trees to pupate in the upper layer of dry, undecomposed leaf litter. Adults are 0.03 inch (0.7 mm) long. Adults are orange-yellow with distinct, thin, brown bands between segments on the abdomen and three small red dots (ocelli) on top of the head. Avocado thrips adults and second instars can be found anywhere on leaves, including on the upper surface, but they most often occur on the underside of tender, reddish foliage before or soon after leaves reach full expansion. Greenhouse thrips also occur on the upper surface of touching leaves, but greenhouse thrips adults are black and sluggish, unlike avocado thrips (Table 15).

Avocado thrips develop well under cool temperatures, conditions that resemble those of its native habitat in the highlands of Central American and Mexico. Populations typically begin increasing in late winter and spring, when avocado thrips feed on young leaves. Abundance peaks in late spring and early summer, when most fruit are young and hardening of leaves induces thrips to move from foliage to feed on young fruit. Populations are suppressed by warm, dry conditions, but this weather usually occurs later in the season, when most fruit are larger and no longer susceptible to new damage.

Avocado thrips has six or more generations a year. Egg-to-adult development occurs in about 20 to 30 days when temperatures average 65° to 75°F (18° to 24°C). You can predict actual development time by monitoring temperatures in degree-days (Table 16).

The brown discolorations on the underside of this avocado leaf are caused by feeding by avocado thrips larvae. This leaf injury is harmless when moderate as shown here, but widespread leaf scarring may be a sign that thrips may be sufficiently abundant to become a problem when they move to feed on fruit.

Low avocado thrips populations produce only slight scarring, like this light brown streak on fruit near the stem.

Fruit are most susceptible to avocado thrips scarring when they are 0.2 to 0.6 inch (5–15 mm) long. Hass remain susceptible to feeding until they reach about 2 inches (5 cm) long, but feeding does not scar fruit larger than about ¾ inch (19 mm).

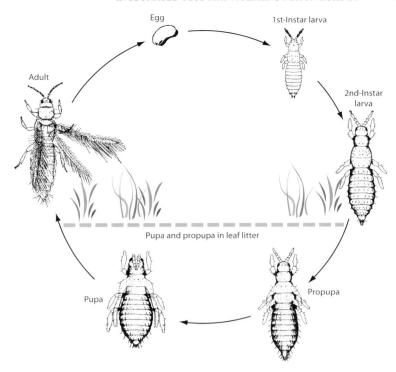

Abundant thrips feeding on young fruit produces injury that becomes visible as severe scarring once the damaged tissue expands when the fruit grow. Thrips scarring often has a webbed pattern.

Figure 26. Thrips life cycle and stages. Thrips typically develop through five or six stages, depending on the species. Eggs are laid singly in the leaf tissue (plant-feeding pest species) or next to their prey (predatory species). The first two immature (larval) stages feed on plant tissue or prey. The one or two pupal stages do not feed. In species with two pupal stages, the active propupa (also called prepupa or pseudopupa) usually drops to the ground (leaf litter or soil) where the pupa (or late pseudopupa) develops into an adult. The adult flies back to the plant to feed and reproduce. *Adapted from:* Hoddle and Morse 2003; adult from Anonymous 1952; immatures from McKenzie 1935.

Table 15. Common Thrips and Their Distinguishing Characteristics in Avocado.

Name		Where most occur	Appearance	
Common	Scientific		Adults	Larvae
Pest thrips				
Avocado	*Scirtothrips perseae*[1]	on both sides of young leaves, on shoulders of young fruit	three red spots atop head, banded antenna, brown lines separating segments on upper side and underside of pale yellow abdomen, wing tips at rest extend beyond abdomen	pale yellow body
Greenhouse	*Heliothrips haemorrhoidalis*[1]	where fruit touch in clusters, upper leaf surface	black body with pale wings	white to yellowish body
Importance unknown				
—	*Neohydatothrips burungae*[1]	on avocado leaves	closely resembles *S. perseae*, but is often darker brownish and has bands only on upper side of abdomen	—
Innocuous thrips				
Citrus	*Scirtothrips citri*[1]	on avocado growing near citrus	body light orangish yellow to white, no bands on abdomen	light orangish, yellow, or white body
Western flower	*Frankliniella occidentalis*[1]	on or near flowers	thick, bristlelike hairs at the tip of the abdomen, which other species lack; body black, brownish, yellow, white, or orange; some individuals have brown abdominal bands; abdomen extends beyond wing tips at rest	yellow to orangish body
Beneficial predatory thrips				
Banded	*Aeolothrips* spp.[2]	among pest mites and thrips	black body, white wings have two distinguishing black bands	yellow body
Black hunter	*Leptothrips mali*[3]	among mites, scales, and pest thrips	dark brown or entirely black body, white wings, much more active than similar-looking greenhouse thrips	reddish brown body
Franklinothrips or vespiform	*Franklinothrips orizabensis, F. vespiformis*[2]	among lace bugs, mites, and pest thrips	mostly black body, with pale or white areas; distinctly narrow where abdomen meets thorax	yellow to orange body, swollen abdomen with red or dark orange band, body more stout or oval-shaped than avocado thrips
Sixspotted	*Scolothrips sexmaculatus*[1]	in colonies of mites	three dark blotches on each forewing, body pale to yellowish	yellow to whitish body

Families:
1. Thripidae
2. Aeolothripidae
3. Phlaeothripidae

Table 16. Avocado Thrips' Average Development Time (in Days) and Adult (Female) Longevity at Five Constant Temperatures.

Life stage	Temperature				
	59°F (15°C)	68°F (20°C)	77°F (25°C)	81°F (27°C)	86°F (30°C)
Egg	21	14	11	10	9
1st instar	4	3	2	1.5	1.8
2nd instar	7	4	3	2	2
Propupa	3	2	1.3	1.1	1.4
Pupa	7.5	4	2.5	2.4	2.5
Egg to adult	42.5	27	19.8	17	16.7
Adult longevity	40	14	8	7.5	3

One generation (egg to adult) requires 620.6 degree-days F (344.8 DD C), above a threshold of 44.4°F (6.9°C), with an upper threshold of 99.7°F (37.6°C). *Source:* Hoddle 2002.

Monitoring Guidelines

Examine newly flushed leaves during February and March to get an indication of whether enough avocado thrips are present to make a problem likely later, when young fruit appear. Monitor regularly every 7 to 10 days beginning as early as April, looking for both mites and thrips. Begin regular monitoring for thrips before young fruit are present and continue your monitoring through fruit set. Use a magnifying lens to inspect the underside of succulent leaves that are reddish brown to light green. Avoid leaves that are fully hardened and dark green, leaves that touch fruit or other leaves, and leaves that are very close to flowers and fruit. Thrips on hardened leaves and leaves that touch other leaves and fruit are often other species. To monitor young fruit, you can clip or pinch stems and examine the entire fruit surface. Depending on thrips densities, treatment decisions may be based on thrips abundance on succulent leaves. A treatment decision generally should be made before most new fruit are set or before most thrips move from leaves to young fruit. Consult the most current *Avocado: UC IPM Pest Management Guidelines: Insects and Mites* (online at www.ipm.ucdavis.edu) for specific monitoring methods.

Management Guidelines

Before making a treatment decision, consider factors that influence the likelihood of thrips damage. These include any history of thrips damage, the abundance of natural enemies, weather, fruit load, and age or size of fruit. If extensive leaf flush continues through fruit set, the need for treatment may be reduced because more of the thrips population will remain on the tender foliage. Conversely, little or no succulent foliage during fruit set increases the extent to which thrips will feed on and damage young fruit. Treatment decisions are also influenced by the grower's tolerance for scarring, the feasibility of treatment and availability of equipment, and the possibility that treatments will disrupt natural enemy populations or promote the development of pesticide resistance. Consult the most current *Avocado: UC IPM Pest Management Guidelines: Insects and Mites* (online at www.ipm.ucdavis.edu) for recommended thresholds.

Researchers are investigating the importation of new natural enemy species and the modification of cultural practices for control of avocado thrips. If you apply insecticides, choose selective materials whenever possible to minimize adverse impacts on the natural enemies that usually provide good control of other avocado pests, including caterpillars, certain mites, scales, whiteflies, and other thrips.

Monitor for avocado thrips by inspecting tender foliage on new shoots. Examine only succulent reddish brown to light green leaves. Do not sample fully hardened, dark green leaves, as avocado thrips rarely occur on old foliage.

When monitoring avocado thrips, inspect both foliage and small fruit, including under the calyx or fruit button.

Biological Control. Natural enemies may suppress avocado thrips, but sometimes not enough to keep populations below damaging levels. Predatory thrips are the most important natural enemies, especially *Franklinothrips orizabensis*. At mild temperatures, about 77°F (25°C), *F. orizabensis* populations can increase readily if avocado thrips populations are increasing. This predator also eats other thrips, mites, and whiteflies, and feeds on avocado pollen and leaf juices. The adult *F. orizabensis* is mostly black with white or pale bands on its body, especially near its thin waist. Females

lay eggs into plant tissue and immatures develop through two larval and two pupal stages. First instars are yellowish with relatively long legs. Second instars have a distinctly swollen, bright orangish or red abdominal area. Pupation occurs in a silken cocoon.

Franklinothrips vespiformis, black hunter thrips (*Leptothrips mali*), and several banded thrips (*Aeolothrips* spp.) also feed on avocado thrips, other pest thrips, and mites. Banded thrips, also called banded-wing thrips, supplement their diet with pollen and plant juice, and can complete their life cycle

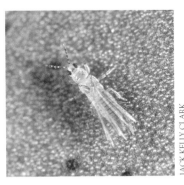

Avocado thrips is a rapidly moving species that occurs on both sides of leaves. The mostly yellowish adult has light- and dark-banded antenna and three red eye spots on top its head. It has thin, brown bands between segments on its upper and lower abdomen. Avocado thrips lack stout tail bristles and their wing tips at rest extend beyond their abdomen.

JACK KELLY CLARK

This western flower thrips (*Frankliniella occidentalis*) larva resembles avocado thrips larvae. Western flower thrips is not a pest in avocado. It mostly consumes pollen, so it is found primarily on flowers and leaves near blossoms.

JACK KELLY CLARK

MARK S. HODDLE

This recently introduced thrips (believed to be *Neohydatothrips burungae*) closely resembles avocado thrips. The arrangement of tiny hairs (setae) is used to reliably distinguish these species. But when compared with avocado thrips, *N. burungae* is often darker brown, with brown bands that occur only on top of its abdomen, not underneath.

In addition to being found anywhere on young fruit, these pale yellow to whitish avocado thrips larvae typically are found along major veins on the underside of succulent young leaves, as on this leaf with a reddish tinge.

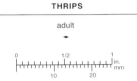

THRIPS

adult

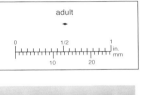

JACK KELLY CLARK

Predatory thrips, especially *Franklinothrips orizabensis*, are the most important natural enemies of avocado thrips. *Franklinothrips orizabensis* and *F. vespiformis* (shown here) are virtually indistinguishable. Both are mostly black with pale to white areas, including at their thin waist.

JACK KELLY CLARK

The *Franklinothrips* larva has a swollen abdomen with a distinct red or dark orange band or dot. Its body is more stout or oval-shaped than avocado thrips's yellowish body.

JACK KELLY CLARK

Western flower thrips like this female can be confused with avocado thrips. Western flower thrips can be black, brownish, yellow, white, or orange. The abdomen of flower thrips has stout, bristlelike hairs at the tip, which can be seen with a hand lens, and the abdomen extends beyond the wing tips at rest.

FRANKLIN DLOTT

Banded (or banded-wing) thrips (*Aeolothrips fasciatus*) is a predator of other thrips and pests such as mites and whiteflies. Banded thrips are black with three broad white bands on each forewing.

and persist even when their prey are scarce. Other general predators (especially green lacewings) and at least one parasitoid (*Ceranisus menes*) also attack avocado thrips.

Cultural Control. Avocado thrips damage may be affected by practices that alter the extent to which trees continue to produce tender foliage during fruit set and growth of young fruit. Consider modifying fertilization (amount, application method, formulation, and timing) and pruning (the extent and timing of branch removal) to induce plants to continue to produce tender foliage during about May and June, which may reduce the extent of thrips' natural migration from hardening leaves to young fruit.

Adding coarse organic mulch beneath trees and maintaining a mulch layer 6 inches (15 cm) thick may reduce the survival of avocado thrips that drop from trees to pupate. The effectiveness of mulching for thrips control is uncertain, though, and the labor costs involved in adding mulch may not be justified simply for thrips control. However, application of coarse organic material such as composted yard waste beneath trees helps control Phytophthora root rot and weeds, and thrips reduction might be an additional benefit.

Neohydatothrips

Neohydatothrips burungae

A new species closely resembling avocado thrips was discovered in San Diego County in 2004. *Neohydatothrips burungae* has previously been reported throughout Central America. In Mexico it is relatively common on avocado and mango. The importance of *N. burungae* in California is unknown.

In comparison with avocado thrips, *N. burungae* has darker brown shading on the thorax, darker abdominal stripes (brownish rings around the top front of each abdominal segment), and brown bands that occur only on top of its abdomen, not underneath. However, this coloration pattern is variable and may not be a reliable way to distinguish these species. The reliable way to distinguish these thrips is according to differences in the position and size of setae (stout hairs) on the thorax and wings (see Figure 27). For example, *Neohydatothrips burungae* has a continuous or complete row of short, stout hairs on both midveins within its forewings. Avocado thrips has relatively few hairs along these midveins on its front wings; there are sizable gaps in both of these rows of hairs on avocado thrips. Careful preparation of several specimens and a good microscope are necessary if you want to recognize these characters.

Greenhouse Thrips

Heliothrips haemorrhoidalis

Greenhouse thrips occurs primarily on broadleaved evergreen plants including citrus and many ornamentals. It occasionally is a serious pest in coastal avocado groves. Damage to leaves from greenhouse thrips, although unsightly, is of no significance to tree health. Feeding on fruit skin causes scarring and the downgrading and culling of fruit at the packinghouse.

Damage

Thrips injury on foliage begins to show in June as small, white-gray patches on upper leaf surfaces where these thrips are found in the greatest numbers. The pale discoloration of foliage and fruit caused by early infestations turns brownish later in the season. The epidermis of injured leaves and fruit becomes thick, hard, and cracked. Black specks of thrips excrement may be noticeable.

Greenhouse thrips prefer to feed where leaves or fruit touch each other. This early feeding damage causes pale to whitish discoloration with specks of black excrement.

Several greenhouse thrips larvae infest the bottom of this fruit. Later in the season, greenhouse thrips damage to leaves and fruit darkens to this brownish discoloration.

PHIL A. PHILLIPS

Most damage occurs when fruit are 2 to 7 months old. Economic damage occurs when thrips cause scars or blemishes larger than ¼ inch (19 mm) in diameter on fruit. Damage usually is most severe on fruit in clusters or where fruit touch leaves, as the thrips are protected where fruit touch. Mexican seedling avocados and Hass avocados are extremely susceptible. Least-susceptible varieties include Anaheim, Dickinson, Fuerte, and Nabal, which are not widely planted in California. On green fruit avocado varieties like Bacon and Zutano, greenhouse thrips are not considered a pest, as they feed primarily on foliage.

Description and Seasonal Development

Adult greenhouse thrips are black with white legs and white wings. Adults seldom fly, and all stages of this tiny insect are sluggish. Males are not found in California, where each parthenogenic female can lay up to 60 eggs during her life. Eggs are inserted singly into fruit or the upper or lower leaf surface.

Eggs hatch after about 4 to 5 weeks during summer, longer during the winter. Before hatching, eggs gradually increase in size, causing a swelling (egg blister) in the leaf cuticle that can be seen with a hand lens.

Greenhouse thrips larvae and pupae are pale yellow to whitish, with red eyes. Larvae carry a greenish red to black globule of liquid feces on the tip of the abdomen. They periodically drop this excrement, leaving dark specks on fruit and foliage that can help you locate infestations during monitoring.

Greenhouse thrips has about five to six generations a year. All life stages are usually present throughout the year. In some colder areas, the thrips overwinter primarily as eggs that produce newly hatched larvae in mid-February. Greenhouse thrips populations are lowest during winter and spring, but can increase quickly enough to cause fruit damage during early summer or fall. On Hass, where most of the greenhouse thrips reside on fruit, much of the population is removed annually at harvest.

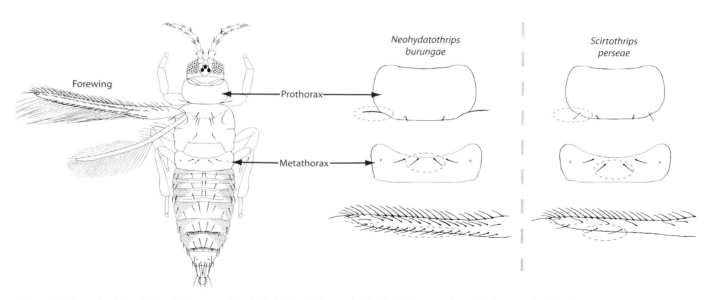

Figure 27. Avocado thrips (*Scirtothrips perseae*) and *Neohydatothrips* sp. (probably *N. burungae*) can be distinguished by the positions and size of the stout hairs (setae) on the thorax and the forewing veins as circled in red. *N. ?burungae* (?="probably") has a long hair projecting from the rear outer edge on each side of its prothorax (top left circle), while in *S. perseae* the corresponding hairs are small. Both species have four hairs on the center front of their metathorax (the last thoracic segment), where the metathorax and middle thoracic segment (mesothorax) meet. In *N. ?burungae* all four hairs are situated along the front edge (middle left circle), whereas in *S. perseae* the middle pair of these hairs is set back from the front edge. *N. ?burungae* also has continuous or complete rows of hairs on both veins on each forewing. In the front row, the second from the last hair is out of line and set back from the edge. In contrast, *S. perseae* has relatively few hairs on the outer part of each forewing and there are sizable gaps in the rows of hairs on both wing veins.

Western flower thrips (*Frankliniella occidentalis*) has two complete rows of forewing midvein hairs, except the second to last hair on *F. occidentalis* is not out of line (not dislocated as in bottom left circle). Western flower thrips also has two long hairs projecting from the rear outer edge on each side of its prothorax, not the single long hair on each side as on *N. ?burungae*.

Citrus thrips (*Scirtothrips citri*) forewing veins closely resemble those of *Scirtothrips perseae*: there are relatively few hairs and sizable gaps between hairs. Citrus thrips has one long hair projecting from the rear outer edge on each side of its prothorax like on *N. ?burungae*.

All these species have numerous hairs on both the front and rear edges of their wings. The hairs along the rear edge are particularly long and slender (shown only on the whole insect diagram). Careful preparation of several specimens and a good microscope are needed to recognize these characters. *Illustrations adapted from: Bailey 1941, Gill 1997, Kono and Papp 1977, Watson 2005.*

Monitoring Guidelines

Map or record the locations of infestations and check these areas each year. Greenhouse thrips problems tend to reoccur at the same sites within a grove, typically where the microclimate is more moderate. From late March through July, monitor for greenhouse thrips about every 10 to 14 days, at least in coastal groves. Concentrate in less-exposed and interior grove areas where temperature and humidity are moderate and wherever your records indicate that greenhouse thrips were most abundant during previous seasons. If greenhouse thrips are present, it is also important to monitor trees where mature fruit was held the longest before harvest.

Monitor on the inside and the north side of trees, away from direct sun exposure. Examine fruit where they touch in clusters and the upper surface of older leaves. Look for colonies of greenhouse thrips, bleached tissue, and black excrement specks. Make sure to correctly identify the species of any thrips you find (see Table 15).

One study indicates that greenhouse thrips damage can be predicted based on "thrips-weeks" (the number of thrips present × the number of weeks they feed). When thrips feed in one spot on a fruit, approximately 25 thrips-weeks (e.g., one thrips feeding for 25 weeks, or five thrips feeding for 5 weeks) may produce a ¾-inch (19 mm) diameter, economically important scar.

Management Guidelines

Biological control, cultural practices, grove microclimate, and weather influence whether greenhouse thrips will be a problem on susceptible (Hass and Mexican seedling) avocados. Conserve the natural enemies of thrips and of other pests. Consider modifying your harvest and pruning practices to control greenhouse thrips. If pesticide application is warranted, spot-treat infested areas and avoid spraying the entire grove. Use selective materials for thrips and other pests whenever possible. Application of broad-spectrum pesticides often leads to outbreaks of pests such as caterpillars and mites. Consult the current *Avocado: UC IPM Pest Management Guidelines: Insects and Mites* (online at www.ipm.ucdavis.edu) for specific pesticide recommendations.

Biological Control. *Megaphragma mymaripenne* (family Trichogrammatidae) is an important parasite of thrips, often killing about 25 to 50% of greenhouse thrips eggs in coastal avocado trees. Parasitized eggs develop a relatively large, round hole, usually in the middle of the egg blister, showing where the *Megaphragma mymaripenne* adult emerged. In contrast, when a greenhouse thrips emerges part of the egg shell is often visible at the side of the egg blister.

Thripobius semiluteus (family Eulophidae) attacks second-instar larvae. The normally yellow to whitish thrips larvae turn black and swell around the head when a larva of this parasitic wasp matures inside. Egg-to-adult development time for *Thripobius* is about 3 weeks when temperatures average 70°F (21°C). Thrips populations decline once about 60% of larvae are parasitized. Natural control from *Thripobius semiluteus* is inconsistent. Release of several thousand *Thripobius* per acre per week has controlled greenhouse thrips in coastal avocado trees, but *Thripobius* may not be commercially available when you need it.

Predaceous thrips including black hunter thrips and vespiform thrips (*Franklinothrips* spp., family Aeolothripidae) prey on greenhouse thrips. However, many predators may avoid greenhouse thrips because of their fecal excrement. Beneficial thrips and thrips-feeding general predators are discussed earlier, under avocado thrips.

Monitor for greenhouse thrips by inspecting fruit where they touch other fruit or leaves. Also examine the upper surface of older leaves.

Greenhouse thrips are relatively sluggish. They feed in groups of black adults and pale larvae. Larvae often carry, and periodically drop, a dark drop of liquidy excrement.

This adult *Thripobius semiluteus* is a black and yellowish parasitic wasp that attacks greenhouse thrips larvae.

Black hunter thrips (*Leptothrips mali*) adults and larvae are dark brown or reddish or entirely black. The adult of this predator has white wings, resembling an adult greenhouse thrips. However, black hunter thrips is much more active than the slow-moving greenhouse thrips.

Cultural Control. The earlier the harvest, the less thrips damage on harvested fruit. Early harvest (about June or July) of all mature fruit on infested trees also reduces damage to the next season's crop. Especially on Hass, where a large proportion of the greenhouse thrips feed and breed on fruit, an early harvest date will minimize the crop-to-crop overlap period, reducing the number of thrips that can move from old to new fruit.

An alternative to early harvesting is to selectively size-pick the larger fruit in clusters and where fruit and leaves touch. Size-picking reduces greenhouse thrips populations by removing some thrips. Thinning fruit clusters and pruning dense canopies eliminates harborage, and that reduces the density of greenhouse thrips as well as caterpillars and mealybugs.

CATERPILLARS

Caterpillars are the larvae of moths and butterflies (order Lepidoptera). Omnivorous looper, western avocado leafroller (amorbia), and (least frequently) orange tortrix are sporadic pests in avocado. Healthy trees can tolerate some loss of chewed foliage and blossoms but extensive defoliation can result in sunburn to fruit and twigs. Economic damage occurs primarily when caterpillars chew and scar fruit. Conservation of natural enemies is the primary strategy, as caterpillars are usually kept naturally under effective biological control.

Identify and Monitor Caterpillars. Where problems may occur, monitor caterpillars and identify the species in your grove. Alternate host plants, damage potential, monitoring methods, and natural enemies vary depending on the caterpillar species. Larvae can be difficult to identify, particularly when they are young, partly because individuals of the same species often vary in color. Closely examine

Greenhouse thrips larvae are yellow to whitish. When parasitized, greenhouse thrips larvae turn black and swell around the head as a *Thripobius* wasp larva matures inside. At left are black, immobile *Thripobius* pupae. The adult greenhouse thrips (bottom) is also black, but it has white wings and moves.

several individuals, perhaps with a hand lens or microscope. Use the photographs and larval key (Figure 28) to identify the prevalent species. Look for caterpillar predators and for larval diseases and parasitism. The abundance of caterpillar natural enemies in the grove will influence your decision on whether to treat and what methods to use.

Monitor at least during spring and summer by looking for caterpillars and damage, trapping adults, or using a combination of methods, depending on which caterpillar species are prevalent and which management methods you plan to use. Consult the latest *Avocado: UC IPM Pest Management Guidelines: Insects and Mites* (online at www.ipm.ucdavis.edu) for specific monitoring recommendations and suggested action thresholds.

Be sure to correctly identify the cause of damage. Earwigs, Fuller rose beetles, grasshoppers, and June beetles chew leaves too, but these species are not pests of avocado except, occasionally, on small, young trees. Certain abiotic disorders can cause leaf damage in the form of necrotic patches that eventually drop out of the leaf, leaving holes that resemble insect chewing damage.

All species of caterpillars can be monitored using timed counts. Spend a fixed amount of time (perhaps 2 to 5 minutes per tree) looking at foliage (especially around chewed leaves) sampled from each of several trees. Pull apart webbing and count and record any live caterpillars and natural enemies.

Foliage shaking is a relatively quick and easy monitoring method when avocado looper is the only caterpillar pest present. Avocado looper produces less webbing so it is more easily dislodged than amorbia and orange tortrix. Place a collecting surface such as a plastic sheet or opened cardboard box beneath chewed foliage. Shake shoots vigorously to knock loopers onto the collecting surface for counting.

Monitoring Adults. Adult moths are nocturnal and consume only liquids and pollen. During the day they rest on the underside of leaves or on shady bark. Moths are strongly attracted to lights at night. Larval infestations are sometimes concentrated near trees adjacent to bright lights.

You can use pheromone-baited sticky traps for adults to identify the species in a grove and indicate peak times for flights of egg-laying adults. Traps are baited with a separate pheromone to attract adult male amorbia, omnivorous looper, or orange tortrix. For amorbia, two different pheromones are used, one for northern California and the San Joaquin Valley (SJV) and another for southern California (SC), including Ventura County. Traps typically are deployed at a density of about one trap per 10 acres around the time that adult moths are expected to be present. Check with suppliers for recommendations on which pheromones to use and what type and number of traps to use.

The trapping results can indicate whether foliage monitoring is warranted and help you time management actions such as the release of egg parasites. Adult traps

---

Identify the caterpillar species in your grove to help you:
- Choose between shake sampling versus timed counts.
- Select pheromone type for trapping adult moths.
- Decide whether and when to release parasites.
- Consider whether management directed at nearby alternate hosts can help control species moving into avocado during the moth stage.

This key will help you identify the larvae of moths that damage avocado in California. Other Lepidoptera species found only occasionally are not included. Ask your farm advisor or agricultural commissioner for help in identifying specimens that do not fit the key. Read both descriptions and compare the specimen with the drawings provided before proceeding. After you arrive at a name, compare the specimen with the appropriate photos and descriptions. Take several specimens through the key individually; your monitoring sample may include more than one species and different age groups of one species.	Parts of a caterpillar useful in identifying the species The features used in the key can be seen with a good hand lens, but you may need a low power microscope to see certain features on small larvae. The key works best for specimens in the third instar or larger; certain characters, such as the number of prolegs and color markings, can be different in very young larvae.

Key:

1. Two pairs of prolegs on abdomen, on abdominal segments 6 and 10: Omnivorous Looper	 prolegs
Four pairs of prolegs in middle of abdomen, on segments 3, 4, 5, and 6: See 2. below	 prolegs
2. Black line on thoracic segment 1, above first pair of true legs: Western Avocado Leafroller (Amorbia)	 Black line on first segment of thorax
Black line absent on thoracic segment: Orange Tortrix	

Compare your specimens to photographs of each species, including pictures in the *Avocado: UC IPM Pest Management Guidelines: Insects and Mites.*

Figure 28. Key to the caterpillars that damage avocado in California.

Caterpillars cause economic damage when they chew fruit. Injury varies from oval craters to scattered gouges in the skin, as caused here by western avocado leafroller (amorbia).

You can monitor for all species of caterpillars by inspecting foliage for damage and insects. Pull open webbed foliage and count it as infested only when live, unparasitized caterpillars are present. This webbed leaf contains only an old, empty pupal case of western avocado leafroller.

Pheromone-baited sticky traps for moths can identify the species in groves, such as the western avocado leafroller adults in this trap. Compare the relative number of moths caught between dates. The peaks in flights of egg-laying adults help you time actions such as foliage monitoring for larvae or release of *Trichogramma* egg parasites.

A re-usable plastic bucket trap for monitoring amorbia or western avocado leafroller. This and certain other traps can also be used to monitor pests such as omnivorous looper or orange tortrix if baited with the appropriate species-specific pheromone.

Orb weaver spider webs are suspended here among chewed avocado leaves. These spiders will capture and feed on flying moths and caterpillars that drop from foliage or balloon (float) through the air attached to a silk thread.

generally are not useful for determining whether treatment is needed, partly because the damaging stage of the pest is the caterpillar, natural enemies kill many eggs and larvae, and the number of moths trapped is not a good indication of the number of caterpillars that will be present.

Caterpillar Management. Learn to recognize and conserve natural enemies, which usually keep caterpillars below damaging levels in most avocado groves. Caterpillar predators include assassin bugs, bigeyed bugs, birds, damsel bugs, lacewings, pirate bugs, and spiders. Naturally occurring viral diseases and *Bacillus thuringiensis*, which is commercially available as a selective insecticide, are important caterpillar pathogens. The most important natural enemies are parasitic flies and wasps. Avoid applying broad-spectrum or persistent insecticides for any pests. Caterpillar outbreaks commonly occur after a grower sprays carbamate or organophosphate insecticides, since those chemicals poison parasites and predators of caterpillars. When pesticides are warranted, limit application to the most infested spots, which provides untreated refuges from which natural enemies can recolonize the rest of the grove after treatment.

Prune the trees to reduce the amount of foliage that touches between adjacent trees and to minimize dead twigs and plant debris accumulated in canopies. Thin or selectively harvest fruit in clusters. Pruning and thinning reduce the availability of protected sites and canopy bridges that facilitate insect movement between trees, thereby reducing the abundance of avocado caterpillars, greenhouse thrips, and mealybugs. Remove abandoned citrus trees to reduce the likelihood that amorbia and orange tortrix will move from citrus to nearby avocado trees. Control weeds that host these caterpillars near avocado trees. Reduce dust in groves by driving slowly and oiling or watering dirt roads. Dusty conditions reduce the effectiveness of parasites and predators that attack caterpillars and other pests, including mites and scales.

Amorbia or Western Avocado Leafroller

Amorbia cuneana

Western avocado leafroller (family Tortricidae) is primarily a pest of avocado. Populations occur in most California groves and occasionally increase dramatically, causing severe fruit damage. This caterpillar also causes damage in citrus groves, where it is called "amorbia," its official common name. In avocado, the pest is often simply called "leafroller," but this can lead to some confusion: amorbia, avocado looper, and orange tortrix all roll avocado leaves and bind plant parts together with silken webs.

Damage

Young amorbia larvae chew the leaf surface, leaving a thin brown membrane or skeleton of leaf veins. Mature caterpillars consume the whole leaf, starting in the center or at the leaf edge. Young larvae often web terminal leaves together and feed within the enclosure they have made. The feeding damage becomes apparent when the terminals grow and unfold. Mature avocado trees can tolerate considerable larval chewing without experiencing severe effects on tree growth or fruit yield.

Fruit damage occurs where larvae feed among touching fruit in a cluster or where they join leaves to fruit with their webbing and feed where they touch. In these protected, sites larvae feed on the fruit skin. The resultant scarring causes downgrading or culling of fruit in the packinghouse.

Description and Seasonal Development

Amorbia adults (like orange tortrix adults) are bell-shaped when their wings are folded at rest. Their variably colored forewings are typically orangish to tan with dark markings. Adult amorbia are about 1 inch (2.5 cm) long, about twice the size of an orange tortrix adult.

Each amorbia female lays about 150 to 200 eggs during her 2- to 3-week lifespan. These light green, oval eggs occur mostly on the upper side of leaves, close to the midrib. Amorbia (and orange tortrix) eggs are laid in an overlapping or shingle-like pattern in a flat mass. Amorbia females lay from 5 to 100 eggs per mass, with an average of 25 eggs per mass. Eggs darken and larvae emerge about 2 weeks after oviposition. Hatched egg masses appear as whitish patches on leaves.

Amorbia larvae develop through five instars. At maturity they are ¾ to 1 inch (1.8–2.5 cm) long. Caterpillars are yellowish green when young and mostly darker green when mature. Older larvae have one short, dark, horizontal line on the side of their thorax just behind the head and above the first pair of legs. Other avocado caterpillars lack these distinctive black marks. Amorbia feed in nests of leaves and fruit that they have tied together with silk. When disturbed, amorbia and orange tortrix larvae often wriggle violently and drop to the ground.

Amorbia pupate for 2 to 3 weeks in rolled leaf shelters. The ½- to ¾-inch-long (12–19 mm) pupae begin as a pale green, gradually turn tan, and are brown when mature.

Egg-to-adult development time is about 1½ months at an average temperature of 75°F (24°C). Amorbia typically goes through three generations per year in warmer growing areas. From inland Ventura County to San Diego County, most adults fly and most females oviposit from January through April, May through June, and September through October. Two generations a year is the average in coastal groves. In Santa Barbara County, most moths emerge and lay eggs during March through June and August through November.

Management Guidelines

Monitor regularly during spring and summer, especially after peaks in moth flights. Inspect foliage (for caterpillars, damage, and natural enemies), trap adults, or do both. Consult the latest *Avocado: UC IPM Pest Management Guidelines: Insects and Mites* (online at www.ipm.ucdavis.edu) for specific monitoring recommendations and suggested treatment thresholds. Conserve natural enemies, modify cultural practices, and avoid applying broad-spectrum insecticides as discussed above under "Caterpillar Management."

Biological Control. Birds, predaceous insects, and spiders commonly prey on caterpillars. A naturally occurring nuclear polyhedrosis virus often kills many amorbia when caterpillar populations are high. Parasites, especially tachinid flies, are the most important natural enemies and usually keep amorbia populations below economically damaging levels. At least 15 different parasitic fly and wasp species attack amorbia. At least seven of these species also parasitize omnivorous looper or orange tortrix or all three avocado caterpillars.

Trichogramma spp. are naturally common parasites of amorbia eggs. *Trichogramma platneri* can be purchased and released as discussed below. *Eumea* (=*Aplomya*) *caesar*, *Nilea* (=*Pseudoperichaeta*) *erecta*, and at least five other fly species (family Tachinidae) parasitize amorbia. The black to dark grayish adult tachinids are about ¼ to ⅓ inch (6–8 mm) long. They resemble common house flies, but have hairs that are more prominent and stout. The female attaches her white eggs on or near the caterpillars' head, and the emerging maggots

Amorbia, and many other adults in the family Tortricidae, are bell-shaped when their wings are folded at rest. Adult amorbia are about 1 inch (2.5 cm) long, with variably colored forewings that are typically orangish to tan with dark markings.

Amorbia (and orange tortrix) lay pale, oval eggs, overlapping and shinglelike, in flat masses.

An early instar larva of amorbia, also called western avocado leafroller, revealed by pulling apart its nest of silk-tied leaves.

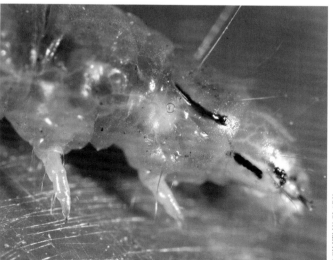

Late-instar amorbia are distinguished by the presence of a short, dark, horizontal line on the thorax just behind the head, above the first pair of legs. Orange tortrix larvae lack this dark line.

The amorbia pupa is 1/2 to 3/4 inch (1.3–1.9 cm) long, as revealed here by uncurling rolled leaves that are tied together with silk. Pupae are pale green at first, turning tan and then brownish before adult emergence.

An adult tachinid fly and its oblong pupal case next to the larger amorbia pupal case within which the immature parasite developed. At least eight tachinid fly species attack amorbia in avocado.

Accurately distinguish pests and beneficials when inspecting foliage for caterpillars and their damage. This rolled avocado leaf contains a jumping spider egg case. This predators' silk might be misidentified as caterpillar presence if you fail to closely examine the webbing.

Commercially reared *Trichogramma* parasites are shipped as pupae inside parasitized moth eggs glued to cards. In the photograph, a pencil tip points to a tiny, recently emerged adult wasp.

This 1/25-inch-long (1 mm) *Trichogramma platneri* parasitic wasp is laying its egg into a caterpillar egg. A complex of natural enemies usually prevent caterpillars from causing problems in avocado.

If naturally occurring biological control of caterpillars is inadequate, you can purchase *Trichogramma* wasps and release them by hanging cards of parasite pupae like this one on several trees per acre. Because *Trichogramma* attack only eggs, any releases must be made starting early and continuing throughout the moths' egg-laying cycle.

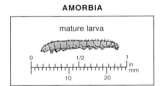
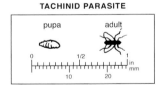

bore into the caterpillar and feed inside. Some tachinid larvae kill and emerge from late-instar caterpillars. Most tachinids emerge from their hosts after the caterpillars pupate and die. Small, brown to reddish, parchmentlike tachinid pupal cases are often found near the larger pupal cases of dead hosts.

Trichogramma Releases. Trichogramma platneri is the most effective parasite of avocado caterpillar eggs. This wasp, 1/25-inch-long (1 mm) or smaller, lays one or a few eggs in each caterpillar egg. If you find amorbia eggs that are black, they are probably parasitized by *Trichogramma*.

Where naturally occurring parasitism is inadequate, amor-

bia has been controlled by the release of 50,000 *T. platneri* adults in each of four uniformly spaced avocado trees per acre. At least two releases about 1 week apart are made during peak moth egg laying in late spring, as determined by monitoring of adults with commercially available phero-mone-baited traps or black light traps. Commercial suppliers typically provide *Trichogramma* as parasitized moth eggs glued to cardboard. The adult wasps should emerge soon after the shipment arrives. Protect the cards from Argentine ants and other predatory insects. Keep a small portion from any purchase in a shady location in a clear container covered

Female tachinids lay oval, white eggs, usually on or near the caterpillar's head as on this amorbia. Tachinid larvae chew into their host and feed inside, hidden until they pupate.

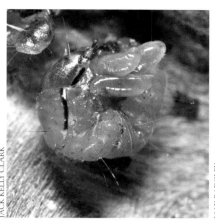

Greenish maggots of a gregarious external larval parasite, *Habrobracon* (=*Bracon*) *xanthonotus*, are feeding on this amorbia. After their host shrivels and dies, these parasite larvae will pupate nearby in a group of small, white, silken cocoons.

The chalcid *Brachymeria ovata* parasitizes pupae of many different caterpillars, including amorbia (shown here) and omnivorous looper. *Brachymeria* adults have enlarged rear coxae (basal leg segments), visible on this recently emerged wasp.

with tightly woven cloth. That way you can observe wasp emergence to assess product quality.

Omnivorous Looper

Sabulodes aegrotata

The omnivorous looper (family Geometridae), also called looper or avocado looper, feeds on several dozen plant species. Hosts include acacia, box elder, California buckeye, chestnut, elm, eucalyptus, fruit trees, ginkgo, magnolia, maple, pepper tree, and willow. Omnivorous looper occurs in most avocado groves, generally in low numbers, unless natural enemies are disrupted by the application of broad-spectrum insecticides.

Damage

Leaf damage is especially evident on terminal shoots. Very young larvae feed only on the leaf surface, leaving a characteristic brown membrane. Older larvae chew all the way through the leaf, often leaving only the midrib and large veins. A full-grown larva can consume an entire leaf in 1 day. Healthy avocado trees tolerate considerable leaf damage without severe effects on growth or yield. Extensive feeding can result in sunburn and may reduce yield the following year.

Fruit damage can be caused by young or old larvae. If young fruit is fed on, it sometimes becomes misshapen. Chewing typically scars the fruit surface, and that may cause fruit to be culled or downgraded.

Description and Seasonal Development

Adults are mostly tan to orangish on top, with a narrow black band across the middle of the wings. They are white on the underside and have a wingspan of about 1¾ to 2 inches (4.5–5 cm). Females live 2 to 3 weeks, laying eggs in clusters of 3 to 80 on the underside of leaves. Each barrel-shaped egg has a ring of tiny projections around one end. Eggs are pale green at first, and later turn shiny reddish to brown. Larvae hatch from the eggs about 8 or 9 days after oviposition, leaving behind transparent shells.

Young larvae are pale yellow and very small, about 0.06 inch (1.5 mm) long. Mature larvae are 2 to 2½ inches (5–6.3 cm) long and mostly yellow to pale green or pink with a gold-colored head. Older larvae have variable dark brown, black, green, or orangish lines along their sides. In addition to three pairs of true legs behind the head, avocado looper has two pairs of appendages (prolegs) near its rear on abdominal segments 6 and 10. Larvae travel in a characteristic "looping" manner, where they extend their body forward, then draw their rear forward to meet their forelegs. This arches the body up into a loop. When disturbed, omnivorous loopers often drop and hang from leaves by a silken thread.

Larvae feed for about 6 weeks, then pupate within rolled or webbed leaves. Pupae are 1 to 1¼ inches (2.5–3.2 cm) long and white when they first form. The case darkens as a moth with brownish wings develops within and can be seen through the pupal case. Pupation lasts 1 to 4 weeks.

Populations increase with increasing temperatures in spring. Omnivorous looper typically has four, perhaps five generations per year in warmer growing areas. From inland Ventura County to San Diego County, most adults fly and oviposit during January through March, May through June, August through September, and October through November. Three generations a year are typical in coastal Santa Barbara County, where moths typically emerge and lay eggs during March through April, June through July, and August through September. Depending on temperature, egg-to-adult development takes 2 to 5 months.

Management Guidelines

Monitor regularly during spring and summer, especially after peaks in moth flights. Shake sample shoots to dislodge larvae, inspect foliage mainly on the south and east quadrants of trees, trap adults, or use a combination of methods. Consult the latest *Avocado: UC IPM Pest Management Guidelines: Insects and Mites* (online at www.ipm.ucdavis.edu) for specific monitoring recommendations and suggested thresholds. Conservation of natural enemies is the most important control method. Modify your cultural practices to help control caterpillars and avoid applying broad-spectrum insecticides, as discussed earlier under "Caterpillar Management."

Biological Control. Spiders are important predators of loopers, especially in groves that have not been sprayed with pesticides and have not recently been subject to a freeze. Birds, predatory bugs, and lacewing larvae also prey on caterpillars.

Granulosis virus often infects and kills larvae when they become abundant. A virus epidemic can cause the looper population to decline rapidly, within 1 to 2 weeks. Infected larvae stop feeding, become lethargic, and eventually liquefy and then dry up. The appearance of virus-killed caterpillars ranges from white and swollen to brownish and shriveled.

These clustered young avocado fruit were chewed by omnivorous loopers. Caterpillars thrive in more protected sites, so pruning and thinning canopies can substantially reduce damage.

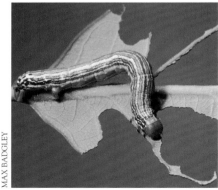

Omnivorous looper larvae have a gold-colored head and a variably colored body with dark brown, black, green, orangish, yellow, or white lines along their sides.

An omnivorous looper-chewed leaf and a silk-covered pupa. Persea mite caused the pale leaf spots.

Omnivorous looper eggs are barrel-shaped with a ring of tiny projections around one end. Eggs are pale green at first, then turn shiny reddish to brown. Hatched eggs are transparent.

These chewed leaf edges are characteristic of damage from older omnivorous looper larvae.

Omnivorous looper adults are mostly tan to orangish on top, with a narrow black band across the middle of the wings.

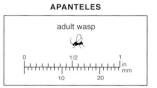

Parasitic wasps, especially *Trichogramma* egg parasites and three larval parasites (family Braconidae), are the most important natural enemies of omnivorous looper. *Apanteles caberatae* and *Meteorus tersus* are solitary internal parasites of larvae. Each develops from an egg inserted into a caterpillar by the female wasp. The parasitic larva feeds inside, and then emerges to pupate near the caterpillar it has killed. The *Apanteles caberatae* adult is a ¹⁄₁₀-inch-long (2.5 mm) black wasp. Its pale larva chews an exit hole, usually near the looper's rear end, and pupates in an elongated, whitish, silken cocoon attached to foliage near its dead host. The *Meteorus tersus* adult is a yellowish brown wasp about ¹⁄₇ inch (3.6 mm) long. Its larva pupates in a brown or yellowish, parchment-like cocoon that can often be found hanging beneath leaves or twigs, suspended on a silken thread about 1½ inches (38 mm) long.

Habrobracon (=*Bracon*) *xanthonotus* is a gregarious external larval parasite. The adult is about ⅛ inch (3 mm) long with brownish legs, a black thorax, and a white abdomen with brown spots. Each female lays from one egg to several dozen whitish eggs on a caterpillar. The emerging larvae feed as pale greenish to yellow maggots attached to the outside of a looper, as pictured near the beginning of the third chapter, "Managing Pests in Avocados." The parasites pupate in a group of small, white, silken cocoons near the shriveled, dead caterpillar.

An omnivorous looper pupa with its silk covering pulled back.

After eating foliage sprayed with *Bacillus thuringiensis* (Bt), caterpillars become lethargic, stop feeding, and excrete liquid. The caterpillar's body becomes dark and soft after it dies (as shown here) and it decomposes into a liquidy, putrid mass.

The adult *Apanteles caberatae* has a black body about ¹⁄₁₀ inch (2.5 mm) long. The caterpillar parasite emerges from an elongated, pale silken cocoon attached to foliage near its dead host.

Granulosis virus frequently infects and kills omnivorous loopers within 1 to 2 weeks after larvae become abundant. Virus-killed caterpillars are immobile, and sometimes hang limply from leaves. Infected larvae vary from white and swollen to brownish and shriveled.

Pupa of *Meteorus tersus*, an omnivorous looper parasite. This brown to yellowish cocoon often hangs beneath twigs or chewed leaves, suspended on a silken thread about 1¹⁄₂ inches (38 mm) long.

Parasitic tachinid adults are dark grayish to black flies about ¹⁄₄ to ¹⁄₃ inch (6–8 mm) long. They resemble common house flies, but have hairs that are more prominent and stout, visible here on the legs and rear end.

Omnivorous looper larvae can be monitored by shaking avocado foliage over a collecting surface, such as this flattened cardboard box.

This mature larva of a parasitic tachinid fly has emerged from the caterpillar it killed. It will form an oblong, brown to reddish pupal case.

At least five tachinid fly species attack omnivorous loopers, including *Eumea caesar*, *Hyphantrophaga* (=*Eusisyropa*) *virilis*, and *Nilea erecta*. Tachinid appearance and biology are discussed earlier under "Amorbia."

Trichogramma Releases. *Trichogramma platneri* is a common, naturally occurring egg parasite. Looper eggs turn black when parasitized by *T. platneri*. Where naturally occurring parasitism does not provide adequate control of omnivorous looper, growers may release 50,000 *T. platneri* in each of four uniformly spaced trees per acre. At least three releases spaced about 1 week apart are timed to coincide with peak egg laying by late spring to early summer moths, as determined by monitoring using commercially available pheromone-baited traps or black light traps. Protect *Trichogramma*-release cards from Argentine ants and other predatory insects. Read under "Amorbia" for more *Trichogramma*-release tips.

Orange Tortrix

Argyrotaenia citrana

Orange tortrix (family Tortricidae) is an occasional problem on avocados grown in coastal areas. It rarely is injurious in inland growing areas. Orange tortrix feeds on many plants, including apple, citrus, grape, and strawberry. Native and weedy hosts include California poppy, coyote brush, curly dock, filarees, lupines, mustards, and pigweeds.

Damage

Most larval chewing occurs within silken webs on outer-canopy shoots. During bloom, tiny larvae sometimes feed among flowers. Larvae also feed on green bark, girdling some twigs. White exudate may cover wounds on larger twigs. Least common is fruit feeding, but it is this that causes economic damage. Fruit injury closely resembles the damage caused by other avocado caterpillars, except that orange tortrix tends to chew deeper holes. Feeding near the stem end of fruit and on the stem itself may cause fruit to drop.

Description and Seasonal Development

Orange tortrix and amorbia adults resemble each other. They are orangish to tan moths with dark shading across their folded wings. At rest, their folded wings flare out at the tips to make their overall shape resemble a bell. Orange tortrix adults are about 0.4 inch (1 cm) long, about one-half the size of amorbia adults.

Orange tortrix and amorbia females lay their eggs overlapping in a mass. Orange tortrix females oviposit on the surface of young leaves, green twigs, or green fruit. Each egg is pale green, flat, and oval, and has a finely reticulated surface. Females lay several clusters that range from a few to more than 150 eggs per mass. Eggs hatch in about 9 days.

Larvae usually feed singly on shoot tips or on succulent leaves in nests that they web together with silk. Larvae develop through 5 to 7 instars over about 40 days. They are about 1/12 inch (2 mm) long at hatching and about 1/2 inch (13 mm) long when mature. Larvae have a brownish or straw-colored head and prothoracic plate (the top of first segment behind the head). The variable body color is dark gray, greenish, straw-colored, or tan. Orange tortrix and amorbia larvae typically wriggle vigorously backward or sideways when disturbed, and may drop to the ground or remain suspended from the leaf by a silken thread.

Larvae form a dense silken cocoon where they pupate within webbed foliage. Adults emerge in about 1 to 3 weeks, depending on temperature. Orange tortrix has two to four generations per year, with all stages present throughout the year. The pest's development rate can be predicted based on temperature, using a degree-day model (Table 17). Taken together with adult-trapping results, the degree-day model can tell you more precisely when to inspect foliage and when to plan treatment for caterpillar management.

Management Guidelines

Look for orange tortrix during spring and summer when you monitor for amorbia as described above. Consult the latest *Avocado: UC IPM Pest Management Guidelines: Insects and Mites* (online at www.ipm.ucdavis.edu) for specific recommendations. Conserve the natural enemies of orange tortrix, which will in most cases provide adequate control. Minimize dust, avoid applying broad-spectrum insecticides, and make only spot applications if possible. Prune canopies and thin clustered fruit to provide some control of the pest. Because orange tortrix has many hosts and moves from one to another, controlling host weeds near avocado trees may help reduce orange tortrix damage to your crop.

Biological Control. More than a dozen parasite species and a variety of predators attack orange tortrix. These usually provide excellent biological control. Parasites include *Trichogramma platneri* and several tachinid flies as described under "Amorbia." Common parasitic wasps are *Apanteles aristoteliae* (family Braconidae) and *Exochus* spp.

Table 17. Orange Tortrix Development Time (Days) at Four Constant Temperatures.

Temperature	55°F (12.8°C)	65°F (18.3°C)	75°F (23.9°C)	85°F (29.5°C)
Days	97	53	35	28

Egg-to-adult development time is 1,136°F (646.1°C) above a threshold of 43°F (6.1°C), with an upper threshold of 78°F (25.6°C). *Source:* Bettiga, Kido, and McCalley 1992.

These orange tortrix adults and eggs resemble those of amorbia and other Tortricidae that appear bell-shaped when resting. Orange tortrix adults are orange to tan moths with dark markings. Orange tortrix adults are about 0.4 inch (1 cm) long, about one-half the size of adult amorbia.

Orange tortrix larvae can be distinguished from amorbia by their smaller mature size and their color pattern. Full-grown tortrix larvae are up to 0.6 inch (1.5 cm) long. Tortrix lacks the dark horizontal line on the thorax that occurs on amorbia just behind the head and above the first pair of legs.

Adult *Exochus* spp. are ichneumonid wasps that lay one egg in each tortrix larva. The parasite larva feeds and pupates inside the caterpillar, leaving a round exit hole in the dead host.

The orange tortrix pupa is about 1/2 inch (13 mm) long and initially pale in color, then brown or orangish. It is shown here on apple, one of its many alternate hosts.

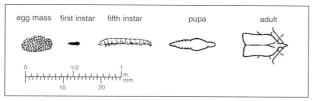

ORANGE TORTIX

egg mass   first instar   fifth instar   pupa   adult

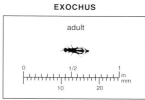

EXOCHUS

adult

(Ichneumonidae). These wasps lay one egg inside each caterpillar, and the egg hatches into a parasitic larva that feeds on the host. *Apanteles aristoteliae* attacks and kills young caterpillars and then pupates in a white cocoon outside the dead caterpillar. *Exochus nigripalpis* oviposits into older larvae. It feeds and pupates inside the caterpillar, eventually leaving a round exit hole in the dead larva.

ANTS

Ants (family Formicidae) are important natural enemies of many insect pests. Ants provide other benefits, such as improving soil. However, ants sometimes chew crop twigs and tender bark or annoy farm workers. In avocado groves, ants are considered pests mostly because they disrupt the biological control of other pests. Ants are primarily a problem in young avocado trees where mealybugs and other honeydew-producers are occasional pests.

Argentine ant (*Linepithema humile* =*Iridomyrmex humilis*), the native gray ant (*Formica aerata*), and southern fire ant (*Solenopsis xyloni*) feed on honeydew excreted by phloem-feeding insects, including mealybugs, soft scales, and whiteflies. They protect these food sources from natural enemies, allowing the phloem-sucking insects to become more abundant. When honeydew-producers are present, ants also increase the populations of armored scales and some other pests that do not excrete honeydew. Ants are general predators that attack most any other predator or parasite they encounter, regardless of what host it is seeking as a natural enemy.

Description and Seasonal Development

Most ants are wingless workers (sterile females). Workers forage for food outside the nest, dig tunnels, and care for the tiny, pale, grublike ant larvae in the nest. Adult ants can also be winged males that die soon after mating or reproductive females (queens), which lay tiny, elliptical eggs in underground nests. Queens and males are usually observed only during their brief mating season when they develop wings and swarm outside the nest.

Ants have a narrow constriction between the thorax and abdomen. Their antennae are distinctly elbowed. Winged ants have hind wings that are much shorter than their forewings. All of these characters distinguish ants from termites. Termites have a broad waist, antennae that are not elbowed, and equal-length wings.

It can be very helpful to identify the species of any ants present in the avocado grove (Figure 29). Biology and management techniques differ between many ant species.

Antenna   Thorax   Petiole node

Figure 29. Identify ants by their shape, the number and arrangement of their antennal segments, and the number of nodes (projections) on the petiole, which is the first (narrow) segment of the waist. The Argentine ant shown here has one distinct petiole node, an unevenly rounded thorax, and a 12-segmented antenna. Identify ants using these characters as illustrated in publications such as *A Key to the Most Common and/or Economically Important Ants of California* (Haney, Philips, and Wagner 1983) or *Key to Identifying Common Household Ants* (Reynolds 2004). *Illustration adapted from: S. H. DeBord in Smith 1965.*

Be especially alert for the highly aggressive red imported fire ant *(Solenopsis invicta =S. wagneri)*. Red imported fire ants run up any object that they encounter. They have a venomous sting that can seriously injure people. Red imported fire ant workers can generally be recognized by their mixed sizes: small and large ants $\frac{1}{12}$ to $\frac{1}{4}$ inch (2–6 mm) long can occur together in the same clump or trail. Except for southern fire ants, which also range in size, workers outside the nest are about the same size for all other ant species likely to be found in California groves. If you suspect you have found a red imported fire ant population, report your suspicions to agricultural officials. Telephone 1-888-4FIREANT toll-free or go online to www.fireant.ca.gov.

Management Guidelines

Periodically inspect for ants and bark damage under trunk wraps of young trees. Check for ants on trees of any age if honeydew-producing insects are a problem. If ants have swollen, almost translucent abdomens, this can indicate they are honeydew-collecting species.

Ants do not have effective natural enemies aside from competition with other ants. Cultivation controls ants but also creates dust and disturbs the soil near trees, damaging roots. An insecticide mixed with bait is the preferred method for chemical control. Baits are slow-acting but effective over the long term because they take advantage of ants' food-sharing behavior. Ants spread the insecticide bait throughout their colony, even to nest-bound immatures and queens.

The best time to bait is from late winter to early spring, when ant numbers are relatively low. Bait effectiveness varies with ant species, availability of alternative food, pesticide active ingredient, type of bait, and time of year. Argentine ants prefer sweet liquid baits. Protein baits can also attract Argentine ants, for instance in spring when colonies are producing young, which need nitrogen for development. To determine which bait will work best, offer small quantities of several baits and watch to see which one the ants prefer.

Apply an effective bait in spots near nests or on ant trails. Spot-treatment takes advantage of ants' trailing behavior, whereby they lead nest mates to places where food is concentrated. Spot-treatment minimizes toxicity to nonpest ant species that compete with pest ants and help to limit the pests' populations. Broadcasting baits or widespread spraying with an insecticide is expensive and may not reach many ants that are in their nests underground.

JACK KELLY CLARK

This Argentine ant is tending a brown soft scale, protecting the pest from natural enemies while it feeds on scale honeydew. These $\frac{1}{10}$-inch-long (2.5 mm) ants are uniformly brown and travel in characteristic trails on trees or the ground.

JACK KELLY CLARK

The native gray ant is $\frac{1}{6}$ to $\frac{1}{3}$ inch (4–8 mm) long and brownish, dark red, and gray. It is noticeably larger than the Argentine ant and southern fire ant. Native gray ants move quickly in irregular patterns. They usually forage individually, not in dense trails of ants.

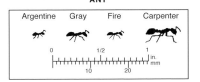

ANT

Argentine   Gray   Fire   Carpenter

A southern fire ant nest exposed to reveal pale pupae and larvae, winged reproductives, and worker ants, which are $^1/_{10}$ to $^1/_5$ inch (2.5–5 mm) long. The yellowish red head and thorax and dark brown abdomen distinguish southern fire ant workers from workers of the red imported fire ant, which are uniformly reddish brown.

Fire ants generally can be distinguished from other ants in California avocado groves by their varying size. Unlike most other species where all workers are of near-uniform length, a trail of red imported fire ants (shown here) or native southern fire ants consists of large and small forms together plus a range of intermediate-sized ants.

HEMIPTERA

Hemipteran insects have piercing or sucking mouthparts and incomplete metamorphosis: eggs hatch into immatures called nymphs that develop gradually into adults without a pupal stage. Nymphs differ from adults primarily in size, lack of wings, and color. The order Hemiptera includes true bugs (suborder Heteroptera) and "Homoptera," an informal group including mealybugs, scale insects, and whiteflies.

Avocado Lace Bug
Pseudacysta perseae

Avocado lace bug (family Tingidae) occurs in the Caribbean, Mexico, and the southeastern United States. It was discovered in San Diego County in 2004. Also known as the camphor lace bug, this pest's only other known hosts are various *Persea* species and the camphor tree (*Cinnamomum camphora*), which is grown as a landscape ornamental and commercially for its aromatic extracts.

Lace bugs do not feed on fruit. Adults and nymphs feed in groups on the underside of leaves. This sucking pest causes chlorotic, then necrotic blotches on foliage. Severely damaged leaves may drop prematurely. Defoliation can result in sunburned fruit and wood and can stress trees, reducing subsequent years' yields.

Adults are oval insects about $^1/_{12}$ inch (2 mm) long with a dark (black or brownish) head and thorax. Their abdomen, antennae, legs, and wing covers have both dark and light (orangish, yellowish, or white) areas. Nymphs are mostly dark and orangish, resembling the adults but without wings. Eggs are laid on leaves within shiny black globs of excrement.

Insects develop from egg to adult in about 1 month during warm weather and have several generations a year. All stages can be present throughout the year (Figure 30).

Little is known about this insect's effects in California. High populations and severe foliage damage have occurred in California on some untreated residential avocado trees. Avocado lace bug is an intermittent pest in Florida avocados.

Avoid spreading lace bugs. Do not move uncertified host material or dirty bins from infested areas. Clean bins and other potentially infested equipment and materials before you bring them into groves as lace bugs may survive and spread on leaf debris. Conserve resident natural enemies that prey on lace bugs, including lacewing larvae and predatory thrips. *Franklinothrips* reportedly are important in controlling avocado lace bug in the Dominican Republic and *Franklinothrips* species and several other predatory thrips occur in California avocados. For potential release in California to provide classical biological control, University of California scientists are searching for natural enemies that feed only on avocado lace bugs. At least two parasitic wasp species kill avocado lace bug eggs in Florida—an unidentified species in the family Mymaridae and an *Oligosita* sp. (Trichogrammatidae). Contact insecticides such as oil and pyrethrins temporarily reduce lace bug populations when applied to thoroughly cover the underside of avocado leaves. Persistent, broad-spectrum insecticides are more effective, but those can disrupt biological control of other potential pests in avocados. Certain systemic insecticides can be very effective and may be available for application through irrigation systems. Consult the latest *Avocado: UC IPM Pest Management Guidelines: Insects and Mites* (online at www.ipm.ucdavis.edu) for specific recommendations.

A colony of lace bugs feeding on the underside of leaves initially causes faint pale green to yellowish discoloration visible on the upper leaf surface (bottom of photo). As lace bugs continue feeding, tissue darkens and dies (top).

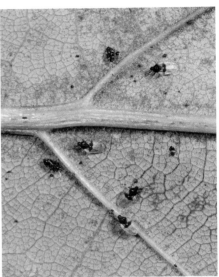

Severe avocado lace bug damage causes large, brown or tan, dead blotches on leaves. Heavily damaged leaves may drop prematurely, resulting in sunburned fruit and trees and stress that can reduce subsequent fruit yields.

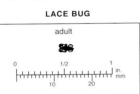

LACE BUG

adult

0   1/2   1
||||||||||||||||||||||||||||||| in.
      10   20   mm

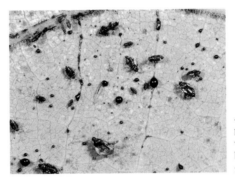

Avocado lace bug adults are oval in shape with a dark head and thorax and lighter-colored wings and appendages.

Avocado lace bug nymphs are mostly black, with paler areas on the back of older nymphs where wings are developing. Eggs usually are hidden beneath black specks of excrement left by the female during egg laying.

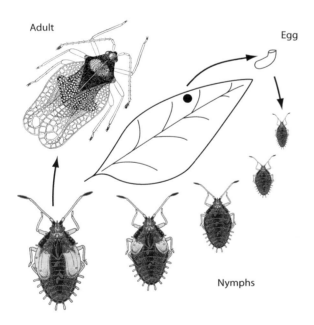

Figure 30. Avocado lace bug life cycle and stages. *Illustrations adapted from:* Heidemann 1909, Moznette 1922.

Armored Scales

Latania scale (*Hemiberlesia lataniae*) occasionally damages avocado trees. California red scale (*Aonidiella aurantii*) is a rare problem, and only on avocados growing near citrus where red scale is abundant. Dictyospermum scale (*Chrysomphalus dictyospermi*) and greedy scale (*Hemiberlesia rapax*) are other species of armored scale (family Diaspididae) that have been reported at innocuous densities in avocados. Scale insects in avocados are usually under good biological control. Damaging outbreaks have occurred, but these appear to have resulted from upsets of natural enemy populations by ants, dust, and pesticide applications.

High latania scale populations on bark can kill twigs, especially on young trees. Unlike many plant-sucking insects, armored scales do not secrete any noticeable liquid. Economic damage is from scale covers on the fruit skin, which appear as tiny dimples or light-colored spots. Feeding may also cause small discolored spots in the skin. Internal fruit quality is not impaired, but infested or spotted fruit may be culled.

Description and Seasonal Development

Armored scales have a flattened, slightly convex cover that at maturity is about ¹⁄₁₆ inch (2 mm) in diameter. This plate-like cover usually can be removed to reveal the actual scale body underneath. Armored scale covers typically have concentric rings, which form as each nymphal stage secretes new material to enlarge its cover. Covers often have a different-colored, slight protuberance or "nipple." Females develop roundish covers. When present, males have covers that are elongated in late instars.

Latania and greedy scale covers are gray, tan, or white. These species can only be distinguished reliably by an expert. Dictyospermum scale has a yellowish brown cover that is somewhat darker than the similar-looking, orange to reddish cover of California red scale. California red scale and latania scale can occur on all surfaces of the avocado tree, with relatively even distribution among fruit, leaf, and wood surfaces. Dictyospermum scale infests mostly fruit and leaves. Greedy scale is usually limited to twigs and branches.

The life stages and development of armored scales (Figure 31) are mostly the same as illustrated for California red scale, but there are several differences. Latania scale and greedy scale females lay eggs beneath their cover, from which crawlers hatch, whereas California red scale and dictyospermum scale give live birth to young crawlers. Greedy scale and latania scale reproduce without males, at least in California, whereas both California red scale and dictyospermum scale do produce males, which as immatures develop under elongated covers. Consult publications such as *Color-Photo and*

Host Keys to the Armored Scales of California (Gill 1982) and *The Scale Insects of California Part 3: The Armored Scales* (Gill 1997) for help in identifying scales.

Monitoring and Management Guidelines

Biological control is the primary method for scale management. Conserve natural enemies by controlling ants, minimizing dust, and avoiding any application of broad-spectrum, persistent insecticides. If certain areas of a grove have high populations of armored scale, determine whether encrusted fruit can be selectively harvested and sent to a packinghouse that uses brushes or pressure-washing equipment that can remove scale covers from fruit. Only very infrequently can direct control measures be justified; on those occasions, it is best to apply oil spray as it has little long-term adverse impact on natural enemies. Time any scale treatments to occur soon after most scale crawlers have emerged.

Monitoring Scale Crawlers. To time an application, monitor scale crawlers by trapping them with transparent tape that is sticky on both sides. Wrap tape traps tightly to encircle each of several twigs near female scales. Replace the traps weekly during times of year when you expect crawlers to be present. Preserve the used traps by sandwiching them between clear plastic and light blue paper, and label each paper with the trap date and location. Visually compare the

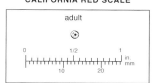

CALIFORNIA RED SCALE

Armored scales secrete a convex cover, which they enlarge each time they molt. This twig is encrusted with all ages of greedy scale, which can be distinguished from latania scale only by an expert.

A California red scale cover has been lifted to reveal the soft, yellow scale body underneath (photo left). Female armored scales secrete a roundish cover (right). California red scale and Dictyospermum scale also produce males, which when immature have an elongate cover (top).

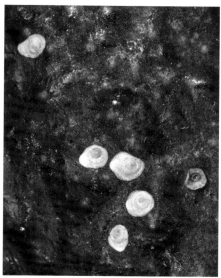

When viewed close-up, latania scale covers appear as roundish gray, tan, or white encrustations on the darker fruit skin.

Latania scales cause economic damage when their covers mar fruit aesthetics by appearing as light-colored spots on the skin. Feeding may also cause small discolorations within the skin.

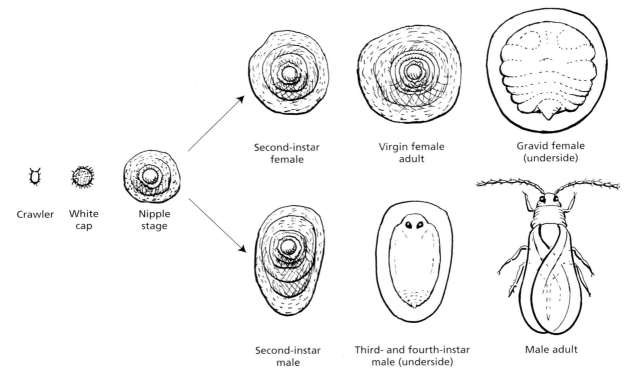

Figure 31. Armored scale life cycle and stages, illustrated here for California red scale. Mobile first instars (crawlers) emerge from beneath the female cover. Nymphs settle, feed, and females secrete a roundish cover. Females molt three times and remain immobile the rest of their life. After the first molt, males secrete an elongated cover. Males molt four times and mature into tiny, winged adults. Adult males emerge, seek virgin adult females, and mate. Greedy and latania scale develop only as shown here for females; greedy and latania scale are parthenogenic and produce no males.

abundance of crawlers caught in traps for the different monitoring dates. If warranted, apply a treatment such as an oil spray after the end of maximum crawler emergence, when it is obvious that you caught more crawlers per trap during previous weeks and catches have definitely started to decline.

Biological Control. Predatory insects and parasitic wasps control most scales. Armored scale parasitic wasps include species of tiny *Aphytis* and *Aspidiotiphagus* (family Aphelinidae) and *Comperiella* and *Signiphora* (family Encyrtidae). If persistent populations of California red scale are present, consider purchasing and releasing a small number (perhaps 10,000) of *Aphytis melinus* parasites near the scale infested trees.

Most scale predators feed on both armored and soft scales and often on other pests as well. Predators include brown and green lacewings, pirate bugs, predaceous mites such as *Cheletomimus berlesei* and *Hemisarcoptes malus*, and sixspotted thrips. Predaceous Coccinellidae include the spotless lady beetle (*Cycloneda sanguinea*), steelblue lady beetle (*Halmus chalybeus*), and twicestabbed lady beetle (*Chilocorus orbus =C. stigma*). As adults, these lady beetles are about ⅙ to ⅕ inch (4–5 mm) long. Spotless lady beetles have a black and white head and thorax and orangish wing covers without markings. Steelblue lady beetles are a bluish metallic color. Twicestabbed lady beetles are shiny black with two large, red spots on their wing covers. Their larvae are black to brown-

ish with a yellowish transverse band and are covered with branched spines. The life cycle of typical scale-feeding lady beetles is illustrated in Figure 32.

Soft Scales

Several species of soft scale insects (family Coccidae) occur on avocados, but rarely are they pests. Soft scales suck phloem sap from foliage and twigs. When abundant, the large quantities of sticky honeydew that scales excrete will promote growth of blackish sooty mold, which can foul fruit.

Black scale (*Saissetia oleae*) is the most common soft scale in California avocados. Other soft scales that are sometimes present include brown soft scale (*Coccus hesperidum*), European fruit lecanium (*Parthenolecanium corni*), and hemispherical scale (*Saissetia coffeae*). Pyriform scale (*Protopulvinaria pyriformis*) occurs on avocado trees in landscapes, but it is rare or absent in commercial groves.

These scales at maturity are 1/12 to 1/5 inch (2–5 mm) in diameter. The soft scale's surface is the actual body wall of the insect and, unlike the visible surface of armored scales, it cannot be removed. Adults are black, brown, or orangish with a hemispherical, humped, or round shape. The exception is pyriform scale, a flattened species that is somewhat pear-shaped or deltoid (pointed at one end

An enlargement of scale crawlers caught in a sticky tape trap. Crawlers emerge from under the female and search for a suitable place to settle and feed. Before settling, crawlers can drop onto uninfested plant parts, be spread by wind, or be moved as contaminants on animals, equipment, or workers.

Adult male scales are minute, yellowish insects with legs and one pair of wings. Males, such as this California red scale, are easily overlooked, but can be observed in yellow sticky traps. Males of scales and mealybugs can be confused with adults of certain tiny wasps that parasitize scales and other pests.

This yellow flag marks the location of a scale crawler monitoring trap. Transparent tape that is sticky on both sides is wrapped tightly to encircle the twig. The tape end is doubled over several times to provide a handle for easy removal. Tapes are replaced about weekly and inspected to determine when scale crawlers are abundant.

This female *Aphytis melinus* is laying its egg in a California red scale. It also parasitizes latania scale. A wasp larva feeds beneath the cover and kills parasitized scale.

Certain predatory mites feed on scale crawlers and eggs. A translucent predaceous mite is on a California red scale (photo center). Mites that are reported to feed on avocado scales include *Cheletomimus berlesei* and *Hemisarcoptes malus*. An oblong predaceous mite egg is pictured in the section on mites.

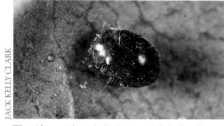

This ¹/₁₆- to ¹/₈-inch (1.6–3 mm) lady beetle (*Rhyzobius lophanthae*) is feeding on the settled first instar scales visible on the underside of this leaf. A similar-looking, ¹/₆-inch-long (4 mm) blackish to reddish brown species (*Rhyzobius forestieri*) also feeds on all stages of scales and mealybugs.

RHYZOBIUS LOPHANTHAE

larva   adult

0   1/2   1 in.
10   20   mm

TWICESTABBED LADY BEETLE

adult

0   1/2   1 in.
10   20   mm

This blackish, late instar *Rhyzobius* (=*Lindorus*) *forestieri* larva has lifted the edge of a European fruit lecanium and is feeding on the scale crawlers and eggs underneath. Younger larvae of scale-feeding lady beetles can be difficult to see because they often feed hidden beneath the female scale cover or body.

This twicestabbed lady beetle (*Chilocorus orbus* =C. *stigma*) feeds on armored and soft scales throughout the United States. It is one of several lady beetles species with ¹/₅-inch-long (5 mm) adults that are shiny black with two red spots. Its spiny larvae are mottled black, tan, and white.

and rounded at the other). White wax projects from beneath the edges of female pyriform scales. Consult publications such as *Color-Photo and Host Keys to the Soft Scales of California* (Gill 1982) and *The Scale Insects of California Part 1: The Soft Scales* (Gill 1988) for help with identification.

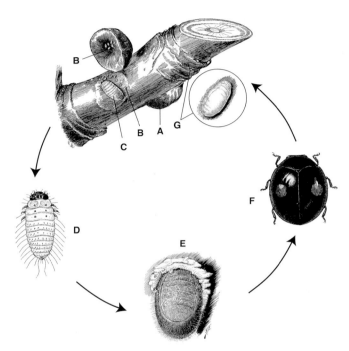

Figure 32. Lady beetle life cycle and stages, illustrated here with a predator of scales. A. Female soft scales such as this are immobile and dome-shaped. B. Scale eggs and crawlers occur underneath, as revealed by lifting the mature female from bark. C. Young beetle larvae and certain other small predators feed on eggs and crawlers beneath the female. D. Beetle larvae develop through four instars, and late instar-larvae feed openly on scales. E. Beetle larvae pupate on or near the host plant. F. The lady beetle adult emerges from the pupal case and locates and feeds on scales. G. The female beetle lays eggs from which larvae hatch and seek prey. *Adapted from:* Simanton 1916.

Blackish sooty mold is growing on honeydew on these leaves. Honeydew is excreted by certain sucking insects such as aphids, mealybugs, scales, and whiteflies. Honeydew is an important attractant and food for adults of many natural enemies, and honeydew and sooty mold are harmless to avocado, except in the uncommon situation when they're abundant enough to foul fruit surfaces.

Mobile first instars (crawlers) emerge from eggs that the female adult lays under her body. First instars settle to feed within a day or two of emergence. These oval nymphs are yellow, pale orange, or reddish. Soft scales retain barely visible legs and are able to move slowly as they molt through three instars. On avocado and other evergreen hosts, scales usually spend all of their life after the crawler stage in one spot.

This mature female black scale is identified by the raised H-shape on its back. A yellowish first instar has settled just below and to the right of the female. At top left is an older nymph that is molting (called the rubber stage).

Two mature European fruit lecanium females, one flipped to reveal many eggs developing underneath. Most soft scales have one generation a year, with females that mature and produce eggs during spring to early summer. An exception is brown soft scale, which can have several generations a year.

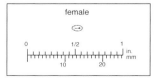

EUROPEAN FRUIT LECANIUM

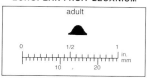

JACK KELLY CLARK

This adult *Coccophagus lecanii* parasite just emerged from a soft scale nymph it has killed. During its larval stage, the wasp feeds inside the scale.

Argentine ants are feeding on honeydew excreted by this black scale. Selectively controlling ants improves biological control of many pests because ants attack any parasites and predators they encounter on plants.

JACK KELLY CLARK

This steelblue lady beetle (*Halmus chalybeus*) was introduced from Australia and occurs in avocado along the central and south coast of California. The 1/6-inch-long (4 mm) adult is metallic bluish. Its prey includes armored and soft scales and mites.

JACK KELLY CLARK

The dark European fruit lecanium nymphs were killed by *Coccophagus lecanii*. Unparasitized nymphs remain orangish. However, some parasite species do not discolor their host. Dissecting the apparently healthy scales (photo right) might reveal that some contain parasites.

This mostly pale larva of the steelblue lady beetle has prominent spines with multiple branches. Larvae of *Chilocorus* species also have numerous spines on spines.

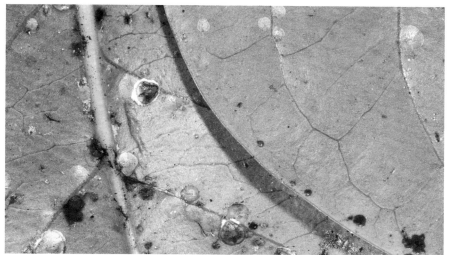

Pyriform scale is named for its deltoid or pyriform shape most apparent in the mature females, which are dark brown to orangish with a white fringe as on the leaf at left in the photo above. Nymphs are yellowish and translucent. Although it infests avocado in Florida and elsewhere, in California pyriform scale has only been found on certain ornamentals.

Soft scales usually are controlled effectively by predators and parasites. Parasitic wasps are especially important, including *Coccophagus* spp. (family Aphelinidae) and *Metaphycus* and *Microterys* spp. (family Encyrtidae). Important lady beetles include many *Chilocorus*, *Hyperaspis*, and *Rhyzobius* species. Lady beetles can easily be overlooked because many are tiny, colored and shaped like scales, or (as small larvae) feeding while hidden beneath a scale's body (see Figure 32). Lacewings, predaceous bugs, and many other predatory insects and mites feed at least occasionally on scales.

Conserve natural enemies by reducing dust and selectively controlling ants. Whenever possible, apply only selective or short-residual pesticides to control other pests (see Table 4).

Whiteflies

Whiteflies (order Aleyrodidae) suck phloem sap. They excrete honeydew, which collects dust and supports the growth of blackish sooty mold fungi that can foul fruit. Honeydew also attracts ants, which interfere with the biological control of whiteflies and other pests. In approximate order of most to least commonly seen, the whitefly species in California avocados are redbanded whitefly (*Tetraleurodes perseae*), nesting whitefly (*Paraleyrodes minei*), greenhouse whitefly (*Trialeurodes vaporariorum*), mulberry whitefly (*Tetraleurodes mori*), and giant whitefly (*Aleurodicus dugesii*). They have many natural enemies and usually are under good biological control.

Description and Seasonal Development

Giant whitefly, greenhouse whitefly, and mulberry whitefly each have hosts in over a dozen plant families. Nesting whitefly prefers citrus but also infests avocado trees and some ornamental broadleaf evergreens. Redbanded whitefly in California has been found only on avocados.

Whiteflies are identified in the field primarily by the color, shape, and waxiness of the fourth-instar nymph or pupa (Figure 33). Adult whiteflies are delicate, powdery-surfaced

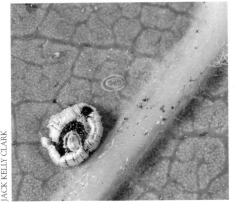

Whiteflies are identified to species primarily by the fourth-instar nymph or pupa. This redbanded whitefly pupa has a relatively continuous marginal fringe of wax, which often curls tightly over the body.

Whiteflies are named for the mealy, white wax covering their wings and body. This redbanded whitefly adult has pale reddish bands on its wings. It most resembles mulberry whitefly, but giant whitefly and nesting whitefly adults also have marked wings.

Greenhouse whitefly adults have yellowish bodies and entirely pale wings. Greenhouse whitefly pupae have distinctive, long, marginal wax filaments.

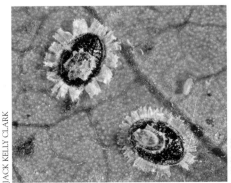

Redbanded whitefly third instars (shown here) and fourth instars are black with a distinct marginal fringe of wax. Eggs and first and second instars are beige. The cast skins from earlier instars are often retained on top, as shown here.

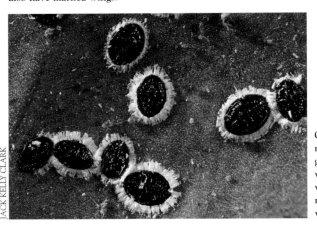

Older nymphs and pupae of mulberry whitefly have marginal wax that extends outward, flat. Unlike redbanded whitefly pupae, the wax does not curl over the mulberry whitefly's black body.

insects, that lay tiny, oblong eggs on foliage. The first-instar nymphs are initially mobile crawlers; after hatching from the egg, crawlers soon become sessile, settling to feed and losing their legs. The subsequent three nymphal stages are also sessile, generally flattened and oval, and may resemble certain soft scales. All whiteflies have similar life cycles (Figure 34). All life stages can be present on a plant host at any one time, with several generations developing each year. For example, one redbanded whitefly generation takes about 6 weeks to grow from egg to adult when temperatures average 77°F (25°C). Consult publications such as *Color-Photo and Host Keys to California Whiteflies* (Gill 1982) for help with identification.

Management Guidelines

Conserve natural enemies, which provide partial to complete biological control of most whitefly species unless disturbed by ants, dust, or insecticides. Have any unfamiliar whiteflies identified by an expert. New species are introduced periodically into California. Do not bring plant materials into California from other states or countries: they may be infested. Avoid moving uncertified or infested plant material from one orchard to another to minimize pest spread. Make sure bins are clean when you transport bins from giant whitefly-infested areas to clean groves.

Parasitic wasps are the most important natural enemies of whiteflies (Figure 34). These include many *Cales, Encarsia,* and *Eretmocerus* species (family Aphelinidae) that feed as larvae inside whitefly nymphs. Predators of whitefly nymphs include bigeyed bugs (*Geocoris* spp.), green lacewings (*Chrysoperla* spp.), lady beetles (*Delphastus* spp.), and pirate bugs (*Orius* spp.). Spiders feed on adult whiteflies.

Control dust by oiling or paving main orchard roads. Use a water truck or trailer to wet unpaved roads, especially during summer months when dust moving up into the tree canopies can be especially disruptive of natural enemy populations. Where ants are abundant on trees, consider applying insecticide baits to control them. When you apply pesticides, conserve natural enemies by choosing selective materials, such as *Bacillus thuringiensis* (Bt) for caterpillars.

Chemical treatment of whiteflies is often ineffective. Temporary suppression may be followed by a resurgence of the pest, especially after application of certain broad-spectrum insecticides.

Nesting whitefly nymphs and pupae are semitransparent pale green, oval, and flat. Pupae have numerous short, fine filaments uniformly projecting from the body margin. The distinctive long wax strands produced by nymphs give rise to the field name, "pasta" or "spaghetti" whitefly.

Giant whitefly adults often leave wax spirals on the leaves where females lay eggs (right side of right leaf in photo). Immatures produce long strands of wax (left leaf), which may extend an inch or more below the leaf surface, giving heavily infested foliage a bearded appearance.

Giant whitefly pupae are distinctly elevated in profile, with edges perpendicular to the leaf surface. The dark pupae are parasitized by *Entedononecremnus krauteri.* A round hole chewed by an emerging adult wasp is visible at the upper right.

Mulberry whitefly, *Tetraleurodes mori*	Redbanded whitefly, *Tetraleurodes perseae*	Nesting whitefly, *Paraleyrodes minei*	Greenhouse whitefly, *Trialeurodes vaporariorum*	Giant whitefly, *Aleurodicus dugesii*
ADULTS				
Reddish to gray wing markings, including a blotch at the base and tip of each wing.	Reddish wing markings, commonly in two broken bands and a blotch at the base of each wing.	Grayish blotches on forewings.	No markings on white wings. Wings usually held flat—parallel to top of its yellowish body.	Grayish blotches or mottling on wings. Larger that other species, about 3/16 inch (5 mm) long.
PUPAE				
A black body fringed with white wax that extends out flat and does not curl over the body.	A black body fringed with white wax that curls over the body.	Pale green to orangish with a marginal fringe of many short filaments. Produces numerous wax strands so that insects appear to be covered with tiny spaghetti noodles.	Pupa has long submarginal wax filaments and a marginal fringe of short filaments. Elevated in profile, with edges parallel to the leaf surface.	Several marginal filaments and covered with powdery wax. Elevated in profile with edges parallel to the leaf surface. Long wax strands, ≥1 inch (2.5 mm) in length (not shown), hang from infested leaves, giving foliage a white bearded appearance.

Figure 33. Whitefly species that occur on avocado in California can be distinguished by pupal shape, filaments, and waxiness, and sometimes by adult wing markings. *Sources:* Flint 1995; giant, nesting, and redbanded whiteflies by David H. Headrick.

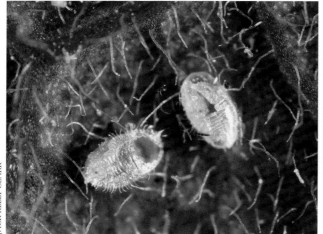

Parasites leave a circular hole when they emerge from immature whiteflies. At left is the case of a pupa killed by *Encarsia pergandiella*. Adult whiteflies emerge through a ragged slit or T-shaped split in the pupal skin (photo right).

This adult *Cales noacki* parasitizes both mulberry and redbanded whiteflies. It typically kills 50 to 90% of redbanded whitefly nymphs in coastal growing areas. Females oviposit in second or third instars. The whitefly is killed as it pupates, and then an adult parasite emerges.

Delphastus species are small, mostly black lady beetles that feed on many different species of whitefly.

Spiders are important predators of many pests. White-flies and thrips have been captured in this spider web.

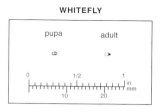

Like the adults, this tiny pale *Delphastus* larva feeds on all whitefly life stages.

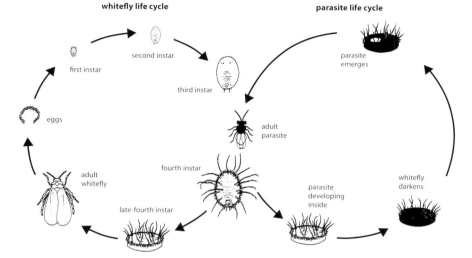

Figure 34. Whitefly and parasite life cycles and stages, illustrated with the greenhouse whitefly and *Encarsia formosa*. Most whiteflies develop through four nymphal instars. The female *Encarsia* lays one egg per host in a late second-instar through early fourth-instar whitefly. The parasite larva develops through three instars as it feeds inside and eventually kills the host. *Encarsia* blackens its host as the parasite matures.

Adult brown lacewings, like this *Hemerobius pacificus*, are about one-half as large as green lacewings. They emerge from flat, white, silken cocoons on plants. Brown lacewing adults and larvae are predaceous, while only certain species of green lacewings are predaceous as adults.

Green lacewing adults, such as this *Chrysoperla carnea*, have golden eyes and slender, green bodies. Lacewings are named for their prominent wings, which have green, netlike or lacy veins. Adults are nocturnal but can be observed flying during the day if their resting place on branches or foliage is disturbed.

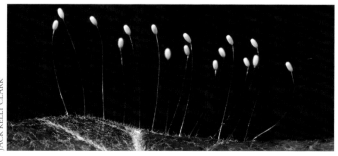

Green lacewings lay oblong eggs, each with a silken stalk attached to the plant. Depending on the species, eggs are laid singly or in clusters (as with these eggs of *Chrysopa nigricornis*). A lacewing larva is pictured in the section on mites.

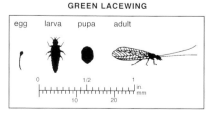

Mealybugs

Mealybugs (order Pseudococcidae) suck phloem sap. When abundant, they can reduce tree vigor, foul plants with sticky honeydew, and promote the growth of blackish sooty mold that fouls fruit. Longtailed mealybug (*Pseudococcus longispinus*) is the only species common in California avocados. Its populations are usually very low. New scion grafts on old (topworked) trees have sometimes been damaged by longtailed mealybugs that are abundant during late winter and early spring. Other species are of potential concern because they infest avocados elsewhere. These include citrus mealybug (*Planococcus citri*), pink hibiscus mealybug (*Maconellicoccus hirsutus*), and vine mealybug (*Planococcus ficus*), which are not reported pests of avocados in California.

Description and Seasonal Development

Mealybugs produce two to four overlapping generations a year. All stages can occur throughout the year. Nymphs and females are soft, oval, and covered with white, powdery wax. Adult males are tiny, two-winged insects with two long tail filaments, but are rarely seen. In many mealybug species the female lays tiny, yellow eggs in an ovisac, a mass of eggs intermixed with white wax. Longtailed mealybug produces no external egg sacs; it gives live birth to nymphs.

Species can often be distinguished based on their waxiness, especially the presence, length, and thickness of marginal wax filaments. The citrus, longtailed, and vine mealybugs have distinct, well-developed wax filaments around their body margin. Female longtailed mealybugs have tail filaments greater than three-quarters of their body length. Citrus and vine mealybug filaments are relatively short. Pink

Pirate bugs prey on mealybugs, mites, scales, small caterpillars, thrips, whiteflies, and insect eggs. This *Orius tristicolor* lays oval eggs in plant tissue. Its yellow to orangish, pear-shaped nymphs are also predaceous.

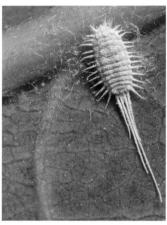

Longtailed mealybug occurs in coastal avocado groves, usually at very low densities. It has well-developed waxy filaments around its margin, including tail filaments greater than three-quarters of the body length.

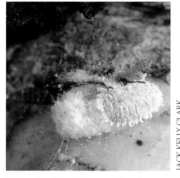

This ovipositing vine mealybug has not been found on avocado in California. This recently introduced species has been reported on avocado elsewhere, so make sure to take any unfamiliar mealybugs to an expert for identification. Female vine mealybugs closely resemble citrus mealybugs; both species have uniformly short marginal wax filaments.

The mealybug destroyer (*Cryptolaemus montrouzieri*) is a dark brown or blackish lady beetle with an orangish head and rear. The larva closely resembles its mealybug prey. *Cryptolaemus* larvae have longer lateral wax filaments and move faster than mealybugs. The lady beetle larva can be recognized if its wax is gently brushed away.

Pink hibiscus mealybug females are covered with powdery wax but lack distinct wax filaments extending from their body's margin. If found in California outside of Imperial County, submit suspected pink hibiscus mealybugs to the local agricultural agency or Cooperative Extension office for identification.

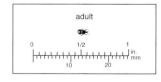

MINUTE PIRATE BUG

BROWN LACEWING

LONGTAILED MEALYBUG

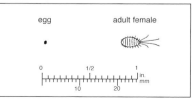

hibiscus mealybug lacks distinct waxy filaments. The mealybug species in California that might occur on avocado and many other crops and ornamentals can be distinguished by consulting *Mealybugs in California Vineyards* (Godfrey et al. 2002), an illustrated key.

If you find unfamiliar mealybugs, get them identified by an expert. For example, the introduced vine mealybug has not been found in California groves although it does infest avocados elsewhere. Pink hibiscus mealybug in California has been limited to Imperial County. Introduced parasites, especially *Anagyrus kamali,* are providing good control. If you find pink hibiscus mealybug elsewhere in California, notify agricultural officials right away as prompt management action may be warranted.

Management Guidelines

Conserve natural enemies, which control most mealybug populations. Selective control of ants will cause longtailed mealybug populations to decline and can prevent outbreaks. Reduce dust, which interferes with natural enemies. Whenever possible, apply only selective or short-residual pesticides when treating other pests (see Table 4). Consult the latest *Avocado: UC IPM Pest Management Guidelines: Insects and Mites* (online at www.ipm.ucdavis.edu) for specific recommendations.

Mealybug predators include green lacewing (*Chrysoperla* spp.) larvae, pirate bugs, predaceous fly larvae, and lady beetles such as the mealybug destroyer (*Cryptolaemus montrouzieri*). Parasitic wasps are especially important in controlling outbreaks. For example, *Acerophagus notativentris, Arhopoideus peregrinus,* and *Anarhopus sydneyensis* (family Encyrtidae) parasitize longtailed mealybug. *Anarhopus sydneyensis* can complete one generation in about a month when temperatures average 80°F (27°C), during which time the wasp larvae feed inside and kill second instar through adult female mealybugs.

Twospotted leafhoppers such as this nymph can be abundant on avocado. This species does not damage avocado.

Twospotted leafhoppers adults have two black, eyelike tail spots. They move quickly when approached or disturbed.

LEAFHOPPERS AND SHARPSHOOTERS

Leafhoppers (family Cicadellidae), including species called "sharpshooters," suck plant juices. They are active insects that walk rapidly sideways or readily jump when disturbed. Glassy-winged sharpshooter and twospotted leafhopper are sometimes abundant in avocados, but they are not pests of avocados.

Twospotted Leafhopper
Sophonia rufofascia

The inadvertently introduced twospotted leafhopper is sometimes abundant on avocado leaves, especially on succulent foliage, but it does not damage avocado trees or fruit. It feeds on more than 200 plant species, but apparently causes severe foliar chlorosis and dieback only on guava and some of its many landscape and ornamental hosts. Adults are about ⅕ inch (5 mm) long, light green to pale yellow with various shades of pink or red, and have a dark stripe down the center of their back. Adults have two dark wing spots near their rear, which resemble eyes and make the leafhopper appear to be moving backwards when it walks. Nymphs are green to translucent yellow with two dark spots near their rear. Nymphs produce clear cast skins that can remain attached to the plant for long periods, resembling pale leafhoppers.

Glassy-Winged Sharpshooter
Homalodisca vitripennis (=H. coagulata)

Glassy-winged sharpshooter was inadvertently introduced into southern California in the late 1980s. It feeds on avocado mostly where citrus or other preferred hosts are abundant nearby. Occasionally at high populations, glassy-winged sharpshooters can cover fruit with whitish excrement. Because of their ability to vector *Xylella* pathogens, sharpshooters are a serious pest in grapes and several other crops.

Damage

Glassy-winged sharpshooter and certain other leafhoppers suck leaf and stem xylem tissue. Because they feed on the nutrient-poor xylem, sharpshooters must consume copious amounts of fluid to gain adequate nutrition. Consequently,

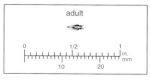

TWOSPOTTED LEAFHOPPER

adult

0   1/2   1 in.

10   20 mm

the adults and nymphs excrete large amounts of liquid while feeding. Their excrement gives fruit and foliage a whitewashed appearance, and that may cause the fruit to be downgraded during packing.

Glassy-winged sharpshooter adults feed on more than 300 plant species and can reproduce (lay eggs) in about 100 species. In avocados, glassy-winged sharpshooters rarely are abundant enough to foul fruit. Study of avocado trees near citrus groves with abundant sharpshooters found no effect on the avocados' plant health or fruit size or yield. The glassy-winged sharpshooter is a serious pest of certain other crops because it vectors *Xylella fastidiosa* bacteria. Different strains of this bacterium cause lethal diseases in other plants, such as almond leaf scorch, oleander leaf scorch, and Pierce's disease in grapes. The bacteria multiply and block the water-conducting system of the plant, causing water stress and eventually the death of the plant.

There is no known cure for the *Xylella fastidiosa* diseases that affect other crops. There many other strains of *Xylella fastidiosa* in other parts of the world that could do damage to crops if introduced into California. *Xylella* causes a serious citrus variegated chlorosis disease in South America. An avocado strain of *Xylella* is believed to exist in Central America, but no leafhopper-vectored avocado diseases have been observed in the United States.

Description and Seasonal Development

The glassy-winged sharpshooter is larger than most other leafhoppers. Adults are about ½ inch (13 mm) long and dark brownish with white and yellowish patches and spots. Pale head spots make it easy to distinguish from the native smoke-tree sharpshooter (*Homalodisca lacerta*), which has light-colored wavy lines on its head.

Females lay eggs in a cluster of about one dozen eggs under the surface of the underside of leaves. The eggs initially resemble a greenish blister on the leaf, which females cover with a white chalky secretion. Eggs turn brown as they mature and they leave a permanent brown to gray scar in leaf tissue after the nymphs emerge.

Immature glassy-winged sharpshooters develop through several stages (instars) and resemble small adults, except that the immatures are wingless and uniformly olive gray, and they have prominent, bulging red eyes. Smoke-tree sharpshooter nymphs look very similar but have blue eyes.

The glassy-winged sharpshooter has two generations per year in California. Although all life stages can be found year-

Glassy-winged sharpshooter eggs occur within leaf tissue in a cluster of about one dozen eggs. Eggs initially resemble a greenish blister (photo right). Mature eggs are brown and leave a permanent brown to gray scar in leaf tissue (left) after insects emerge.

The adult glassy-winged sharpshooter is mostly dark brown with white and yellowish patches and spots.

Glassy-winged sharpshooter nymphs are uniformly brown to olive-gray and wingless. Nymphs have prominent, bulging red eyes.

GLASSY-WINGED SHARPSHOOTER

round, reproduction and immature stages occur mostly from late winter through fall. Overwintering adults oviposit in late winter and early spring. Nymphs mature into first-generation adults from about April through early June. Most second-generation adults appear from later summer through fall and can survive overwinter until the following season.

Management Guidelines

Avocado nurseries may be required to treat stock and meet other requirements when producing and shipping young avocado trees. Contact your county department of agriculture for current quarantine compliance rules.

In established avocado groves, glassy-winged sharpshooter generally requires no management. Monitoring may be warranted, though, if the avocados are grown near untreated citrus or other favored hosts. Yellow sticky traps are useful for monitoring glassy-winged sharpshooter adults and their primary parasites (*Gonatocerus* spp.). Midsummer through fall is the best time to deploy and inspect traps. Glassy-winged sharpshooters become most abundant during their second generation, and at this point they may move into avocados from nearby citrus.

If glassy-winged sharpshooter is abundant in avocados, consider removing or replacing nearby alternate hosts such as favored ornamentals and abandoned citrus trees. Because glassy-winged sharpshooters reproduce in great numbers on citrus, consult with nearby citrus growers regarding any plans to promote biological control (e.g., conserve egg parasites) or treat sharpshooters in citrus.

Biological Control. Several wasps (*Gonatocerus* spp.) have become established as parasites of glassy-winged sharpshooter eggs in California. The remains of parasitized eggs are easily recognized by the tiny, round hole at one end of the glassy-winged sharpshooter egg through which the adult parasite has emerged. The egg parasite *Gonatocerus ashmeadi* is commonly found wherever glassy-winged sharpshooter occurs in California. In southern and coastal areas of California a closely related species, *Gonatocerus morrilli*, can be very effective in the late summer, when the second generation deposits its eggs. At least two other *Gonatocerus* species (*G. fasciatus* and *G. triguttatus*) parasites also now occur in California.

EXOTIC PESTS

Fruit Flies

Exotic fruit flies (family Tephritidae) are frequently introduced into California. Species that threaten avocados have thus far been eradicated. The Mexican fruit fly (*Anastrepha ludens*) is often found in San Diego County because it is established in neighboring Mexico. Mediterranean fruit fly (*Ceratitis capitata*) and Oriental fruit fly (*Bactrocera dorsalis*) are other repeatedly detected and eradicated species that can infest avocado.

This tiny adult female *Gonatocerus triguttatus* is one of several species of egg parasite introduced to help control glassy-winged sharpshooter.

Glassy-winged sharpshooter eggs killed by parasites are easily recognized; eggs have a tiny, round hole at each egg through which an adult parasite has emerged. Glassy-winged sharpshooter nymphs leave a hard-to-see slit when they emerge. Unparasitized eggs lack any obvious exit hole.

The adult Mexican fruit fly is mostly brown and yellowish with broad wing bands. Mexican fruit flies are distinguished from similar looking species by the female's long ovipositor, which is one-half the body length or longer.

The adult Oriental fruit fly's body is about 1/3 inch (8 mm) long. It is variably colored, often brownish with black and yellow markings.

Females lay eggs in various fruit. Feeding by the maggots directly damages the fruit and introduces microorganisms that decay its flesh. Because these are quarantined pests, eradication treatments and restrictions on shipping fruit are required where fruit flies are found. Typical treatments are spraying with an insecticide combined with fly bait, release of sterile flies to prevent pest reproduction, or both methods conducted at regular intervals over several months. Fruit shipments from eradication zones may be banned or growers may be required to comply with other restrictions related to managing groves and shipping fruit.

Take steps to avoid introducing exotic pests and to assist in their eradication. Be aware of any movement out of quarantine zones and into groves; fruit flies can hitchhike in vehicles or spread in contaminated materials. Do not bring any plant material into California unless agricultural officials have inspected or approved it for importation. Supervise workers who may cross the border from Mexico. For example, consider providing lunch for picking crews and make sure they do not bring fruit from home. Consider removing alternate hosts and abandoned orchard trees, such as old citrus growing near your avocado trees.

Diaprepes Root Weevil

Diaprepes abbreviatus

Diaprepes root weevil (family Curculionidae), also called citrus root weevil or Diaprepes, occurs in Florida, Texas, and the Caribbean region. In 2005, introduced populations were found in California in more than two dozen locations in Los Angeles and Orange Counties. The extent to which Diaprepes may establish and spread and become a potentially serious pest in avocado groves in California is unknown. Make sure that you report suspected sightings of Diaprepes root weevils to agricultural officials if you see it outside of areas where it is known to occur.

Damage

Diaprepes feeds on more than 270 species of plants in 59 families. It can damage or kill citrus and many ornamentals. Larvae chew roots, sometimes girdling the root crown. Before plants die, the foliage may fade and wilt on severely damaged trees. Larval feeding injury may also make trees more susceptible to root diseases such as avocado root rot. Adult Diaprepes root weevils prefer to chew young, tender leaves from the leaf edges, causing irregular or semicircular notches. They are strong fliers, but tend to remain for life on a good host unless they are disturbed or inadvertently moved by people with infested material.

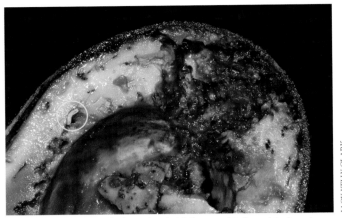

A Mediterranean fruit fly larva (circled left center) infests this decaying avocado.

Mediterranean fruit fly and other Tephritidae develop through four life stages. Displayed here (left to right) are the eggs, third-instar larva, pupa, and adult.

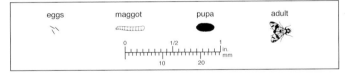

MEDITERRANEAN FRUIT FLY

Adult Diaprepes root weevils are variably colored, ranging from gray to yellow to orange and black. Report suspected Diaprepes root weevils to agricultural officials.

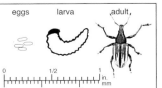

DIAPREPES ROOT WEEVIL

Description and Seasonal Development

Adult *Diaprepes abbreviatus* are colorful weevils about ⅜ to ¾ inch (10–19 mm) long. These snout beetles typically have black longitudinal striations on their back alternating with variable colors, commonly gray, orange, or yellow. Females oviposit on leaves in a gelatinous mass containing about 2 dozen to 20 dozen eggs. Each egg is oval and about 0.04 inch (1 mm) in length. Newly laid eggs are white, but they turn grayish before they hatch about 7 to 10 days after oviposition. The emerging, grublike larvae drop to the soil, where they may wander on the surface before boring underground to feed on roots or the root crown. Larvae develop through 10 or 11 instars over about 4 to 16 months before they mature to a length of about 1 inch (2.5 cm). Pupation takes place in a soil cell. Adults emerge, move to leaves, and then feed, mate, and reproduce. Adults can live for months. Development time from egg to adult ranges from about 5 months to 18 months, depending on temperature.

Diaprepes root weevil and Fuller rose beetle have similar life cycles and their immature stages look a lot alike. Adults of both species are nocturnal, hiding during the day, and their larvae live in soil, so these insects are easily overlooked. Many other invertebrates also chew avocado leaves, although many of these species do not damage avocados unless the trees are young. As always, make sure that you correctly identify the cause of any damage before you take action.

Monitoring and Management Guidelines

Detect Diaprepes root weevil by checking for chewed shoots and notched edges on succulent leaves. Shake chewed foliage over a light-colored collecting surface (such as a white sheet) to dislodge weevils, which will drop and may behave as if they were dead. Look near chewed foliage for leaves that are folded or stuck together and open glued leaves to inspect them for egg clusters. Where well-established, populations of adults emerging from soil can be monitored with a Tedders ground trap (a pyramidal stand set on infested soil to guide adults to walk up and be captured in an inverted funnel). If you know Diaprepes to be present, scrape away soil at the base of infested plants and look for weevil larvae and pupae and for chewed roots and root crowns.

If you find a weevil resembling *Diaprepes abbreviatus* in an area where this pest is not known to be established, place adults in a small jar filled with rubbing alcohol and take them to your local county agricultural commissioner for positive identification. Where they are established and eradication is not feasible, you can still practice good sanitation to greatly reduce their spread. Remove all soil and plant material from equipment, bins, picking sacks, and other items before you move them from an infested area. Control populations on favored hosts such as citrus and certain ornamentals near your avocado trees. Improve root growth and the soil environment to help trees tolerate any weevil feeding.

Appropriate irrigation and good soil drainage are especially important. In infested areas, use *Phytophthora*-resistant rootstocks to lessen any Diaprepes root weevil and *Phytophthora* spp. interactions. Entomopathogenic nematodes applied to infested soils provide some control under certain soil conditions. Certain foliar or soil-applied insecticides can also be used, but it is especially difficult to contact all immature weevils in the soil, and certain pesticides can disrupt natural enemy populations and interfere with the management of other pests. Parasitic wasps are being introduced in infested areas to help provide biological control as part of a long-term Diaprepes root weevil management program. Nurseries may be required to follow special inspection and management procedures to ensure that all plants they ship are weevil-free. For more information, consult publications such as *Diaprepes Root Weevil* (Grafton-Cardwell, Godfrey, Peña et al. 2004).

PESTS OF YOUNG TREES

Certain invertebrates damage avocado only when the trees are young. These include branch and twig borer, false chinch bug, and various leaf- and shoot-chewing pests such as brown

These young trees will need to be regularly monitored for pests that migrate from adjacent grasslands and uncultivated areas. False chinch bug, Fuller rose beetle, grasshoppers, and June beetles are invertebrates that can damage young trees when they migrate from drying weeds.

garden snail, earwigs, Fuller rose beetle, grasshoppers, and June beetles (scarabs). The ants and mealybugs discussed earlier can be common on both young and old trees, but usually they are only pests on young trees.

Fuller Rose Beetle

Pantomorus cervinus

Fuller rose beetle (family Curculionidae) is an occasional problem in young avocado plantings. It can also damage top-worked, recently grafted, or severely pruned trees that have relatively little foliage. Leaf chewing on older, well-foliated trees does not cause economically important damage.

Fuller rose beetle adults chew leaf margins, causing a ragged, notched, or serrated appearance. Most chewed leaves are on lower branches because adults cannot fly and must climb trunks and branches to reach foliage. Fuller rose beetle

Adult Fuller rose beetles chew and notch leaf edges, occasionally stunting the growth of young trees. Caterpillars, brown garden snail, earwigs, grasshoppers, and June beetles also chew avocado leaves. You must correctly diagnose the cause of damage so you can identify effective controls.

Adult Fuller rose beetles are brown to grayish snout beetles (weevils). Their hard body narrows toward the head, which has elongated mouthparts. Weevil presence can easily be overlooked as these night-feeding adults hide during the day.

usually is abundant only on avocados growing near citrus or other preferred hosts.

Adult Fuller rose beetles are brown to grayish snout beetles (weevils) about ⅜ inch (9 mm) long. All adults are females, and they lay their eggs in clusters of several dozen

The Fuller rose beetle larva (right) is grublike, without prominent legs or other appendages. The pupa (left) and larva occur in soil. Larvae feed on roots but apparently are not pests of avocado roots.

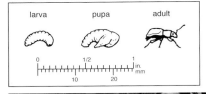

FULLER ROSE BEETLE

larva   pupa   adult

Sticky barriers around trunks can exclude insects that rarely fly or are flightless, such as ants, earwigs, and Fuller rose beetle. Apply material over wrapping to protect tender bark from potential injury. Leave a wide strip without sticky material near the bottom of wrapping. Sticky materials may drip or run when hot, promoting sunburn if materials run off tape onto tender, sunny bark.

in crevices on the tree or under loose bark. Larvae drop to the ground and feed on the roots of weeds or trees, but larval feeding does not damage the trees. They overwinter as grubs that pupate beginning in about May to July. Adults emerge during about June through September. They feed for 2 weeks before laying their first eggs. Feeding and egg-laying can continue into winter. There is one generation each year.

During late winter or early spring, apply a sticky barrier to trunks to exclude weevils if they pose a potential problem. Encircle a smooth section of trunk with a flexible wrap or tape and apply the sticky material on top to prevent direct contact with, and injury to, bark. Starting in June, inspect susceptible young or top-worked trees for leaf notching from newly emerged adults. Be aware that other pests such as caterpillars, earwigs, June beetles, grasshoppers, and snails also chew leaves. Larvae and pupae of the exotic Diaprepes root weevil resemble immatures of Fuller rose beetle, and the adults of both species chew leaves. Make sure to identify the cause of any problems before you take action: management practices vary depending on the pest.

A parasitic wasp (*Fidiobia citri*, family Platygastridae) parasitizes up to 50% of Fuller rose beetle eggs in citrus. This parasite's importance in avocado trees is unknown. Parasitized eggs darken and may persist long after unparasitized eggs have hatched. If chewing from weevils is extensive, consult the latest *Avocado: UC IPM Pest Management Guidelines: Insects and Mites* (online at www.ipm.ucdavis. edu) for management recommendations.

June beetles that sometimes damage young avocado are often orangish brown species with faint longitudinal lines on the wing covers. Adult scarabs fly in from uncultivated areas and chew foliage at night. During the day, adults burrow and hide in topsoil, reappearing the next night to feed.

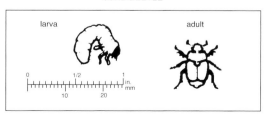

June Beetles (Scarabs)

June beetles (sometimes called Junebugs) and May beetles include various species in the family Scarabaeidae. During spring they sometimes injure young, newly planted trees, typically near uncultivated land away from the sea coast. Chewing on mature trees with a well-developed canopy is generally of no economic importance.

Adult beetles fly into avocado trees from untilled fields and brushlands during late spring or early summer. Adults chew tree foliage at night, and when they persist night after night they can completely defoliate a large number of young trees in a single grove. During the day, adults hide under litter or burrow into the upper 2 inches (5 cm) of soil, reappearing the following night to resume feeding.

Species attacking avocado include *Coenonycha testacea, Serica fimbriata,* and *S. alternata.* The *Serica* species are the more common and widely distributed. The *Serica fimbriata* adult is 0.6 inch (1.5 cm) long and velvety brown with faintly striated wing covers. *Serica alternata* and *Coenonycha testacea* adults are 0.4 inch (9 mm) long and uniformly shiny brown. Adult scarabs are robust beetles, although *C. testacea* is almost rectangular and is distinctly more narrow than either of the *Serica* species. Scarab larvae are C-shaped, cream colored, soil-dwelling grubs. June beetles go through one generation per year.

Chewing caused by June beetles can be confused with that caused by other nocturnal pests, including earwigs, Fuller

June beetle larvae are C-shaped, cream-colored grubs. Scarab grubs live in the soil and feed on roots of grasses and other resident vegetation, but are not known to damage avocado roots.

rose beetle, and snails. Beetles can be detected, and perhaps controlled to some extent in small plantings, if you deploy blacklight traps at night during late winter and spring. There is a risk, however, that the traps may attract adult beetles from outside the grove. Rather than place traps among young trees, it may be best to deploy them somewhere nearby, such as among mature trees that are near new plantings or along grove edges that border unmanaged vegetation. Consult the latest *Avocado: UC IPM Pest Management Guidelines: Insects and Mites* (online at www.ipm.ucdavis.edu) for more management recommendations.

Grasshoppers

Grasshoppers (order Orthoptera) become pests when young tree foliage is chewed by large numbers of insects migrating from unmanaged vegetation. Mature trees are not harmed by grasshopper feeding. Widespread, damaging species include the devastating grasshopper (*Melanoplus devastator*) and the valley grasshopper (*Oedaleonotus enigma*).

Grasshoppers are robust, elongate insects with winged adults that are good flyers. Commonly they are brown, gray, green, or yellowish insects with greatly enlarged hind-leg femurs adapted for jumping. Grasshoppers have relatively short antennae, and this distinguishes them from crickets, katydids, and other groups in the order Orthoptera, which have long antennae.

Most grasshopper species overwinter as eggs and have only one generation a year. Adults live and feed for 2 to 3 months, during which females typically deposit elongate pods of about 20 to 100 eggs in the topsoil of undisturbed areas. Eggs hatch when the soil warms in spring. The nymphs feed on nearly any species of nearby green plant, molting five or six times before they become adults.

Nymphs and adults readily move from place to place. Each individual typically feeds on several different plants. As vegetation is consumed or as it dries when the rainy season ends, grasshoppers migrate to more succulent plants. Adults,

sometimes in large swarms, can fly several miles a day. Nymphs readily jump, walk, or are carried by wind.

Grasshopper population levels vary from year to year. Grasshoppers become more numerous after a warm, moist spring produces abundant vegetation in uncultivated areas, favoring their survival. Conversely, parasites and bacterial, fungal, and protozoan diseases can cause grasshopper populations to crash. Many grasshoppers are eaten by arboreal predators such as birds and robber flies (family Asilidae) and soil-dwelling egg predators such as blister beetles (Meloidae).

Do not take control action based solely on the appearance of feeding damage. Caterpillars, earwigs, Fuller rose beetle, June beetles, and snails also chew leaves. Some management methods vary depending on the cause. Where abundant, grasshoppers can be observed during the day feeding openly and flying or jumping among plants.

Grasshoppers can be difficult to manage once large numbers move onto young trees. If you believe grasshoppers may become a problem, monitor for them in uncultivated areas near young trees. Before adjacent vegetation dries or is cut, consider applying an insecticide combined with bait or spraying border areas to kill grasshoppers before they migrate and start to damage your crop. Consult the latest *Avocado: UC IPM Pest Management Guidelines: Insects and Mites* (online at www.ipm.ucdavis.edu) for specific recommendations.

European Earwig
Forficula auricularia

The European earwig and related species (family Forficulidae) feed on dead and living insects, other organisms, and succulent plant parts. Earwigs occasionally damage buds and leaves on young or newly grafted trees. Earwigs can be especially problematic on trees with trunk wrappers

Earwigs sometimes chew buds and leaves on young or newly grafted trees. Trees with trunk wraps where pests can hide are especially susceptible, but earwigs rarely are abundant enough to warrant treatment.

This adult devastating grasshopper is a common species that feeds on various plants and occasionally is a pest of young avocado trees.

EUROPEAN EARWIG

adult

0   1/2   1 in.
          mm
    10   20

JACK KELLY CLARK

JACK KELLY CLARK

or cardboard guards. The damage can be difficult to distinguish from that caused by other chewing pests that hide during the day and feed at night, including brown garden snail, Fuller rose beetle, and June beetles.

If you suspect that earwigs are causing damage, lift and shake or sharply tap any trunk wrappers and look for earwigs dropping to the ground, where they quickly scurry for cover. Alternatively, use folded newspapers or burlap bags as traps, placing them near the bases of several trees with chewed foliage. Check these traps for earwigs the next morning. Cans with sardine or tunafish oil are highly attractive to earwigs, which will climb into the containers and drown, but you may have to cover liquid traps with heavy screening to prevent feeding by domestic and wild animals drawn to the fish odor. Earwigs rarely are sufficiently abundant to warrant treatment. Remove trunk wrappers where pests hide as soon as the wraps are no longer needed.

Brown Garden Snail

Cantareus aspersus (=Helix aspersa)

The brown garden snail (Phylum Mollusca, family Helicidae) sometimes damages young trees, especially following wet winters and springs. Extensive chewing of blossoms, leaves, and shoots stunts the growth of young trees. Brown garden snail is not a problem in mature groves. Thick, dry leaf mulch suppresses snail numbers and large trees tolerate any modest amount of chewing.

Description and Seasonal Development

The brown garden snail has a soft, slime-covered brown body. It can withdraw its body and its pair of antennalike sensory appendages into its shell. The hard, spiral shell will grow up to about 1¼ inches (30 mm) in diameter over the snail's lifetime. The shell is brown, tan, and yellow, and patterned in bands, flecks, and swirls.

Snails are hermaphroditic; each one contains both male and female sexual organs, but it still takes two snails to reproduce. After mating, snails drop their eggs in a scattered group in a sheltered spot on the topsoil. Mature snails lay eggs as many as six times a year, depending on climate and moisture conditions.

Snails are most active during the night and early morning when surfaces are damp. In southern California, particularly along the coast, young snails are active throughout the year. Mature snails hibernate in topsoil during cold weather.

Brown garden snail eggs (left) are about ⅕ inch (5 mm) long and spherical or teardrop-shaped with a protuberance at one end. Egg color ranges from pale milky or translucent to light or dark brown or orange.

Inspect young trees regularly for chewing damage. Look for earwigs, snails, and other pests hidden under trunk wraps and other nearby shelters.

Brown garden snails occasionally damage young avocado trees, typically after prolonged wet weather. Spittle exuded by this snail will dry to a silvery sheen, which indicates this pest is present even when snails are hiding. Fresh snail feces is on the left leaf.

Management Guidelines

Inspect young trees regularly for chewing damage. Make sure to determine the cause of damage. Caterpillars, earwigs, Fuller rose beetle, grasshoppers, and June beetles also chew tree foliage. Inspect surfaces for slimy or dry, silvery trails characteristic of snails and slugs. Look for snails hidden under trunk wraps or in other shelters near young trunks.

Modify your cultural practices, encourage biological control, and exclude snails from tree canopies to provide good control in young groves. Control weeds in young groves, as low vegetation favors snails. Retain dropped leaves and apply a coarse, organic mulch around trunks to retard snail populations and suppress root rot and weeds. Frequent microsprinkling encourages snail problems, so increase the intervals between irrigations to the extent compatible with good tree growth. Restrict snail access to canopies and expose the soil surface to drying by trimming back branches that touch the soil.

Snails and slugs are repelled by copper. Commercially available bands of copper foil can be wrapped around a tree's trunk to exclude snails. Alternatively, you can spray a slurry containing Bordeaux mixture or tribasic copper onto trunks to provide a snail barrier.

Birds and other small vertebrates, parasitic flies, and several types of predatory beetles commonly prey on snails. The predatory decollate snail (*Rumina decollata*, family Subulinidae) is widely distributed in southern California and it feeds on brown garden snail and other mollusks. Decollate snails are commercially available for introduction into areas where they are not yet present, but introductions are legal only in southern California counties. Decollate introductions are not recommended in avocado. Brown garden snail is a pest primarily when avocado trees are young, and establishment of a significant population of decollate snails usually takes several years after introduction.

Certain snail baits are available for spot applications. Molluscicides that kill brown garden snails also kill predatory decollate snails. Pesticides are rarely warranted for mollusk control in avocado. Consult the latest *Avocado: UC IPM Pest Management Guidelines: Insects and Mites* (online at www.ipm.ucdavis.edu) for specific recommendations.

Some growers apply snail barriers such as the tribasic copper sulfate slurry on this lemon tree trunk. Snails avoid crossing copper, which can be applied in various ways, such as commercially available bands of copper foil that can be wrapped around trunks.

JACK KELLY CLARK

The predatory decollate snail is about 1½ inches (38 mm) long at maturity. Its elongated shell is distinguished by its broken-off tip.

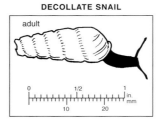

DECOLLATE SNAIL

False Chinch Bug

Nysius raphanus

False chinch bug (family Lygaeidae) occasionally causes severe injury by sucking sap from shoots and young stems. Infested shoots wither and die suddenly after attack. Only young trees are damaged, primarily in groves adjacent to uncultivated areas or grasslands away from the sea coast. Damage typically occurs in May and June.

The adult false chinch bug is mostly light to dark gray, elongate, and about ⅛ inch (3 mm) long. Females lay their eggs on host plants or in cracks in the soil. The mostly pale gray nymphs have inconspicuous reddish to brown abdominal markings. There are from four to seven generations per year. All stages can be present throughout the year.

False chinch bugs, such as this adult, suck sap, causing shoots to wither and die. Only young trees are damaged, primarily during late spring in groves adjacent to uncultivated areas away from the coast.

False chinch bugs nymphs are pale gray with brown or reddish areas on their abdomen.

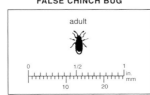

FALSE CHINCH BUG

adult

During winter and early spring, false chinch bug feeds primarily on foliage, stems, and seeds of wild grasses and cruciferous weeds. When vegetation dries or is cut, the bugs move to feed on virtually any nearby green plants, including irrigated fruit and nut trees, grains, and vegetable crops. Young avocado trees in inland plantings in border rows can be severely affected. Otherwise-healthy, mature avocado trees tolerate feeding from false chinch bug.

Monitor during late winter and early spring if young avocado trees are growing inland near unmanaged areas that are most susceptible to false chinch bug migrations. Before the winter weeds dry or are cut, look for bugs on fences and in weedy areas adjacent to the young trees. If false chinch bugs are abundant, consider treating the weedy borders to kill bugs before they can migrate. Consult the latest *Avocado: UC IPM Pest Management Guidelines: Insects and Mites* (www.ipm.ucdavis.edu) for specific recommendations.

Branch and Twig Borer

Melalgus (=Polycaon) confertus

The branch and twig borer (family Cerambycidae) is not common in avocado groves and seldom causes economic injury there. When present, borers cause a recognizable hole in branches. This is the entrance to a larval feeding

This pile of recently pruned limbs can attract wood boring pests into the grove. If the limbs were infested when cut, borers may emerge and attack nearby trees.

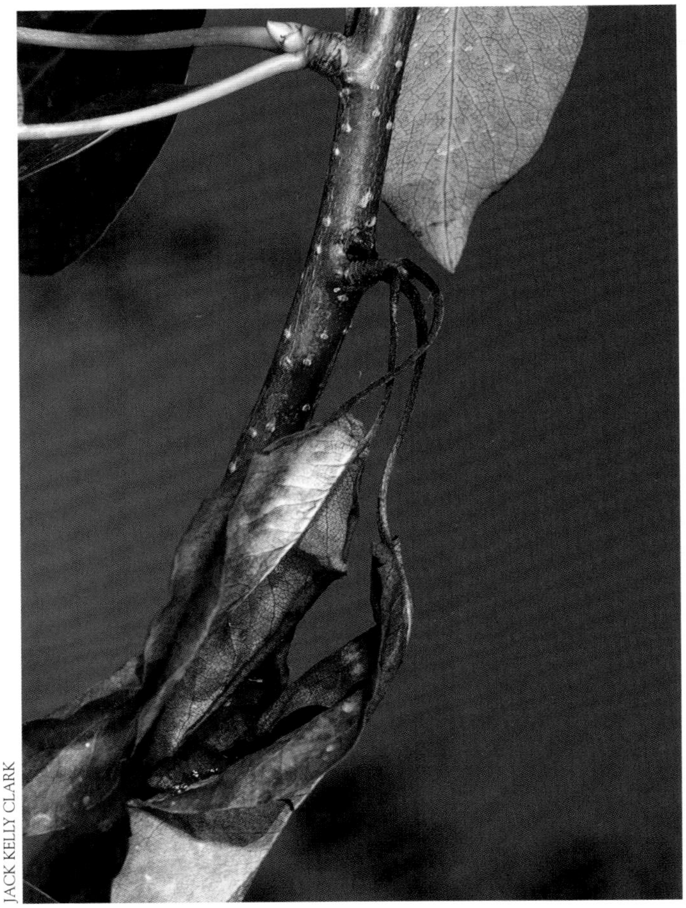

JACK KELLY CLARK

This shoot was killed by an adult branch and twig borer, which chewed a feeding pit at the crotch. This scattered shoot death is not serious, but can indicate that larvae are boring in trees, which can cause economic damage to young trees.

tunnel and often exudes sugary sap that turns white and flaky. Infested branches with tunnels are easily broken by wind.

Branch and twig borer adults are slender, brown beetles about ½ to ¾ inch (13–19 mm) long. The beetle's body is cylindrical, and its head and prothorax are narrower than its body. Females lay eggs in the wood of many different species of native and cultivated trees and shrubs. Larvae bore into the heartwood and feed there for a year or more. Pupation occurs within the tree and adults emerge in early summer. There is one generation per year.

Borers prefer injured, dying wood and stressed, slow-growing trees. Use standard measures to protect trees from sunburn and injuries, such as whitewashing exposed bark. Provide appropriate irrigation to keep the trees healthy. Remove any badly diseased or borer-infested trees and branches from the orchard. Promptly destroy brush piles. Branch and twig borers can emerge from the cut limbs of many species and attack nearby trees. Insecticide sprays do not kill borer larvae. Pesticides are not recommended for control of this insect.

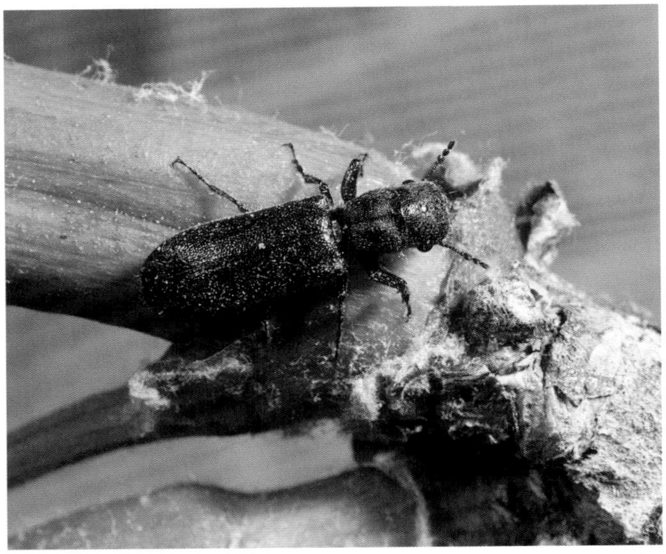

JACK KELLY CLARK

The adult branch and twig borer is a dark, cylindrical beetle with a head and prothorax narrower than its abdomen.

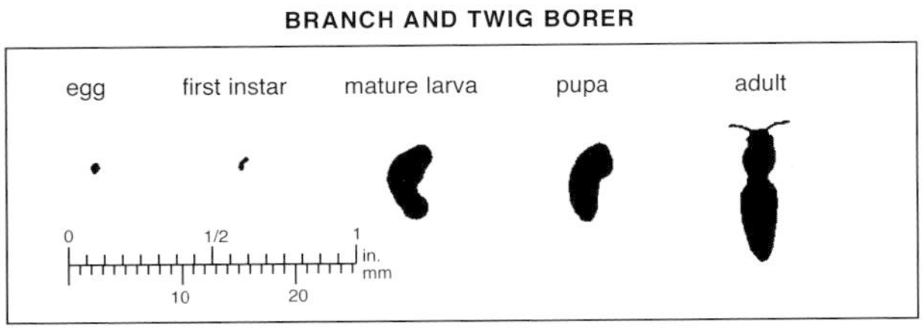

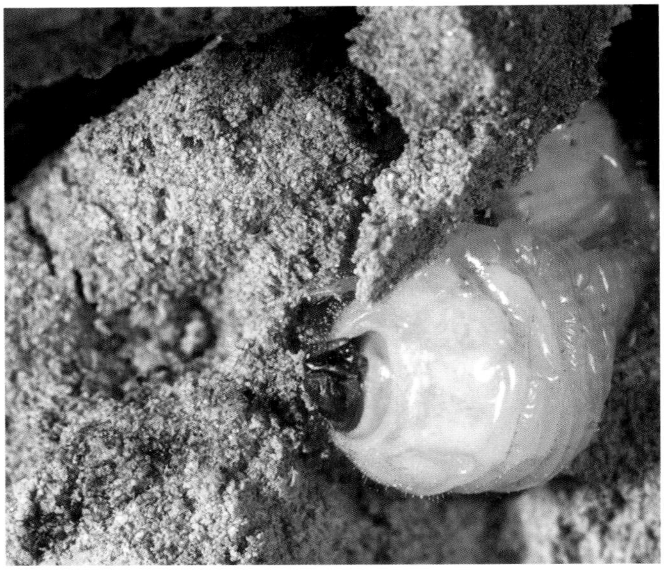

JACK KELLY CLARK

This pale larva exposed in its tunnel is the damaging stage of the branch and twig borer.

NEMATODES

Nematodes are rarely if ever a pest of avocado trees in California. Root lesion nematode (*Pratylenchus vulnus*) reportedly caused damage to avocado trees planted in Ventura County where the nematodes had become abundant on walnuts previously grown at that site. Certain nematodes are beneficial because they kill pests: for instance, entomopathogenic *Steinernema* spp. are applied to control Diaprepes root weevil.

Nematodes are microscopic roundworms. Plant parasitic species feed in or on roots, where they puncture and suck cell contents using a spearlike mouthpart (stylet). Each pest species typically feeds on a variety of different plants, both crops and weeds. Certain stages can persist in the soil even when plants are not present. Nematodes are readily spread by anything that moves contaminated soil or water or plants with infested roots.

Feeding by a large nematode population typically causes pale, stunted growth aboveground and possible shoot dieback. If you examine the roots of an infested plant, you may find very few fine feeder roots; this lack of fine roots can be caused by a high population of root lesion nematodes or other adverse soil conditions. There are no symptoms that can be used in the field to reliably diagnose root lesion nematodes as the cause of the damage. It is prudent instead to suspect other problems that are much more likely to cause these symptoms in avocados, such as canker diseases, Phytophthora root rot, and improper irrigation.

If no other causes of damage are evident and you do suspect nematode infestation, collect small roots and soil from the root zone of symptomatic trees and submit these to a laboratory for analysis. Separately collect soil and roots from apparently healthy trees and submit those samples for comparison testing. For recommended sampling methods and help in interpreting test results, contact your farm advisor or diagnostic laboratory.

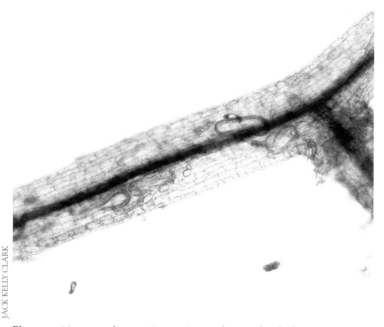

Plant parasitic nematodes are microscopic roundworms that feed in or on roots. Root lesion nematodes (*Pratylenchus* sp.) are visible inside this root. Nematodes are rarely if ever pests of avocado in California.

Weeds

Weeds can be a major problem around young avocado trees, in older groves where trees have been heavily pruned or are unhealthy and have a sparse canopy, and in nurseries. Vegetation management can also be important along grove borders and roadsides. Weeds usually are a minor concern within healthy mature groves that have thick mulch and a dense canopy that shades the ground.

Vegetation management has several goals, to:

- minimize competition with young trees
- control problem weed species
- improve infiltration of irrigation water and precipitation
- reduce soil erosion
- prevent offsite movement of potential surface water contaminants
- reduce wildfire hazards
- enhance management of other pests, including invertebrates, pathogens, and vertebrates

Weeds compete with trees for water and nutrients, primarily during the grove's early years of growth. Competition is strongest from perennial and summer annual weeds. Tall or dense weeds near trunks can increase the number of years it takes for newly planted trees to begin yielding fruit. Weeds can harbor or hide pests such as rodents and snails, increasing the potential for damage to trees.

Grove vegetation also provides many benefits, such as reducing soil erosion, improving water infiltration, and limiting movement of potential contaminants offsite into surface water. Where soil becomes waterlogged around young trees, it is beneficial to allow weeds to grow: their transpiration will reduce soil moisture and the likelihood of resultant damage from root asphyxiation. Vegetation provides alternative hosts and shelter for parasites and predators of invertebrate pests and reduces dust that can favor mite outbreaks. Cover crops on slopes and vegetative filter strips along borders and roads can be especially beneficial.

A thick layer of organic mulch will provide the best weed control in most situations. Provide trees with appropriate cultural care and good growing conditions to keep them healthy so they can develop a dense canopy to shade the soil and exclude weeds. Other methods such as applying herbicides, cultivation, and mowing are important, at least during site preparation before planting. After planting, though, avocado trees can be injured by herbicides used for weed control and by any activity that compacts or disturbs the soil. To provide young trees with a weed-free area from the trunk to just beyond the drip line, rely on methods such as mulching and hand-weeding.

Life Cycles

A plant's life cycle affects both its importance as a weed and the strategies used for its control. Weeds are grouped as annuals, biennials, or perennials based on their life cycles. An annual weed completes its life cycle of germination, growth, flowering, and seed production within 1 year. Winter annuals germinate in the fall, grow through the winter, flower in late winter and early spring, produce seed in the spring, and die by early summer. Summer annuals germinate in late winter, spring, or early summer. They produce seed in summer or fall and die in fall or early winter. Biennials complete their life cycle in 2 years. Their first year's growth is vegetative; flowering occurs in the second year. Perennials live for 2 years or more. In some perennial species, the aboveground parts die back in the winter and then regrow in spring or summer from underground structures.

Winter annuals are the least troublesome species because they grow when competition for water is less of a concern. Many winter annuals can be managed as desirable cover crops on slopes, in orchard row middles, and along borders to reduce soil erosion and runoff. Summer annuals are more problematic. They compete for moisture during the dry season and may interfere with the distribution of irrigation water.

Perennials are the most difficult weeds to control. They form extensive rhizomes, stolons, tubers, or taproots from which they regrow after aboveground parts are killed (Figure 35). Because management of perennials can require repeated cultivation and herbicide application to destroy underground structures, control established perennials before you plant the grove. Even after established weed plants are destroyed, the seeds of many species remain viable in the soil for years.

Monitoring

Identify the weed species that are present in your grove and know their likely emergence dates. Monitoring will help you select effective control methods and tell you when to take action. Monitor beginning at least 1 year before you plant the site and then at regular intervals after planting. Monitor for weeds at least twice each year, in midwinter and late spring. Additional monitoring in midsummer and late fall

Weeds can harbor vertebrates and increase the risk from wildland fires spreading into the adjacent grove. Well-managed border vegetation can minimize these problems.

This bare slope has a steeply eroded gully. Properly managed grove vegetation can provide many benefits, such as controlling soil erosion, improving water infiltration, and reducing movement of potential contaminants offsite into surface water.

Some weeds directly annoy people and reduce worker productivity. These longspine sandbur fruit cling to fur of domestic animals and attach to clothing, such as the bootlace shown here.

is desirable, especially before planting and during the first several years of grove growth, to give you a picture of the full spectrum of weed species that are present.

Keep records of when and where you monitored, what species were present, and some measure of the weeds' relative abundance so you will be able to make sound decisions on cultural and chemical controls. Information collected over several years tells you how weed populations may be changing and how effective your control operations have been. When monitoring, pay special attention to perennials. It is a good idea to draw a map of the grove and mark a copy with the monitoring date and the location of any perennials that you find. That way you can quickly return to see how well your control actions are working and know whether further control action is needed in that area. A handheld GPS (global positioning system) device is useful during monitoring: it allows you to accurately describe specific locations in the grove and then find them again on a later inspection. Figure 36 provides an example weed monitoring form.

Fall Monitoring. Fall rains stimulate weed germination and growth. If fall rains occur early (in September and early October) during months that are typically warm, weeds develop sooner, grow larger, and require earlier or more vigorous control actions. If rains begin later, after temperatures have cooled, winter annuals grow more slowly.

At sites to be planted and, at least, around young trees, monitor after the first fall rains. Look for and record the species of perennial seedlings or sprouts, winter annual seedlings, and mature summer annuals, which are easier to identify than seedlings. In planted groves, inspect the thickness and effectiveness of the mulch layer and assess whether additional controls are warranted near trunks. Check the row middles, primarily for perennial seedlings and sprouts.

Winter Monitoring. Cold, dry winters delay weed emergence. A warm, rainy winter means that winter annuals will grow large and be capable of producing many seed, and perhaps require earlier and more vigorous weed control action than during a drier winter.

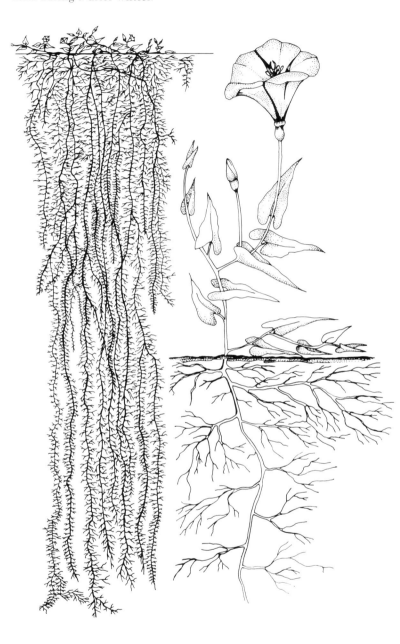

Figure 35. Field bindweed has deep rhizomes from which plants repeatedly regrow. Control established perennials before you plant the grove, since their extensive rhizomes, stolons, taproots, or tubers make control even more difficult after planting. *Redrawn from:* Klitz 1930 by Jacqueline Lamer Lockwood.

Johnsongrass rhizomes are exposed after digging in soil. Perennials are the hardest weeds to control because they form extensive rhizomes, stolons, taproots, or tubers from which plants can regrow after treatment.

Grove location			Monitoring date, season	

Treatments (method or material, dates):

			Infestation level rating	
Common name	Scientific name	Season	Near trunks or in treated areas	Borders or in untreated areas
Annual Grasses				
barley, hare or wild	*Hordeum murinum* ssp. *leporinum*	W		
oats, wild	*Avena fatua*	W		
ryegrass	*Lolium* spp.	W		
bluegrass, annual	*Poa annua*	W + S		
barnyardgrass	*Echinochloa crus-galli*	S		
crabgrasses	*Digitaria* spp.	S		
foxtails	*Setaria* spp.	S		
longspine sandbur	*Cenchrus longispinus*	S		
stinkgrasses (lovegrasses)	*Eragrostis* spp.	S		
sprangletop, bearded	*Leptochloa fascicularis*	S		
witchgrass	*Panicum capillare*	S		
Annual Broadleaves				
mallow (cheeseweed)	*Malva parviflora*	W		
mustards	*Brassica, Sinapis* spp.	W		
groundsel, common	*Senecio vulgaris*	W + S		
knotweed, common or prostrate	*Polygonum arenastrum*	W + S		
nettles	*Urtica* spp.	W + S		
sowthistle, annual	*Sonchus oleraceus*	W + S		
cocklebur	*Lolium* spp.	S		
goosefoot, nettleleaf	*Chenopodium murale*	S		
lambsquarters, common	*Chenopodium album*	S		
nightshades	*Solanum* spp.	S		
pigweeds	*Amaranthus* spp.	S		
puncturevine	*Tribulus terrestris*	S		
purslane, common	*Portulaca oleracea*	S		
starthistle, yellow	*Centaurea solstitialis*	S		
thistle, Russian	*Salsola tragus*	S		
velvetleaf	*Abutilon theophrasti*	S		

Common name	Scientific name	Season	Infestation level rating	
			Near trunks or in treated areas	Borders or in untreated areas
Perennials				
bermudagrass	*Cynodon dactylon*	**YR**		
bindweed, field	*Convolvulus arvensis*	**YR**		
cacti, prickly pear	*Opuntia* spp.	**YR**		
dallisgrass	*Paspalum dilatatum*	**YR**		
fescues	*Festuca* spp.	**YR**		
Johnsongrass	*Sorghum halepense*	**YR**		
nutsedges	*Cyperus* spp.	**YR**		
wild cucumbers	*Marah* spp.	**YR**		

Key

S summer annual

W winter annual

W + S winter or summer germination and growth

YR Year-round growth, although aboveground parts may dieback or become dormant seasonally, typically during winter

Notes:

Directions: Use this form each time that you monitor weeds:
- Inspect all groves for weeds two or more times a year, at least once each during mid-winter and late spring:
- In the blanks to right of each species that is observed, record the relative level of infestation, such as using a scale from 0 to 4 to indicate the extent of weed-covered surface area:

  0 (or left blank) = no weeds

  1 = light infestation, ≤1 to 2% of soil surface is covered with weeds

  2 = moderate, 3 to 10% weeds

  3 = heavy, 11 to 25% weeds

  4 = very heavy infestation, greater than 25% weeds.
- Record separately weeds near trunks (where management is focused) and weeds in borders or row middles (where control may be less intensive).
- If weed abundance and species differ greatly among locations within a grove, use separate forms for each area. Number each form and mark that number on a map that indicates the area corresponding to each form.
- Conduct vegetation management where warranted before seeds are produced or dispersed.

Figure 36. Weed monitoring form and directions.

Early tree growth is a critical time to monitor and manage weeds. Young trees can be stunted and the time to production increased if weeds are allowed to grow near trunks. Perennials such as this Johnsongrass can be highly competitive for moisture and nutrients.

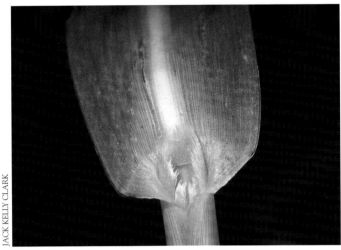

Monitoring and identifying what weed species are present, then learning their biology, helps you select effective control methods and tells you when to take action. Grasses are identified in part by the presence and appearance of their ligule, a membranous or hairy projection on the inner side of the leaf blade where it meets the sheaf or grass stem. This Johnsongrass ligule has a fringe of dense, fine hairs.

Examine bare or untreated ground in February to get an idea of the full range of winter annual species present and the vigor of their development. If weeds are abundant near trunks, consider taking actions such as flaming, hand-weeding, or postemergence herbicide applications during winter or early spring.

Spring Monitoring. Monitor in late spring, after summer annuals have germinated, when winter annuals are flowering and perennial weeds are evident. Spring monitoring a year before you plant the avocado grove will tell you what species are present at a time when you can use virtually any control method and most actions will be more effective and easier to use. After the grove is planted, spring monitoring around trunks will tell you which species have not been controlled by actions such as cover cropping, mulching, and application of preemergence herbicides.

Summer Monitoring. Monitor in midsummer for perennials, especially before planting. Monitor for perennials

This scout is monitoring weeds that should be controlled around young avocado trees. Recording what weed species are present and their relative abundance will help you select effective management actions.

Eliminate weeds, especially perennials, before planting and around young trees. To provide the best weed control, cover this weed-free soil with a thick layer of organic mulch, within the trees' drip line and somewhat beyond.

at least 2 weeks before any cultivation. If present, treat perennials with a translocated herbicide 1 to 2 weeks before cultivation to kill underground structures so the weeds will not be spread by cultivation. Monitor again a few weeks after cultivation and retreat any regrowth.

Management before and during Grove Establishment

Begin weed management before you plant the grove. Do a weed survey at least twice during the year before planting, at the times of year described above, to learn and record what species are present before you clear, cultivate, or grade the site.

Take steps to provide for proper drainage during site preparation, such as ripping through any impervious soil layers or hardpan near the surface, installing drains, and grading soil to eliminate areas of standing water. Consider planting trees on a berm or raised mound of soil.

Coordinate preplanting weed management with other site preparation activities such as amending the soil to improve pH and installing the irrigation system. Be aware that weed problems are changed or created any time that soil is disturbed. It is especially important to eliminate perennial weed species before you plant or move soil around the site.

Control Perennial Weeds. Aggressive control of perennial weeds should be the focus of your program. Repeated cultivations of dry soil during the summer before planting will expose rhizomes and stolons to drying, killing the vegetative propagules of perennials such as bermudagrass, dallisgrass, and Johnsongrass. Cultivation does not eliminate the reservoir of seeds, which will continue to germinate for a period of years. Control emerging seedlings with cover cropping, cultivating, flaming, mulching, and application of herbicides to prevent seedlings from forming perennial structures. In early fall, treat perennials with a systemic postemergent herbicide when the plants flower and, where feasible, cultivate again after 10 to 20 days to expose the root systems to further drying. Monitor the next spring and spot-treat any regrowth.

If field bindweed is present, the above program will reduce infestations, but because of its deep perennial root system (see Figure 35) field bindweed will likely persist and require ongoing control measures until a mature tree canopy heavily shades the ground. Even in mature groves, perennials such

Strip weed control uses mulch and herbicides to control weeds in the tree row. Resident vegetation in the middles is maintained here by mowing.

This annual ryegrass cover crop planted in row middles helps to control weeds and dust. Special mowers can blow clippings into the tree row, providing mulch that helps suppress weeds near trunks.

as field bindweed and wild cucumber can be common along borders and roadsides. These vinelike weeds often grow up from these sites and into trees.

Control Annuals and Seedlings. Control annual weeds and seedlings by using cover cropping, cultivation, flaming, hand-weeding, mowing, mulching, herbicide sprays, and cultural practices that promote a dense tree canopy. Where irrigation is feasible, reduce the population of annual weeds and perennial seedlings by first cultivating, then irrigating to germinate seeds near the soil surface, and then following up with a shallow cultivation to destroy the seedlings. Repeat this irrigate-wait-then-cultivate cycle at least once.

You can solarize the soil of the entire grove before planting (and, in sunny middles, after planting) to control most annuals and certain perennials for 6 months to 1 year. Solarization also suppresses certain soilborne pathogens. The practice is limited to relatively flat, cultivated, smooth soil that can be irrigated. It is less effective or requires more treatment time in cool, coastal locations. To solarize the soil, cover bare, moist, smooth ground with clear plastic for at least 4 weeks during the hottest part of the year. Consult *Soil Solarization* (Stapleton and DeVay 1995) and *Soil Solarization* (Elmore et al. 1997) in the suggested reading for more information.

Before planting you can apply a preemergence herbicide to the entire grove or to strips several feet wide where the trees will be planted. Alternatively, you can control emerged

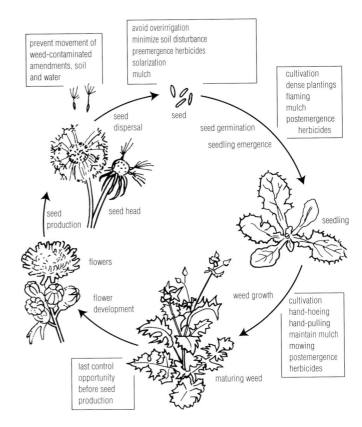

Figure 37. Methods and timing for annual weed control, illustrated here with annual sowthistle. The best times for effective weed management are before planting, before weeds emerge, and before weeds mature.

weeds using methods such as cultivation or contact herbicides, then plant your trees, and then apply a preemergence herbicide after planting. Be aware that some preemergence herbicides should not be applied before planting or close to trees because they can injure avocados. Be sure to follow label restrictions.

Apply and maintain a thick layer of organic mulch, or perhaps a weed barrier fabric, as discussed under "Mulching," later in this chapter. Hand-weed or spot-treat any weeds that grow in or near the edges of the mulch. Be careful not to injure trees with herbicides or damage roots or trunks when using tools such as flamers, hoes, machetes, mowers, and weed trimmers.

After-Planting Strategies. Focus on controlling perennials and any weeds near trunks after the avocado trees are planted. Management strategies include strip weed control, basal control, and total control.

Strip Weed Control. In strip weed control, you maintain a weed-free area in the tree row. By allowing vegetation to grow in the row middles, strip control improves soil structure, reduces erosion, and requires less effort than trying to control weeds over the entire grove floor. However, perennials can establish quickly in the tree rows because there is no compe-

In older groves, the most economical and effective weed control is thick organic mulch and healthy trees with a dense canopy that shades the soil.

tition from other weeds, so you have to check regularly for perennials and spot-treat them.

Basal Weed Control. Basal control eliminates weeds in a several square-foot area or a several foot diameter area around each tree trunk. If you allow vegetative cover in middles and in rows (some distance back from trunks), you reduce the area that requires control actions in comparison with total weed control.

Total Weed Control. Any attempt to keep the entire grove floor free of vegetation will generally require extensive use of herbicides. Even then, though, herbicides should be used in combination with other methods, especially with mulching near trunks.

Soil compaction, erosion, reduced water infiltration, contaminant movement offsite, and injury to trees can be serious problems associated with total weed control. Because no single chemical controls all weed species, combinations of herbicides or sequential treatments usually must be made. Weeds must be more carefully monitored to determine which herbicides to apply and when to apply them. Perennials such as bermudagrass and nutsedges may become established quickly in the absence of competition. Repeated applications of a single herbicide may lead to the buildup of species tolerant of or resistant to that herbicide. It is very difficult to avoid herbicide injury to avocado trees if the groves are frequently sprayed.

Management in Established Groves

As healthy trees develop a wide, dense canopy, other vegetation is increasingly shaded out of groves. Borders and roadsides become the primary locations for weeds, and so for weed control. Weeds can also be a problem around trees that are extensively pruned or are unhealthy (sparsely foliated), especially if the soil beneath them is disturbed and not thickly covered with mulch.

The choice of control method depends on many factors: the extent of canopy shading and mulching, irrigation frequency and method, need for erosion and runoff control, soil type and rockiness, spectrum of weeds present, terrain, tree spacing, and considerations such as economics and grower preference. Combine several control methods and take action at the appropriate time to obtain good control, as illustrated in Figure 37 for annual weeds.

Sanitation. Avoid introducing weeds and eliminate conditions that favor weed development. Clean all equipment after you work infested ground to keep from spreading the seeds and perennial structures of weeds. When you need to work several sites, thoroughly clean your equipment between sites and work the most heavily infested sites last.

Irrigation. Avocado trees are irrigated with sprinklers, microsprinklers, or drip irrigation. The method and frequency of irrigation strongly affect weed growth. If sunlight reaches the soil, the frequency of weed management activities will increase when water is applied over a larger surface area or when water is applied more frequently. Weed management is needed less often when trees are planted on berms since the tree row surface remains drier.

Mulch. Mulch is a layer of material that covers the soil. Mulch controls weeds by blocking sunlight to the soil and to some extent by providing a physical barrier to weed growth. Applying mulch is expensive because it requires significant labor, especially if mechanical access within the grove is limited, but mulching yields substantial benefits in improved tree health and increased fruit yields.

Weed fabrics (water-permeable polypropylene or polyester mulches) have certain advantages over organic mulches and are sometimes used around young trees. Weed fabrics suppress perennials that can grow through organic mulch. Weed fabrics are relatively easy to apply and are longer-lasting than organic mulch. However, weed fabrics are relatively expensive and the exposed dark-colored fabrics can cause soil to become hot, damaging the avocado tree's roots. Unless you cover them with material such as a coarse organic mulch, the fabrics break down within a few years from exposure to ultraviolet (UV) light.

A layer of coarse organic material about 4 to 6 inches (10–15 cm) thick provides the best weed control. Bark, greenwaste (residential yard trimmings), straw, and wood chips make good mulch. Apply organic mulch over a several-foot-wide area around newly planted avocado trees. Reapply mulch annually during the first several years of tree growth. Consider applying additional organic mulch at least once every few years throughout the trees' life, especially when leaf mulch has been blown or washed away. Avoid using mulches that may be heavily contaminated with weed propagules, such as seeds or rhizomes. Keep the layer of any applied mulch thin near trunks or just keep all mulch about 6 inches (15 cm) away from the trunk.

Avoid removing or disturbing dropped avocado leaves, which provide a natural mulch. Take steps to retain leaves under the trees: for instance, keep tree skirts low or install leaf barriers such as a moat of other organic material encircling the tree's drip line. In addition to weed control, organic mulch provides many benefits, such as reducing Phytophthora root rot, conserving soil moisture, and gradually improving soil quality. Look under "Mulch" in the third chapter, "Managing Pests in Avocado," for more discussion on the benefits of mulching.

A planted cover crop or resident vegetation that produces a large amount of biomass can be a source of mulch. Where terrain and tree spacing permit their use, specially designed mowers blow vegetation from middles into the tree rows, providing mulch that suppresses subsequent weed growth. Be sure to control any vegetation near the trunks before you blow on the mulch. Cereal cover crops such as forage oats work particularly well for this "mow-and-throw" technique because their biomass does not degrade as quickly as that of broadleaf vegetation such as vetch. Plant the cover crop in about October and mow it in late March (the exact timing for best results depends on the location and local weather conditions).

Cover Crops. Cover crops are useful in young groves and among older trees that have been extensively pruned. Vegetation along grove borders and roadsides can also be managed as a cover crop.

A cover crop consists of either the resident vegetation (the least expensive choice), one or more seeded annual species (such as commercially available self-seeding mixes), or a blend of resident and seeded vegetation. The best cover crop for your grove depends on the age of the grove, the type of irrigation system you use, grove location, soil conditions, and weather. For example, with sprinkler irrigation you have more cover crop options than with drip or microsprinkler systems.

Proper cover crop management minimizes the need for additional water applications, improves water infiltration, and reduces erosion and off-site movement of potential water contaminants. Cover crops provide habitat for beneficial insects and reduce the dusty conditions that favor mite outbreaks. Competition from desirable cover crop species helps keep weeds from building up.

Mulching within the tree drip line and good species selection reduce the need to manage the cover crop. Depending on the situation, cover crop management methods can include applying herbicides, cultivating, hand-weeding, mowing, rolling with a ring roller to injure the stems, and withholding irrigation. Keep cover crops away from tree trunks to minimize competition with trees and to reduce potential habitat for pests such as pocket gophers, snails, and voles. Cover crops may increase a grove's frost risk, especially in low-lying areas, compared to the risk with bare soil.

You can find detailed information on a wide range of cover crops in the Cover Crops Database website at www.sarep.ucdavis.edu, provided by the UC Sustainable Agriculture Research and Education Program. You can also learn more from *Covercrops for California Agriculture* (Miller et al. 1989), *Cover Cropping in Vineyards* (Ingels et al. 1998), and *Managing Cover Crops Profitably* (Sustainable Agriculture Network 1998) all in the suggested reading, and by consulting with cover crop specialists and your local Cooperative Extension farm advisor.

Hand-weeding. Cutting weeds with a portable string trimmer or mechanical weed whip, hoeing, using a machete, and hand-pulling large weeds are common practices in avocado culture. Hand-weeding controls weeds near trunks, including scattered weeds that sprout in mulch and tall weeds or problem species that grow near the edge of mulch. Avoid injuring trees by using careful technique, using trunk guards, and reapplying mulch to maintain a thick layer of organic material within the drip line.

A planted clover cover crop is grown in row middles in this grove between older trees that were severely pruned several years earlier. Clover blossoms attract bees that may improve avocado pollination and yield.

Cultivation. Cultivate the grove before planting, along borders of planted orchards, and possibly in the middles when trees are young, for instance in the spring to turn under a cover crop. Cultivate when the weeds are small, preferably less then 4 inches (10 cm) tall. Cultivation soon after emergence is especially important for perennials such as dallisgrass and Johnsongrass; once these weeds have developed more than a few leaves, they produce underground rhizomes from which they will regrow after cultivation.

Rugged terrain, rocky soil, the presence of a fixed irrigation system, and avocado's spreading shallow root system make cultivation infeasible or undesirable in many situations. Cultivating too closely cuts the trees' feeder roots, reducing water and nutrients uptake. Cultivation may spread pathogen propagules and increase the risk that pathogens will infect roots. Excessive cultivation increases dust, erosion, and soil moisture loss. Cultivation also damages the soil structure, reducing its capacity for water infiltration.

Cultivation can spread perennial weeds. When combined with applications of translocated herbicides, though, cultivation can control some established perennials as described under "Control Perennial Weeds," earlier in this chapter.

Mowing. Mowing weeds offers several advantages over cultivated or bare soil: mowing reduces erosion and allows the roots of cover crops or resident vegetation to maintain good water penetration into soil. During dry weather, dusty conditions are less severe. Mowing equipment is less expensive and easier to operate than cultivators. The equipment is lighter, so it causes less soil compaction. Special mowers can be used in the tree row to mow weeds around trunks or to blow cuttings from the middles into the tree row for mulch.

Repeated mowing promotes a shift to species that tolerate mowing, especially grasses. When mowed, healthy cover crops are more resistant to invasions of new weeds than is resident vegetation.

Flaming. Weeds can be controlled with specially designed flamers, most using propane. Other equipment includes hot water or steam applicators and infrared devices that contain heating elements without an open flame. Flamers can be handheld or mounted on a hand cart or tractor. Mechanized flamers have multiple burners, while small devices have a single flame source.

Fire is a serious hazard when flaming weeds. Only an experienced operator with demonstrated skill and good judgment should be allowed to flame weeds. Wet conditions during the rainy season or after a thorough irrigation, when surfaces are moist and humidity is high, can be good times to flame.

Work in early morning or late evening when winds are lower and an open flame is more visible. Move the flamer slowly through the grove or briefly touch the basal stem area with the tip of a flame. Do not flame weeds to the point that they char and burn; it only takes a brief contact with high temperatures to disrupt the plants' cells. Proper flaming technique should not create smoldering vegetation or air pollution.

Take care to avoid starting a fire. Use good judgment to identify hazardous situations where flaming should be avoided. Be especially cautious around dry vegetation, mulch, and leaf litter. Do not use flames in dry areas or during the dry season where fire is a hazard. Keep fire suppression equipment—such as a fire extinguisher, shovel, and water—handy in case of accidents. Keep flamers away from unguarded trunks.

The advantages of flaming include its broad spectrum of broadleaf weed control, relatively low cost (depending on fuel and labor costs), and lack of chemical residue. One good target for flaming is winter weeds that germinate after wet weather, after the end of the wildland fire season. Disadvantages of flaming include its lack of residual control, its poor control results with some grasses and perennials, the critical timing that is requires to ensure adequate control, the

JACK KELLY CLARK

Pigweed (*Amaranthus* sp.) and velvetleaf *(Abutilon theophrasti)* before (bottom right) and after flaming (top left). Soon after flaming for weed control, plants may wilt (as shown here) or change color, or they may appear unaffected. Only brief contact with high temperatures is needed to cause plants to die within a few days. Do not flame weeds so long that they smoulder, char, or burn. Use good judgment to identify fire hazard situations in which flaming should be avoided.

The best possible weed control is a thick layer of organic mulch and a weed-free area within the tree's drip line.

hazards associated with handling pressurized flammable gas, and the potential for uncontrolled fire.

Flame weeds while they are less than about 2 inches (5 cm) tall. Broadleaved seedlings are most sensitive to flaming. Perennials and grasses are less susceptible, and repeated flaming leads to perennial and grass domination of the vegetation unless you also use other controls.

Determine the correct working pace or travel speed by checking weeds after you flame a test area. Weeds are being killed if gentle pressure on a leaf between your thumb and index finger creates a water-soaked appearance, indicating that cell membranes have ruptured. Plants may wilt or change color, or they may appear unaffected just after flaming. Even if no change in the weeds is immediately evident, proper flaming will cause plants to yellow and die within several days.

Herbicides. Postemergence herbicides are applied after weed emergence. Preemergence herbicides are applied before weeds emerge, for instance as a winter application to minimize the number of perennial seedlings and summer annuals. Growers sometimes apply a preemergence herbicide and a nonselective postemergence herbicide in combination if some weeds have already emerged.

When using herbicides, choose materials and rates according to the weed species you need to control, your soil type, your irrigation method, and the age of your grove. Combinations of materials or sequential treatments with different materials are often needed, since no single herbicide controls all weed species. The relative susceptibility of common weed species to certain herbicides can be found in the *Avocado: UC IPM Pest Management Guidelines: Weeds* (online at www.ipm.ucdavis.edu). For current registration status of herbicides, check with your county agricultural commissioner. ALWAYS READ AND FOLLOW LABEL DIRECTIONS CAREFULLY. Make sure your spray equipment is calibrated accurately and functioning properly as discussed in *The Safe and Effective Use of Pesticides* (O'Connor-Marer 2000), listed in the suggested reading.

Phytotoxicity. Certain herbicides can severely injure avocado trees. Nonselective translocated (systemic) herbicides and certain preemergents can cause phytotoxicity by contacting trees' shallow surface roots. Avoid applying most herbicides if there is a chance they may contact avocado roots. Make sure not to spray postemergence herbicides onto cracked bark, green wood, leaves, or shoots. Do not use a material around trees or before planting unless you are confident that no phytotoxicity will occur. Use herbicides primarily before planting, in areas away from trees, and for control of perennials.

Herbicide-Resistant Weeds. Tolerance and resistance prevent some herbicides from controlling certain weeds. Tolerant plant species have a natural lack of susceptibility to certain herbicides. Tolerance can be desirable when it allows you to use selective herbicides, such as those that control grasses but do not damage avocado trees or other broadleaves.

Resistance is evident when a pest population is no longer controlled by pesticides that previously provided control, as illustrated in Figure 11 in the third chapter, "Managing Pests in Avocado." After a weed population is repeatedly exposed to the same herbicide or group of herbicides with the same mode of action, the weed population may become dominated by plant biotypes that are resistant to that class of herbicide. For example, rigid ryegrass (*Lolium rigidum*) that is resistant to glyphosate (Roundup) has developed in California where glyphosate has been repeatedly applied.

Minimize the development of resistance by using cultivation, mulch, and hand-weeding as alternatives to herbicide applications. Avoid repeated application of a single herbicide or of herbicides with the same mode of action. Scout growing areas and note weed escapees and species shifts over time. Avoid spreading weed seeds and propagules from infested areas: for example, control runoff water and clean equipment before you move it to another site.

Postemergence Herbicides. Foliar-applied or postemergence herbicides are sprayed on the leaves of weeds that have emerged. They are classified as *contact* herbicides if they kill only the plant parts that are sprayed. Contact herbicides are most effective on seedlings and young weeds.

Translocated or *systemic* herbicides such as glyphosate are transported via the plant's vascular system from contacted foliage to other parts of the plant, including roots and rhizomes. They are more effective on actively growing weeds and are the most effective materials for control of perennials (Figure 38). However, in comparison with contact herbicides, translocated herbicides pose a greater risk of phytotoxicity to avocado.

Special sprayers have been designed to apply postemergence herbicides only where they detect the presence of weed foliage. Often called "smart sprayers," they reduce the amount of herbicide applied by 40 to 80% when weed populations are low. They are especially useful for strip weed control and spot-treating perennial weeds such as bermudagrass, dallisgrass, field bindweed, and nutsedges.

Preemergence Herbicides. Preemergence herbicides kill susceptible plants as they germinate. Most are effective only against germinating seeds. To be effective, the chemical must be moved into about the upper 2 inches (5 cm) of soil by rain, light irrigation of about ½ inch (1 cm), or cultivation. Some preemergence herbicides must be moved into the soil immediately, while others may remain on the surface for a short time before incorporation. Certain materials lose effectiveness if the soil is cultivated after application. Follow label directions regarding incorporation.

Efficacy typically persists for 2 to 5 months after application, but sometimes it lasts for more than a year. Persistence is affected by application rate, soil conditions,

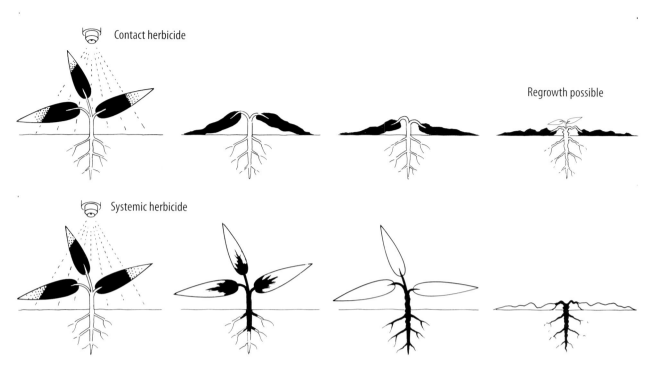

Figure 38. Contact herbicides usually kill only those green plant parts on which spray is deposited. Thorough coverage is vital for good control, and even then certain weeds (e.g., established perennials) may regrow from underground parts. Systemic herbicides are taken up by green plant tissue and are transported to the growing tips of roots and shoots. Because they are translocated, systemic herbicides more effectively control perennial weeds, as illustrated in the bottom figure for the herbicide that moves within the plant (black color) from sprayed leaves to roots. *Adapted from:* David Kidd in Marer 1991.

amount of rainfall or frequency of irrigation, and whether the soil is disturbed. For example, herbicide activity dissipates more quickly during prolonged wet weather and in areas that remain wet, such as around low-volume drip emitters.

Lower-than-labeled rates may be effective if the weed spectrum in the grove is particularly sensitive to herbicides, in areas with annual rainfall of less than 11 inches (28 cm), and where trees are planted on berms, because there is less leaching and breakdown from moisture. Consider avoiding preemergence herbicides for 1 or 2 years before you plant or replant as a way to minimize the possibility that residues will injure the new trees.

Chemical Mowing. You can use a low rate of herbicide to retard the growth of weeds without killing them (chemical mowing), thus maintaining a ground cover. The application rates and timing for chemical mowing (perhaps two or three times per season) depend on the vegetation present, its stage of growth, and growing conditions. Young winter annuals can be controlled with very low rates applied in about January or February. Summer annuals and older winter annuals are harder to control. Plants are harder to control in spring or summer. When stressed by periods of drought, weeds require even higher herbicide rates.

Repeated use of low rates of an herbicide can cause a shift in the weed population; careful monitoring is essential. Perennials or annuals that are not controlled by chemical mowing may quickly take over because of the reduced competition; spot-treat these before they become dominant and extremely difficult to manage. Chemical mowing may select for herbicide-resistant plants. Use alternate strategies within a season, between seasons, or both.

Identifying Major Weed Species

Flowers are used to reliably identify the species of most plants, but weeds should be identified and controlled before they flower. Seedling appearance and the shape and arrangement of vegetative parts such as leaves, stems, and veins are used to identify weeds (Figure 39).

Seasonal growth patterns also help identify the species of a weed. Weeds are classified as annuals, biennials, or perennials based on their growth habit. Certain annuals such as annual bluegrass and mustards typically germinate in the fall or early winter, so they are called "winter annuals." Barnyardgrass and crabgrasses germinate in the spring or early summer, so they are "summer annuals."

Weeds are also classified as broadleaves, grasses, or sedges based on botanical characteristics. Broadleaf seedlings

Herbicides are used here for strip weed control near trunks, with resident vegetation allowed to grow in row middles. Grasses are encouraged to grow and outcompete broadleaves near trunks. Selective herbicides that control grasses but do not damage avocado can then be applied near trees in spring.

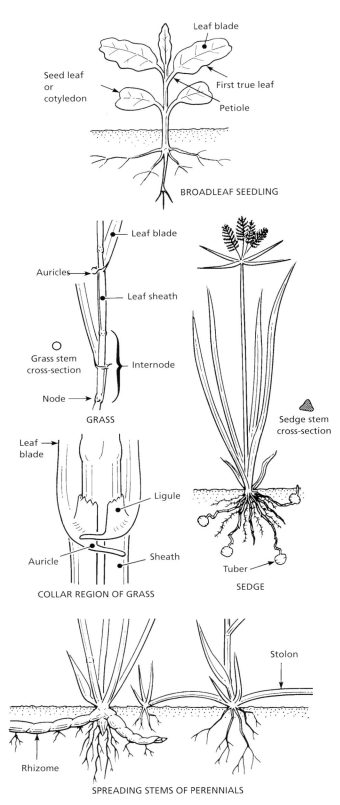

Figure 39. Vegetative parts of weeds and terms used in identification. Note that not all sedges have tubers (sometimes called nutlets). For the most effective control, the species should be identified and control action taken before the weeds mature beyond the seedling stage.

have two seed leaves (cotyledons). The seed leaves of each broadleaf species have a characteristic shape, texture, and color, that make the seedlings relatively easy to identify. Seed leaves (and sometimes also the first true leaves) are different from true leaves that form later. Most broadleaf weeds have true leaves with netlike veins, and most develop showy flowers as they mature.

Grass leaves are longer than they are wide and have parallel veins. Specific grass seedlings are more difficult to identify than broadleaves because the seed leaves of different species are similar and grass seed leaves differ little from true leaves. Characteristics of the collar region (where the leaf blade joins the leaf sheath) help to distinguish grasses. Perennial grasses may be distinguished by the appearance of their rhizomes or stolons.

Grass and sedge seedlings have one seed leaf. Grasses and sedges resemble one another but in many ways they are very different. The true leaves of grasses alternate from one side of the stem to the other; sedge leaves are joined to the stem in groups of three. Grass stems are hollow, rounded, and have nodes (joints) that are hard and closed. Sedge species have three-sided, solid stems that are triangular in cross-section. The most important sedges are yellow and purple nutsedge, perennials that form characteristic tubers on their rhizomes.

Examples of weeds found in avocado groves are listed in Figure 36 and discussed below. Photographs and descrip-tions of all of the weeds mentioned in this chapter can be found in the weed photo gallery at the UC IPM Web site (www.ipm.ucdavis.edu) and in publications such as *Weeds of California* (Robbins, Bellue, and Ball 1970), *Weeds of California and Other Western States* (DiTomaso and Healy 2007), and *Weeds of the West* (Whitson et al. 1991) listed in the suggested reading.

PERENNIAL GRASSES

Bermudagrass and dallisgrass (discussed below), along with fescues and Johnsongrass (pictured early in this chapter), are common perennial grasses (family Poaceae or Gramineae) in avocado groves. Dallisgrass, fescues, and Johnsongrass cause problems most often in low-lying, wet areas of groves. Bermudagrass tolerates drought.

Destroy established perennial grasses by combining repeated dry cultivations and systemic herbicide applications as discussed early in this chapter under "Control Perennial Weeds." The reservoir of seeds will continue to germinate for years. Seed (and rhizomes and stolons) in the upper few inches of the soil can be controlled with solarization. After you plant the grove, you can use cover cropping, very shallow cultivation, flaming, mulching, and herbicide applications to prevent seedlings from forming perennial structures.

Bermudagrass

Cynodon dactylon

Bermudagrass is a drought-tolerant perennial grass and thrives in hot, sunny locations. It is less aggressive in dense shade. In cold locations it becomes dormant and turns brown during the winter.

Bermudagrass reproduces from rhizomes, stolons, and seed. Depending on the situation, complete control usually requires some combination of methods. For more informa-tion, consult *Avocado: UC IPM Pest Management Guidelines: Weeds* or *Bermudagrass Pest Notes* (Elmore and Cudney 2002), both available online at www.ipm.ucdavis.edu.

JACK KELLY CLARK

A. Bermudagrass seedhead.

B. Bermudagrass.

A. Bermudagrass seedheads consist of three to seven slender flower spikes that arise from a single point at the tip of the stem. As with most perennials, if not eliminated before planting this weed can be difficult to control around trees.

B. Bermudagrass forms dense mats of spreading, branching stolons. The plants have short leaves and erect stems 4 to 18 inches (10–46 cm) tall. There is a papery sheath around the stolon at the base of each leaf (not shown here).

C. Dallisgrass rhizomes.

Dallisgrass

Paspalum dilatatum

Dallisgrass is a bunchgrass that is highly competitive with trees for water. Mature plants typically form loose clumps about 1 to 4 feet (30–120 cm) tall. Dallisgrass reproduces from seed and very short rhizomes. Seed are easily transported in water or by machinery. Dallisgrass can become dominant in mowed groundcovers because mowing stimulates seed production. If dallisgrass becomes established in a young grove, repeated applications of a translocated herbicide may be needed to provide control.

C.   Dallisgrass rhizomes are very short, with shortened internodes that resemble concentric rings. The leaf sheath is somewhat flattened; at the base, it is hairy and often tinged red. The ligule *(not shown here)* is firm and membranous with a few spreading hairs at the margins and no auricles.

D.   Dallisgrass flower heads consist of three to six spikes that arise from different points along the flower stem.

SUMMER ANNUAL GRASSES

Barnyardgrass, crabgrasses, and longspine sandbur (discussed below), along with bearded sprangletop, foxtails, stinkgrasses or lovegrasses, and witchgrass are common summer annual grasses (family Poaceae) that can infest avocado groves. They should be controlled near young trunks because their dry-season growth competes aggressively for moisture. Effective control methods include cover cropping, cultivation, flaming, hand-weeding, mowing, mulching, herbicide treatment, and the use of cultural practices that maintain and promote a dense tree canopy.

D. Dallisgrass flower heads.

Barnyardgrass

Echinochloa crus-galli

Barnyardgrass grows in dense, tall or spreading clumps. Several varieties that differ in growth habit and floral appearance occur in California. The stout plants range from 6 inches to 6 feet (15–180 cm) tall. Plants often root at the lower nodes. Spikes at the low end of the flower head are spaced apart; those at the top are crowded together. Because barnyardgrass produces huge quantities of seed, in sunny locations it can be difficult to control without the use of herbicides.

E. Barnyardgrass is the only common summer annual grass that has neither a ligule nor auricles where the leaf blade meets the stem. This characteristic helps distinguish barnyardgrass from young Johnsongrass (a perennial).

E. Barnyardgrass ligule.

Crabgrasses

Digitaria spp.

Large crabgrass *(Digitaria sanguinalis)*, also called hairy crabgrass, is a low-growing annual. It has a papery ligule but no auricles, and there are small tufts of hairs where the leaf blade meets the sheath. Smooth crabgrass *(D. ischaemum)* is a smaller species without hairs and it is less commonly a problem. You have to correctly distinguish crabgrass from other species so you can identify the most effective form of management. For example, large crabgrass plants root deeply at the nodes, giving them the appearance of stolons, and this may cause you to confuse crabgrass with perennials such as bermudagrass. Established crabgrass plants are difficult to remove, but most preemergence herbicides are highly effective at preventing crabgrass seed germination. For more information, consult *Avocado: UC IPM Pest Management Guidelines: Weeds* or *Crabgrass Pest Notes* (Elmore 2002), both available online at www.ipm.ucdavis.edu.

F. Large crabgrass seedlings have rather wide leaves that are covered with coarse hairs. Leaves unroll as they grow out of the center. Crabgrass is a summer annual, but new seedlings can appear as early as February in warmer areas of California.

G. Large crabgrass flower stalks arise in a group near the stem tip, but often there are additional flower spikes branching from beneath the tip as shown here. Flower heads branching from multiple points on the stalk distinguish crabgrass from bermudagrass flower branches that always arise from a single terminal point. Also, bermudagrass spreads primarily by rhizomes and stolons, which are lacking in crabgrass.

F. Large crabgrass seedling.

G. Large crabgrass flower heads.

H. Longspine sandbur fruit.

Longspine Sandbur

Cenchrus longispinus

Longspine sandbur seedlings closely resemble those of barn-yardgrass. Seedling leaves are flattened and have a purplish tinge at the bottom. The most distinctive seedling character-istic is the bur from which the young plant emerges. You can find this bur by digging carefully around the roots.

H. Longspine sandbur flowers produce spiny, yellowish green fruit. As many as 40 fruit or burs may occur in a flower spike that is partially enclosed by a leaf sheath. When dry, these burs cling to clothing or fur that brushes against them. The burs contain seeds that start new infestations wherever they drop.

I. Mature longspine sandbur plants are branched, usually spreading in mats. This summer annual grass favors sandy or well-drained soil in young groves and along borders.

I. Longspine sandbur.

WINTER ANNUAL GRASSES

Annual bluegrass, bromes, and wild oats (discussed below), and ryegrasses and hare barley or wild barley are common winter annual grasses (family Poaceae). They can be abundant in borders and nurseries and around young trees. They are generally only a minor problem, compared to perennials and summer annuals.

Annual Bluegrass

Poa annua

Annual bluegrass is a winter annual in warm inland locations, but it can grow at any time of year in irrigated coastal areas of California. Although it is a weed if it grows in situations such as nurseries, annual bluegrass can be a desirable ground cover in groves away from the coast. It is low-growing and dies out where temperatures become warm in early summer. Although it should be kept back from trunks, at inland sites it is not very competitive with trees for irrigation water. Mature plants grow as dense, low-spreading tufts 3 to 12 inches (7.6–30 cm) tall. Plants often root at the lower nodes. For more information, consult *Avocado: UC IPM Pest Management Guidelines: Weeds* or *Annual Bluegrass Pest Notes* (Cudney, Elmore, and Gibeault 2003), both available online at www.ipm.ucdavis.edu.

J. Annual bluegrass seedling.

J. Annual bluegrass can be distinguished from other grasses by the blunt leaf tip that is shaped like the bow of a boat on both the seedling (*shown here*) and mature plant. The leaf blade is often crinkled at midsection. Usually a winter annual, this grass is relatively short, at most 12 inches (30 cm) or less tall, at maturity.

Bromes

Bromus spp.

Ripgut brome (*Bromus diandrus*), rescuegrass (*B. catharticus*), and soft brome (*B. hordeaceus*), also called soft chess, are winter annuals that grow well in open, moist areas. They can become a problem around young trees, for instance when they germinate in mulch near trunks.

K. Soft brome is a common winter annual in open, disturbed areas. Mature plants are distinguished from many other grasses by the dense, soft hairs on the sheaths (where the leaf blade base wraps around the stem).

Wild Oat

Avena fatua

Wild oat grows 1 to 4 feet (30–120 cm) tall at maturity. Its seedlings can be distinguished from those of most other grasses by their large seed coat, which usually remains attached for a long time. Wild oat becomes a problem around young trunks where it provides shelter for voles or creates a fire hazard if left to grow tall and then dry out. This weed is difficult to control because it may emerge several times during the year and the large seed can germinate deep in the soil, beyond the effective zone for most preemergence herbicides. Maintain a thick mulch near trunks to minimize germination.

K. Soft brome.

L.   Mature wild oat plants are recognized by their widely spaced, downward hanging spikelets (flowers or seed coats). Where the blade meets the grass stem (the collar region), wild oat has a tall, pointed ligule with toothed margins and no auricles *(not shown here)*.

SEDGES

Sedges resemble grasses. They can be distinguished by characteristics such as sedge's three-sided stem, which is triangular in cross-section, and other differences summarized in Figure 39 and under "Identifying Major Weed Species," earlier in this chapter.

Nutsedges

Cyperus spp.

Yellow nutsedge *(Cyperus esculentus)* is the most common weedy nutsedge (family Cyperaceae) in California. Purple nutsedge *(C. rotundus)* can be prevalent at wetter sites. Nutsedges, sometimes called nutgrasses, reproduce from tubers (incorrectly called "nutlets") that form on their rhizomes. The tubers are spread easily by cultivation and when moving infested soil.

Nutsedges may become troublesome in groves where herbicides are used for total weed control. Most chemicals do not control nutsedges well, and in the absence of competition nutsedges quickly spread. To prevent the formation of tubers, kill the young plants before they reach the 5-leaf stage. See *Avocado: UC IPM Pest Management Guidelines: Weeds* or *Nutsedge Pest Notes* (Wilen, McGiffen, and Elmore 2003), both online at www.ipm.ucdavis.edu, for more information.

M.   This yellow nutsedge seedling resembles grass, but nutsedge leaves are thicker and stiffer than most grasses. Nutsedge leaves are V-shaped in cross-section and grow from the base in sets of three; grass leaves are opposite in sets of two.

N.   Mature nutsedge plants are 1 to 2 feet (30–60 cm) tall with a flower head at the tip of each stem. Yellow nutsedge seed are rarely viable. Flowering stems are triangular in cross-section. This yellow nutsedge has three long, leaflike bracts at the base of each flower head. These bracts are short in purple nutsedge.

O.   The tubers of this yellow nutsedge are produced singly on rhizomes. The tubers have a pleasant nutlike flavor. Tubers of purple nutsedge *(not shown here)* are produced in chains; several tubers occur on a single rhizome and they have a bitter flavor. Rhizomes and tubers can develop into new plants and are the main means for dissemination of nutsedges.

L. Wild oat seedhead.

M. Yellow nutsedge seedling.

N. Yellow nutsedge.

O. Yellow nutsedge tubers.

P. Purple nutsedge tubers.

Q. Field bindweed seedling.

R. Field bindweed.

P.   In contrast with the single tuber per rhizome on yellow nutsedge, these purple nutsedge tubers are linked together in chains on rhizomes. Each purple nutsedge tuber is oblong, rough, and scaly.

PERENNIAL BROADLEAVES

Field bindweed, prickly pear cacti, and wild cucumbers are among the perennials that infest avocado.

Field Bindweed

Convolvulus arvensis

Field bindweed (family Convolvulaceae), also called perennial morningglory, competes with trees for moisture and nutrients during summer months. Established infestations are nearly impossible to eradicate because plants produce perennial roots (see Figure 35) and seed can remain dormant for as long as 60 years. Take care not to transport viable rootstock fragments on field equipment. Kill seedlings before they develop five leaves. Treating plants with a translocated herbicide, then cultivating, and then treating regrowth when flowers begin to form will reduce infestations substantially if you repeat the entire program over a period of years. See *Avocado: UC IPM Pest Management Guidelines: Weeds* or *Field Bindweed Pest Notes* (Elmore and Cudney 2003), both available online at www.ipm.ucdavis.edu, for more information.

Q.   Field bindweed seed leaves are nearly square with an indented tip (bottom right). The variable true leaves often resemble blunt-tipped arrowheads. Leaves are attached to flattened petioles that are grooved on the upper surface. The presence of seed leaves demonstrates that this plant germinated from seed rather than developing from a rhizome.

R.   Field bindweed has slender stems 3 feet (90 cm) or more long that trail along the ground or climb up plants. Flowers are funnel- or trumpet-shaped and occur singly on slender stalks in leaf axils. The light red, purplish, or white flowers close each afternoon and reopen the next morning.

Prickly Pear

Opuntia spp.

Prickly pears are low-growing, fleshy perennials that spread by seeds or stems. Also called cholla (pronounced "choya"), they typically occur in dry, sandy soils. Many species grow throughout arid areas of the western United States.

S.   Prickly pear cacti can become undesirable weeds around groves, sometimes after spreading from where they were planted as living fences to exclude people and animals. Plants consist primarily of thick, succulent, flat to cylindrical, segmented stems covered with sharp spines.

S. Prickly pear cactus.

Wild Cucumber

Marah spp.

Several species of wild cucumber (family Cucurbitaceae) are native to California and are not considered weedy in natural systems. In California avocado groves, cucamonga manroot (*Marah macrocarpus*) is probably the most common *Marah* species. These perennial vines develop a large tuber, and that makes established plants difficult to eliminate. Wild cucumber vines have clinging tendrils. Stems climb up and entwine young trees and the sides of mature trees that are exposed along grove edges and roadsides. Cultivation, flaming, hand-weeding, or translocated herbicides are effective for control, but they must be repeated to kill regrowth until the plants exhaust the energy stored in their tubers.

T.   Wild cucumber (*Marah macrocarpus*) flowers and stems with tendrils are growing in this avocado. Wild cucumber is named for the greenish, round to oblong fruit capsules that contain seed. Depending on maturity and species, these fruit are 1-⅕ to 8 inches (3–20 cm) long and their surface is slightly to very spiny.

T. Wild cucumber.

SUMMER ANNUAL BROADLEAVES

Common summer annual broadleaves include lambsquarters, knotweed, nettle-leaved goosefoot, pigweed, purslane, Russian thistle, and velvetleaf. These are described and illustrated in the UC IPM weed photo gallery (online at www. ipm.ucdavis.edu) and in publications listed under "Weeds" in the suggested reading. Cocklebur, nightshades, and puncturevine are examples of summer annual broadleaves, and are discussed below.

Whenever possible, control summer annual weeds before they produce seed. Soil solarization (before planting) and cover cropping, cultivating, flaming, hand-weeding, and mulching will control seedlings of most species. With most species, preemergent herbicide applications can prevent germination and postemergent herbicides can be used to control young plants. Infestations of some species, including mature nightshades and puncturevine, can be relatively difficult to control with herbicides.

Common Cocklebur

Xanthium strumarium

Common cocklebur (family Asteraceae) infests moist, open areas. When it grows near trunks, it competes with trees. Cocklebur produces fruit that stick to clothing and annoy workers. Each bur contains two seeds: one is capable of germinating immediately, while the other usually germinates the next year. The bur may remain attached to the base of the seedling that sprouts from it, and this can help you identify the weed when you pull it. Mature plants have thick, highly branched, fleshy stems with purple or black spots.

U. A common cocklebur's cotyledons are bright green, shiny on the upper surface, pointed, and about 6 times longer than they are wide. True leaves are notched on the margins and taper to the tip. This seedling is at the four-leaf stage.

V. Cocklebur leaves are lobed, somewhat triangular, and coarsely toothed. The plant produces clusters of green male flowers at the top. Female flowers occur in burs on short stalks where the leaf axils meet the stem. Burs are oval-shaped with a pair of beak-like hooks.

V. Common cocklebur.

U. Common cocklebur seedling.

Nightshades

Solanum spp.

Black nightshade (*Solanum nigrum*) and hairy nightshade (*physalifolium* =*S. sarrachoides*) are the most bothersome of the nightshade species (family Solanaceae). A single mature nightshade plant can produce thousands of seedlings in subsequent seasons. The flowers develop in clusters, each blossom about ¼ to ⅜ inch (6–9 mm) wide, with five white or pale blue petals and a yellow center. Plants grow up to 2 feet (60 cm) tall.

W.   Most weedy nightshade species have seedlings with elongate-oval and pointed seed leaves. The first true leaves of hairy nightshade have wavy edges and prominent veins. These true leaves have numerous fine, short hairs, especially along the underside of the main vein. The first true leaves of black nightshade (*not shown here*) are spade-shaped with smooth edges. With black nightshade, leaves, petioles, and stems have some hairs, but are not densely hairy or sticky.

X.   These black nightshade berries turned from green to black at maturity and the calyx covers only a small part of the fruit surface. With hairy nightshade (*not shown here*), berries are green or yellowish brown when mature, but never black, and the calyx covers the entire upper surface of the fruit.

X. Black nightshade.

Puncturevine

Tribulus terrestris

Puncturevine (family Zygophyllaceae) produces hard, spiny fruit that can penetrate tires and are easily spread on shoes or tires. Plants are prostrate in open areas but somewhat erect in dense vegetation. Single yellow flowers arise from leaf axils.

Control puncturevine as seedlings, when most control methods are effective. Be aware, though, that the seed can germinate beyond the effective depth of some preemergence herbicides. Mature plants are much harder to control than seedlings. A seed weevil and stem weevil generally keep puncturevine populations under control in undisturbed and unirrigated areas. If you cut inside the plants, you may be able to see the pale weevil larvae or pupae in plant crowns, stems, and seed capsules. Weevils are not effective if sites are cultivated or if puncturevine is irrigated, and weevil populations are greatly reduced for several years after freezing weather. See *Puncturevine Pest Notes* (Wilen 2006) online at www.ipm.ucdavis.edu, for more information.

W. Hairy nightshade seedling.

Y. Puncturevine seedling.

AA. Puncturevine fruit.

Z. Puncturevine fruit.

Y. Puncturevine seed leaves are thick, oblong, and brittle. They are grayish below and green above, with a groove along the prominent midvein. True leaves have 8 to 12 leaflets, and the first true leaves are covered with soft hairs.

Z. These green puncturevine fruit at maturity break into five nutlets, each of which has two hard, sharp spines. *Microlarinus* spp. weevils provide biological control in certain circumstances, and have fed on this puncturevine. Weevil feeding scars are the lighter patches on the stem and brownish areas on the green fruit. An adult weevil emerged from the hole in this stem after feeding inside.

AA. Puncturevine fruit turn brown and readily detach from plants when mature, as with these snared in a worker's bootlace.

WINTER ANNUAL BROADLEAVES

Burning nettle and mustards (discussed below) and annual sowthistle, common groundsel, little mallow or cheeseweed, and yellow starthistle are some of the winter annual broadleaf species found in avocado groves. Except when they grow densely near the trunks of young trees, winter annual broadleaves are relatively minor pests in avocado. They can be controlled with virtually all of the methods discussed above under "Control Annuals and Seedlings."

BB. Burning nettle.

Nettles

Burning nettle (*Urtica urens*, family Urticaceae) is a winter annual in interior valleys but is especially troublesome in coastal counties of California, where it grows all year. Both leaves and the square stems have stinging hairs. Burning nettle has entire, rounded seed leaves with a small notch at the tip. A related species, stinging nettle (*U. dioica*), is taller and has less-rounded leaves.

BB.   Burning nettle grows 5 to 24 inches (12.5–60 cm) tall, with square stems branching from the base. Its leaves are opposite, stalked, and distinctly toothed. Small, greenish white flowers form in clusters at the base of leaf petioles.

Mustards

Several species of mustard (family Cruciferae) occur in avocado groves. These include black mustard (*Brassica nigra*), wild mustard (*Sinapis arvensis*), and birdsrape mustard (*B. rapa*), also known as common yellow mustard or wild turnip. Although considered to be winter annuals, in milder coastal locations mustards may grow year-round.

Mustards are characterized by distinctive seed pods, ½ inch (13 mm) or longer, that are tipped with short, slender beaks. Pods lay close to the stem, often overlapping one another.

Mustards are sometimes used in ground covers or as green manure crops. Taproots help loosen heavier soils and their flowers attract beneficial insects. Because of their large size, mustards near trunks can create conditions that favor crown diseases, provide refuge for voles, and compete for moisture in lower-rainfall areas.

CC.   All mustard seedlings have broad seed leaves with a deep notch at the tip. The first true leaves are bright green above, pale green below, deeply lobed, and often hairy. Lower leaves are large and usually are more or less deeply cut into irregular lobes.

DD.   Mustards have dense clusters of yellow flowers that arise at the tips of the stalks. The mature plant is erect and about 2 to 6 feet (0.6–1.8 m) tall.

CC. Birdsrape mustard seedling.

DD. Birdsrape mustard.

Vertebrates

Avocado groves provide food and shelter for vertebrate pests that can cause significant damage. The major vertebrate pests are deer, rabbits, and rodents (including ground squirrels, pocket gophers, roof rats, and voles). Occasional pests include bears, coyotes, dogs, opossums, raccoons, and tree squirrels. Deer, rabbits, and rodents are serious pests when their feeding stunts or kills trees. Irrigation tubes and sprinklers can be gnawed, most often by coyotes, gophers, ground squirrels, and rabbits. Black bears, opossums, roof rats, and tree squirrels primarily cause the loss of fruit. Bears can also injure trees and destroy bee hives to obtain honey. Some vertebrates host diseases that can be passed to humans and domestic animals. Vertebrate activity in groves may pose some risk of animal pathogens contaminating fruit and causing food-borne illnesses.

The grove's location influences whether certain vertebrates are likely to be pests of concern. For example, black bears, coyotes, deer, and (most) rabbits do not live in avocado groves; they pose problems only when avocados are grown adjacent to forests, rangelands, or unmanaged areas.

Rabbits chewed the bark off of this tree, girdling the trunk. Voles cause similar damage, but vole gnawing occurs no higher than about 2 inches (5 cm) above the ground. Squirrels can chew virtually anywhere on trunks and limbs, while pocket gopher girdling is usually hidden below ground.

Coyotes (*Canis latrans*) and dogs (*Canis familiaris*) can leave distinctive triangular canine tooth marks when they chew fruit. Their main type of damage is chewed irrigation lines or enlargement of burrow openings when they dig for rodents. Coyotes can be trapped or shot (where shooting is permitted) when they are causing problems.

Rodents (and occasionally rabbits in young groves) can reside within avocado groves year-round and are potential pests in all groves, but they can also invade from adjacent areas. They cause the most damage in groves next to rangeland or unmanaged land, where their populations may build up unchecked.

Managing Pest Vertebrates

Take these four key steps to successfully manage vertebrate pests:

1. identify the damaging species
2. assess the available management options
3. implement appropriate control actions
4. monitor to assess the efficacy of your actions and the need for additional control

Observation and Identification

Positively identify the damaging species before you choose your control actions. Identify vertebrates through direct observation of the pest and of its signs, such as burrows, feces, and tracks. The nature of the damage provides a clue as to which species is causing problems, but you should not rely solely on this kind of evidence. Many species can cause similar types of damage, such as tree girdling or chewing marks on fruit or irrigation equipment. Management tactics differ depending on the pest species. The descriptions, line drawings, and photographs in this book can help you identify the vertebrate pests that are causing problems in your groves. Consult the *UC IPM Pest Notes* (online at www.ipm.ucdavis.edu) on individual species as well as *Wildlife Pest Control*

around Gardens and Homes (Salmon, Whisson, and Marsh 2006), and other publications listed in the suggested reading for additional information on vertebrate pest biology, identification, and management.

Monitoring

Follow the recommendations below on when and how to monitor for specific vertebrate pests. Monitor groves more often and more carefully if conditions in or near the groves especially favor vertebrates. For example, certain types of habitat near groves (adjacent forests, riparian areas, or unmanaged lands) and conditions within groves (ground covers, thick mulch, and trees on or near berms) can increase the likelihood of damage from certain vertebrates. If vertebrate pest populations build up, respond quickly with control actions. After you take a control action, establish a routine monitoring program so you can assess the effectiveness of the control and detect any further problems that may develop. Keep a record of the management procedures you use and their effects on vertebrate pest activity. Good records will help you plan future control strategies and improve their effectiveness.

Control Actions

For most vertebrates, you will have more than one control option for reducing populations and damage. Table 18 summarizes the control options you can use against various vertebrate pests in avocado groves. Details on how to use these controls are given later in this chapter. Before you use any of these controls, consult your county agricultural commissioner to find out which procedures work best in your location and what restrictions apply to these techniques. The timing of control actions is often critical and timing is determined largely by the season and life cycle of the target pest. Become familiar with the biology of the vertebrates affecting your groves as well as the available control options so you will be able to plan the most cost-effective strategy for management.

When preparing the land and planting the grove, take steps to prevent or reduce potential vertebrate problems. Baiting, fencing, fumigating burrows, shooting, and trapping are easier and usually more effective if employed before you plant the grove instead of after. Where feasible, deep-plow and disc to destroy burrows, disperse or kill resident populations, and reduce the risk of reinvasion by pocket gophers, voles, and (to a lesser extent) ground squirrels. Carefully manage border vegetation to minimize the risk of invasion by voles. Encircle the growing area with properly installed fences to exclude deer and rabbits that may injure or kill young trees. When you plant the trees, install tree guards to keep rabbits from chewing the bark and to reduce damage from voles. After the grove is planted, develop and implement a monitoring and management program to promptly address any vertebrate pest problems that may arise.

Table 18. Control Methods for Vertebrate Pests of Avocado.

Pest	Control method							
	Habitat modification	Trapping	Baiting	Fencing	Tree guards	Frightening	Shooting	Fumigation
coyote		◆		◆			◆	
deer				◆		◆	◆ [1]	
eastern fox squirrel	◆	◆					◆	
ground squirrel	◆	◆	◆				◆	◆
opossum	◆	◆					◆	
pocket gophers	◆	◆	◆					◆
rabbits	◆	◆ [2]	◆ [3]	◆	◆		◆	
rats	◆	◆	◆					
voles	◆		◆		◆			

1. During hunting season or with a permit.
2. Cottontails are relatively easy to trap. Jackrabbits are difficult to trap, but trapping may be useful.
3. Permitted only for jackrabbits.
Adapted from: Salmon and Lickliter 1984.

Most birds do not cause problems in avocado groves. Crows sometimes knock fruit from trees and return to feed on avocados that have softened on the ground. Crows will also tear wraps from young trees and may injure young grafts.

Habitat Modification. Changes to the environment in and around groves affect vertebrate pest problems and their management. Brush piles provide shelter and resting places for brush and cottontail rabbits, ground squirrels, and opossums. Remove any brush piles and debris in or near the grove to reduce activity of these vertebrates in the grove and make it easier to observe and control any vertebrate pests that are present.

Ground covers, mulches, and soil berms in and near groves tend to increase the population of certain rodents. For example, thick ground cover provides the type of habitat preferred by voles, and certain ground covers attract pocket gophers and sometimes rabbits. Ground squirrels and pocket gophers often burrow in berms. However, eliminating this habitat is not generally desirable since planting on berms and providing organic mulch beneath trees are both recommended practices that improve avocado growth and reduce the severity of diseases such as avocado root rot. Ground covers, thick mulch, and vegetative borders may also be desirable since they reduce the offsite movement of potential water contaminants such as fertilizers, pesticides, and soil. Where this kind of habitat favors vertebrates, monitor more carefully and respond quickly with control actions if populations

build up. If you are not able to modify habitat to discourage vertebrate pests, you will have to rely more on controls such as burrow fumigation, poison baits, and trapping.

Biological Control. Vertebrate populations are affected most by the availability of food and cover. Predators such as coyotes, foxes, hawks, owls, and snakes eat some of the vertebrates that can become pests, but predators play a relatively minor role in keeping small mammal populations low in groves. Installation of nest boxes for barn owls and perches for other raptors are common wildlife conservation practices, but they do not appear to reduce vertebrate damage levels in groves. Even though natural enemies seldom keep vertebrate pests from reaching damaging levels, take precautions to avoid harming predators and other nontarget species when you use toxic baits or traps.

Exclusion. Tree guards, trunk wraps, and fencing exclude deer and rabbits. Tree guards and trunk wraps can also reduce problems from voles. Deer fencing excludes coyotes and dogs. Although the initial costs can be high, fencing, tree guards,

This debris pile of cut avocado branches provides nesting sites and daytime shelter for vertebrates such as brush and cottontail rabbits, ground squirrels, rats, and opossums. When you eliminate harborage, you help control several species of vertebrate pests and make it easier to monitor pest presence and abundance.

This Pacific gopher snake *(Pituophis catenifer catenifer)* eats pocket gophers and other pests. Although predators play a relatively minor role in keeping small mammal populations low in groves, conserve these beneficial species wherever possible.

and trunk wraps provide long-term control and can be the most effective methods for certain species.

Trapping. When direct control is warranted, live or kill traps appropriate to the species are effective for certain vertebrate pests, especially when populations are relatively low or localized. Any pre-baiting typically varies depending on the pest species. Unlike baits, which often cause vertebrates to die somewhere out of sight, traps provide prompt and reliable evidence as to whether a particular species is present or is being killed.

Endangered Species Guidelines. Many avocado groves are located within the range of one or more federally or

state-protected endangered vertebrate species. Species likely to be of concern when using traps or poison bait include the San Joaquin kit fox and several species of rare kangaroo rats. If you use burrow fumigants in the San Joaquin Valley and the surrounding foothills, the blunt-nosed leopard lizard is a concern as this insect feeder seeks shelter in rodent burrows. Special guidelines apply to the use of certain traps, fumigants, and toxic baits for vertebrate pest control in these areas. Modification of ground squirrel bait stations to exclude protected species is one common practice (Figures 40 and 41). Other typical guidelines restrict broadcast applications of bait, limit the percentage of active ingredient in baits, prohibit fumigation at certain locations or during some times of the year, and require that applications be supervised by someone trained to avoid harming endangered species.

Contact your county agricultural commissioner for the latest maps that show the ranges of endangered species and for current information on restrictions that apply to pest control activities in your area. More information on endangered species regulations is also available online at the DPR Web site (www.cdpr.ca.gov/docs/es).

Baits. Single- or multiple-dose baits are available for control of many vertebrates (Table 19). Sometimes a bait can be applied openly on the ground, but often they must be contained in bait stations specially designed to keep nontarget animals from getting the bait.

Anticoagulant baits are often the preferred option because they are fairly economical and very effective and they do not produce "bait shyness." Also, an antidote is available in case a domestic animal is accidentally poisoned. Active ingredients in anticoagulants that require multiple feedings over a

This Conibear trap is set and placed without bait over the entrance to a ground squirrel burrow, then secured to a stake. Follow restrictions to protect endangered species, such as covering traps with a box that has an entrance no larger than 3 inches (7.6 cm) wide to exclude the San Joaquin kit fox.

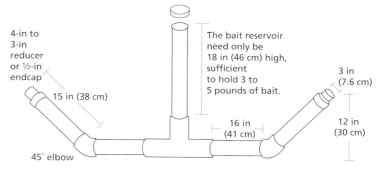

Materials required for modifications
30-in PVC pipe (4-in diameter)
2 45° elbows
2 4-in to 3-in reducers or ½-in endcaps

Figure 40. A ground squirrel bait station designed for use within the range of endangered kangaroo rats and the San Joaquin kit fox. End pieces are angled up and the diameter of their opening is reduced to 3 inches (7.6 cm) to restrict protected species' access to bait. *From:* Whisson 1997b.

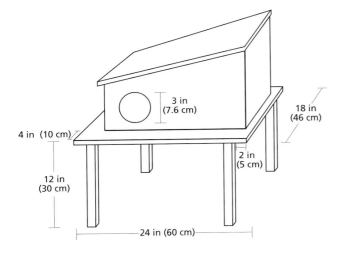

Materials (others may be substituted)
Legs: 1.5 in x 1.5 in pine
Platform: 18 in x 24 in x ¾ in exterior plywood

Figure 41. A ground squirrel bait station elevated on a platform to prevent access by protected kangaroo rats. Construct the station to be sufficiently rigid and anchor it well enough to the ground so that it cannot be easily tipped. *From:* Whisson 1997a.

scavengers. Retrieval and proper disposal of poisoned animals' carcasses, when feasible, is recommended and in some cases required. Check the bait's current registration status before you use it. FOLLOW LABEL DIRECTIONS CAREFULLY and understand the hazards when using baits.

Fumigants. Fumigants control ground squirrels and pocket gophers. The fumigant is applied in an active burrow and any soil openings to the burrow are closed. Ignitable gas cartridges are used to fumigate ground squirrel tunnels. Aluminum phosphide* is applied inside ground squirrel and pocket gopher burrows. Especially when using aluminum phosphide, all application personnel should be trained in the material's proper use and its potential hazards. When aluminum phosphide pellets come into contact with moist soil in the burrow, they produce a gas that is highly toxic to any animal. FOLLOW LABEL DIRECTIONS CAREFULLY and understand the hazards when using fumigants.

This bait station constructed of PVC plastic pipe is one of several designs for control of California ground squirrel. When used within the range of the San Joaquin kit fox, entrances must be restricted to 3 inches (7.6 cm) in diameter. Place baffles inside the pipe to keep bait inside the station.

period of several days include chlorophacinone, diphacinone, and warfarin. Death generally occurs 2 to 6 days after the bait is first consumed. Anticoagulant baits are available in block, kernel, meal, or pellet form containing the poison and a food attractant.

Strychnine* and zinc phosphide* are single-dose baits. They can be more hazardous to humans than multi-dose anticoagulants, and the use of single-dose baits is more strictly regulated. For example, strychnine may be available only for direct underground application and only in pocket gopher tunnels. Zinc phosphide baits have the advantage that they do not accumulate in the tissue of poisoned rodents, eliminating the danger of secondary poisoning of predators and

Table 19. Pesticides Available for Controlling Vertebrates.

	Baits			Fumigants	
Pest	Multiple-dose anticoagulants	Strychnine*	Zinc phosphide*	Aluminum phosphide*	Gas cartridges
Ground squirrels	•		•	•	•
Pocket gophers	•	•[2]		•	
Rabbits	•[1]				
Rats	•		•		
Voles	•		•		

FOLLOW LABEL DIRECTIONS CAREFULLY and understand the hazards when using fumigants. Contact your county agricultural commissioner for current product registrations and the latest information on legal pesticide use, including current information on restrictions that apply to pest control activities in order to protect endangered species.
* Restricted materials, which require a permit from the county agricultural commissioner before possession or use.
1. Use only for jackrabbits.
2. Considered the most effective material for pocket gopher control.

*Restricted-use material. Permit required for purchase or use.

VERTEBRATE PESTS

Ground Squirrels

Spermophilus beecheyi

Ground squirrel damage is most prevalent in groves adjacent to uncultivated areas where squirrels are not controlled. Ground squirrels gnaw fruit and bark and girdle trunks and scaffold limbs. They occasionally chew plastic irrigation lines and their burrows can contribute to soil erosion.

The adult California ground squirrel has a head and body 9 to 11 inches (23–28 cm) long. Its somewhat bushy tail is about as long as its body. The fur is mottled dark and light brown or gray. Ground squirrels live in colonies that may grow very large if left uncontrolled. They are active during the cooler times on hot days and are usually most active in morning and late afternoon.

Each ground squirrel burrow system can have several openings with scattered soil in front. Individual ground squirrel burrows may be 5 to 30 feet (1.5–9 m) long, 2½ to 4 feet (75 cm–1.2 m) below the surface, and about 4 to 6 inches (10–15 cm) in diameter. Burrows provide the ground squirrels a place to retreat, sleep, hibernate, rear their young, and store food. Ground squirrels often dig their burrows along ditches and fence rows and on other uncultivated land. When uncontrolled, they frequently move into groves and dig burrows beneath the trees.

The California ground squirrel can be active throughout the year in coastal areas of Southern California. Especially in hot locations, adult ground squirrels become temporarily dormant (aestivate or estivate) when food is scarce or temperatures are extreme, primarily in late summer. Winter hibernation and summer aestivation are more typical among ground squirrels in inland areas where temperature variations are more extreme. Regardless of location, young squirrels tend to be active all summer. In avocado growing areas, those squirrels that do hibernate generally emerge around January when weather begins to warm. In late winter and spring, the squirrels feed on green vegetation. They switch to seeds and fruit including avocados in late spring and early summer as the vegetation dries up. Females have one litter, averaging 8 young, in the spring. The young squirrels emerge from their burrow when about 6 weeks old. Young ground squirrels do not aestivate their first summer, and most do not hibernate during their first winter. Figure 42 illustrates the seasonal periods of activity for the California ground squirrel and the best times to control them.

Management Guidelines

Remove brush piles, debris, and stumps in and around the grove to make it easier to monitor squirrel activity and perhaps help to limit population buildup. Ground squirrels quickly

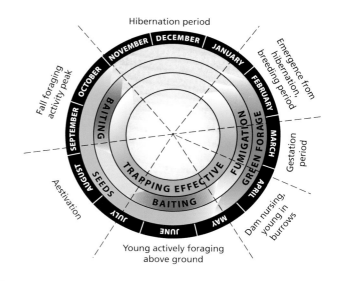

- Squirrels foraging mostly on green grasses and forbs.
- Squirrels foraging mostly on seeds.
- Trapping can be effective any time squirrels are active.
- Ideal time to fumigate burrows.
- Best times for baiting.
- Baiting marginally effective because of aestivation.

Figure 42. California ground squirrel reproductive cycle and seasonal food preference, and the best times to take specific control actions. Actual activity varies among growing areas, depending primarily on local climate and weather, and occurs earlier at warmer sites. *From:* **Salmon, Whisson, and Marsh 2006.**

occupy abandoned burrow systems. If feasible, after controlling squirrel infestations outside your grove use thorough cultivation or deep plowing to destroy burrow entrances and help slow the rate of reinvasion.

The type of direct control action needed for ground squirrels depends primarily on their activity patterns and feeding preferences during the time of year when control action is taken. The choice of tactics is also influenced by the location of the infestation and the number of squirrels present. Watch for signs of squirrel activity within the grove, especially the appearance of burrows, during routine grove activities. Check the perimeter of the grove at least once a month during the times of year when squirrels are active. Midmorning usually is the best time of day for observing squirrels. Keep records of when squirrels emerge from hibernation. Record the approximate number of squirrels you see and the location and number of burrows.

Apply controls as soon as you see squirrels or burrowing activity within or adjacent to the grove. Select the control method best suited for the time of year (see Figure 42). From a biological point of view, the most effective time to control ground squirrels is in early spring when adults have emerged from their burrows but before they reproduce. For best control then, use burrow fumigation about 3 weeks after the first squirrels emerge from hibernation. Because squirrels feed almost exclusively on green vegetation early in the season, poisoned grain baits are generally not effective until late spring or early summer.

Traps. Trapping controls small populations any time of year when squirrels are active. Trapping is especially effective from mid-spring through fall (Figure 42). Ground squirrel traps include Conibear traps and modified gopher box traps (Figure 43).

Conibear kill traps are usually placed unbaited in the burrow entrance, where squirrels are trapped as they pass through. If you are using this type of trap within the range of the San Joaquin kit fox, you must place the trap in a covered box with an entrance no larger than 3 inches (7.6 cm) wide to exclude the fox, or you must spring the traps at dusk and reset them again in the morning.

Modified gopher box traps (a joined pair of box traps [Figure 43]) are baited with foods such as almonds, barley, melon rinds, oats, or walnuts. Place bait in traps well behind the trigger or tied to the trigger without setting the traps for several days, until the squirrels become used to taking the

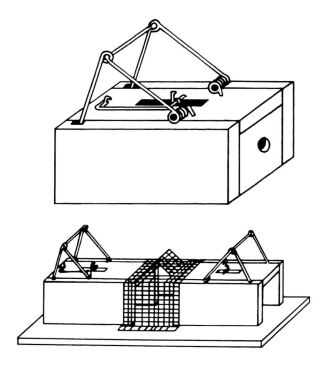

Figure 43. The single box gopher trap *(top, shown not set)* can be used in pairs to capture ground squirrels and tree squirrels. To use box traps in pairs, remove the backs, connect the two traps with wire mesh, and attach them to a board as shown here *(bottom). Adapted from:* Salmon and Lickliter 1984.

bait. Then put in fresh bait and set the traps. Place traps so that nontarget animals are not likely to be caught. For example, place traps inside a larger box with openings no larger than 3 inches (7.6 cm) wide, just large enough to allow ground squirrels to enter.

Fumigants. Fumigation can be very effective against ground squirrel populations. The best time to fumigate is late in the winter or early in spring when the squirrels are active and soil is moist (Figure 42). Fumigation is not effective when squirrels are hibernating or aestivating: at those times, they seal off their burrows. When the soil is dry, fumigation is much less effective because more of the fumigant escapes from burrows through cracks in the soil. When using a fumigant, make sure to treat all active burrow systems in and around the grove. Re-check all areas a few days after fumigation and re-treat any that have been reopened. For safety's sake, do not fumigate burrow systems that are adjacent to buildings or may open under structures. FOLLOW LABEL DIRECTIONS CAREFULLY and understand the hazards when using fumigants.

Gas cartridges provide a relatively easy fumigation method. Use one or two cartridges for each burrow that shows signs of activity. A large burrow system may require more than two. Quickly shove the ignited cartridges into the burrow using a shovel handle or stick and seal the burrow entrance with soil. Watch nearby burrow entrances; treat and seal any that begin to leak smoke. The larger and more complex the burrow system, the more smoke it takes to be effective.

Take care to avoid starting a fire. Keep fire suppression equipment handy. Use good judgment to identify hazardous situations where gas cartridges should be avoided.

Baits. Poison bait is usually the most cost-effective method for controlling ground squirrels, especially for large populations. Bait consists of grain or pellets treated with a poison registered for ground squirrel control. To be effective, the bait must be used at a time of year when ground squirrels are feeding on seeds (see Figure 42) and will readily accept baits. Baits are most effective in late spring or early summer. In the fall, squirrels cache a lot of seeds (they store them instead of eating them), so it may require more bait to control the population. Before you use baits, place a small amount of untreated grain near burrows in the morning and check in the late afternoon to see if the squirrels have taken it (this ensures that nocturnal animals have not eaten the grain). If the grain is taken during the day, proceed with baiting. If it is not taken, wait several days or a week and try again. Remember: bait is not effective unless it is eaten by the target pest. When using poison baits, make sure to follow label directions carefully to reduce hazards to nontarget species.

Multiple-dose anticoagulant baits can be applied in bait stations, as spot treatments near burrows, or broadcast over larger infested areas. Check the label to make sure that the bait you plan to use is registered for the method or bait station you intend to use. For a multiple-dose bait to be effective, animals must feed on it over a period of several days. Various kinds of bait stations are commonly used; all are designed to let squirrels in but to exclude larger animals. One design is made of PVC pipe (see Figure 40). Make the openings about 3 inches (7.6) in diameter and incorporate baffles to keep the bait inside the station. Special types of stations must be used within the ranges of the San Joaquin kit fox or endangered kangaroo rats to ensure that these species are excluded (see Figures 40 and 41). Place bait stations near runways or burrows and secure them so they cannot easily be tipped over. If squirrels are moving into the grove from adjacent areas, place bait stations along the perimeter of the grove where squirrels are invading, one station every 100 feet (30 m). Use more stations when the number of squirrels is high. Check bait stations daily at first, then as often as needed to keep the bait replenished. If bait feeding is interrupted, the bait's effectiveness will be greatly decreased. Make sure to pick up any bait that spills and to replace bait that is wet or moldy. Successful baiting usually requires 2 to 4 weeks. Continue to supply bait until feeding ceases and you observe no squirrels; then properly dispose of unused bait.

When specified on the label, anticoagulant baits can be applied as spot-treatments, which are economical and effective for small populations. Reapply according to label directions to make sure there is no interruption in exposure

Positive identification of the damaging species is important because it allows you to choose effective control actions. Do not rely solely on recognizing the type of damage caused by the pest. Ground squirrels chewed this microsprinkler, but coyotes and gophers also cause gnawing damage to irrigation systems, and dogs and rabbits also sometimes cause this type of damage.

The adult California ground squirrel has mottled, dark and light brown to gray fur.

to the bait. Scattering the bait takes advantage of the ground squirrels' natural foraging behavior and minimizes risks to nontarget species that are not as effective at foraging for seeds. Never pile the bait on the ground, since piles increase the hazard to livestock and certain nontarget wildlife. After treatment, pick up and dispose of any carcasses whenever possible to prevent secondary poisoning of dogs or other scavengers. Burial is a good method for disposal as long as the carcasses are buried deep enough to discourage scavengers. Do not touch dead animals.

When you use a bait, the primary hazard to nontarget animals is that they will eat the bait. Assess the potential hazard to humans, livestock, and nontarget wildlife before you use this type of bait and application method; if it is risky, use another method for ground squirrel control.

Consult your local agricultural commissioner or the DPR Web site (online at www.cdpr.ca.gov/docs/es) for the latest recommendations on use of poison baits in areas that are within the range of endangered species. For more information, consult publications such as *California Ground Squirrel Pest Notes* (Salmon and Gorenzel 2002), online at www.ipm.ucdavis.edu, and the vertebrates section in *IPM for Walnuts* (Strand 2003), listed in the suggested reading.

Eastern Fox Squirrel
Sciurus niger

The introduced eastern fox squirrel is an occasional pest in coastal avocado groves near wooded or riparian areas. It feeds on avocados, oranges, and various nuts. Tree squirrels nest aboveground in cavities in wood or they build nests of leaves and twigs lodged in limbs. Tree squirrels have a bushier tail than the ground squirrel, and their fur is not flecked or mottled.

JACK KELLY CLARK

Ground squirrel burrow entrances are open and about 4 inches (10 cm) in diameter, but can vary considerably. Ground squirrels living in groves sometimes chew and girdle trunks, and such damage to avocado trees will greatly reduce fruit yields and may contribute to premature death of the tree.

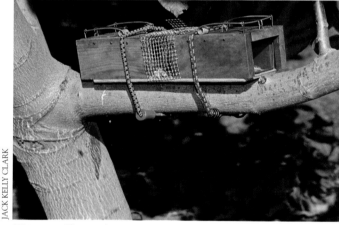

JACK KELLY CLARK

This pair of box gopher traps is set on tree limb to trap the eastern fox squirrel. If you maintain them continuously, you only need relatively few traps to control tree squirrels.

Trapping is the primary control method for eastern fox squirrel. If maintained continuously, relatively few traps are needed to control tree squirrels. For example, a single box-type gopher trap or two traps set back-to-back (see Figure 43) can be nailed to a board attached atop a horizontal limb where squirrels are feeding. Check with local game officials regarding any regulations on shooting tree squirrels. Some dogs (such as active terriers) may help to keep tree squirrels away. It is illegal to poison tree squirrels. For more information, consult publications such as *Tree Squirrels Pest Notes* (Salmon, Whisson, and Marsh 2005), online at www.ipm.ucdavis.edu.

Pocket Gophers
Thomomys spp.

Pocket gophers can be serious pests, primarily in young groves. Herbaceous cover crops, especially legumes, are their preferred food, but pocket gophers also feed on the bark of tree crowns and roots, girdling and killing young trees and reducing the vigor of older trees. Gophers sometimes gnaw on plastic irrigation lines.

Adult pocket gophers are 6 to 8 inches (15–20 cm) long with stout brown, gray, or yellowish bodies and small ears and eyes. They rarely are seen above ground, spending most of their time in a tunnel system they construct 6 to 18 inches (15–46 cm) beneath the soil surface. A single burrow system can cover several hundred square feet. It consists of main tunnels with lateral branches used for feeding or for pushing excavated soil to the surface. Gophers are extremely territorial; except for females with young, you rarely find more than one gopher per burrow system. The conspicuous, fan-shaped soil mounds over tunnel openings are the most obvious sign of gopher infestation. These tunnel openings are almost always closed with a soil plug. Gophers feed primarily on the roots of herbaceous plants. They may also come aboveground to clip small plants within a few inches of their burrow and pull vegetation into the burrow for feeding.

Gophers breed throughout the year on irrigated land, with a peak in late winter or early spring. Females bear as many as three litters each year. Once weaned, the young travel to a favorable location to establish their own burrow system. Some take over previously vacated burrows. The buildup of gopher populations in the grove is encouraged by extensive weed growth or the presence of most cover crops, especially perennial clovers. When cover crops or weeds dry up, gophers may feed extensively on the bark of tree crowns and roots. Damage to trees is always underground and usually not evident until the trees show signs of stress.

Management Guidelines

The best times to monitor for gophers are after irrigation and when mound building peaks in the fall and spring. Monitor monthly in the spring, paying close attention to grove perimeters to determine whether gophers are invading the grove. Monitor more closely in weedy areas such as roadsides and in young groves with extensive weed growth or ground covers. This type of vegetation is more likely to support gophers, and low-growing vegetation makes signs of burrowing activity harder to see. Look for darker-colored mounds, which indicate newly removed soil.

Begin control as soon as you see any signs of gopher activity in the grove. For infestations that cover a limited area, use traps or hand-applied poison bait. Trapping and hand-baiting can be used at any time of year, but they are easier when the soil is moist and not dry and hard. In addition to control within groves, you may want to control gophers in areas adjacent to your groves, thus reducing the potential for further gopher problems.

For infestations that cover a large area, a mechanical burrow builder is effective and economical. This device is pulled behind a tractor to make artificial gopher tunnels into which it places bait. Use of a mechanical burrow builder may be feasible in situations such as unplanted borders or between widely spaced young trees, if the terrain is relatively level and the soil is not too rocky. Rough terrain makes mechanical burrow builders infeasible in many groves and the likelihood of severe damage to the avocado trees' extensive shallow root system makes it infeasible around older trees.

Mechanical burrow builders are discussed in *Integrated Pest Management for Walnuts* (Strand 2003), listed in the suggested reading. For more information on biology and management, consult publications such as *Pocket Gophers Pest Notes* (Salmon and Gorenzel 2002), online at www.ipm. ucdavis.edu.

Traps. Traps are effective against small numbers of gophers but are labor intensive and therefore relatively expensive to use. You can use either a pincer-type or a box-type kill trap.

To place traps, probe near a fresh mound to find the main tunnel, which usually is on the lower side of the mound (Figure 44). The main tunnel usually is 8 to 12 inches (20–30 cm) deep, and the probe will drop quickly about 2 inches (5 cm) when you find it. Place two traps in the main tunnel, one facing each direction (Figure 45). Be sure to anchor the traps to a stake with wire. After placing the traps, cover the hole to keep light out of the tunnel. If a trap is not visited within 48 hours, move it to a new location.

Baits. Single-dose acute baits are generally the most effective for gopher control. Multi-dose anticoagulants are also available (Table 19). Bait must be applied below ground.

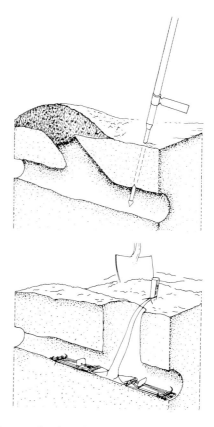

Figure 44. Using a soil probe to locate gopher tunnels *(top)* to determine where to place traps. Probe 8 to 12 inches (20–30 cm) from the plug side of the mound. The probe will suddenly drop a few inches when you hit the main tunnel. Excavate with a shovel to expose the main tunnel and place 2 two-pronged pincher traps (such as Macabee traps) in the tunnel, one facing in each direction *(bottom)*. Tie the traps to a stake on the surface that is tall enough to be easily seen. Push each trap well back into the tunnel. Place a board over the hole and cover it completely with soil so that no light can enter the tunnel. *Illustration from:* Salmon and Lickliter 1984.

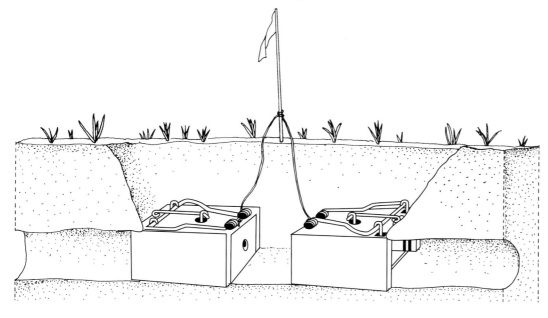

Figure 45. Two box traps used to trap pocket gophers. After locating and excavating the main tunnel as described in Figure 44, push each trap tightly against the tunnel opening. Secure traps to a tall stake and carefully cover the excavated hole to ensure that no light enters the tunnel. The traps shown here are set (their triggers are down). *Adapted from:* Valerie Winemiller in Strand 2002.

Make sure to follow label directions carefully for application rates and safety considerations.

Apply baits by hand for small infestations or where the use of a mechanical burrow builder is not feasible. Use a probe

Adult pocket gophers are 6 to 8 inches (15–20 cm) long with stout brown, gray, or yellowish bodies and small ears and eyes. They rarely are seen above ground except when pushing soil from their burrow as shown here and sometimes when clipping small plants near a burrow opening.

Pocket gophers are rarely are seen above ground. Evidence of their presence underground includes fresh soil mounds without obvious openings formed at entrances to their tunnels, as shown here in the foreground.

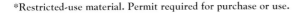

*Restricted-use material. Permit required for purchase or use.

This root crown and the surrounding soil were excavated to reveal pocket gopher girdling hidden below ground. In avocado groves, gophers primarily damage young trees.

to find the main tunnel next to a fresh mound or between two fresh mounds (Figure 44). Once you find the main tunnel, drop bait into the burrow. After you place the bait, put a board, dirt clod, stone, or other cover over any holes to keep out light and prevent soil from falling onto the bait. Place bait in two or three places along the tunnel. This hand-application method can be used for single-dose or multiple-dose baits. Reservoir-type hand probes designed to deposit single-dose baits are available. Bait application is faster with these devices because they eliminate the need to stop and place the bait by hand.

Fumigants. Fumigants such as gas cartridges are not effective because gophers quickly seal off their tunnels when they detect the smoke or poison gases. Aluminum phosphide* can be effective if applied underground into tunnels during a time of year when soil is moist enough to retain the toxic gas, typically in late winter to early spring. Carefully follow all label directions and safety instructions.

Opossum

Didelphis virginiana

Opossums eat a variety of foods, including avocados and other fruit, eggs, insects, garbage, meat, nuts, and vegetables.

These nocturnal marsupials are about the size of a house cat, with a pointed-nose and rat-like tail. Their moderately long fur ranges from white to dark gray, and frequently is darker on their legs and lighter on their back. Opossums rest during the day in debris piles, buildings, hollows in a tree or the ground, or virtually anyplace that offers protection. Females generally have two litters a year, each of about 7 young. Young opossums stay with their mother for about 3 months, initially suckling within the female's abdominal pouch. Messy food remnants, gnawing marks that appear on fruit overnight, or prints in soft soil resembling little human or monkey hands about 1½ to 2 inches (38–50 mm) long can indicate the presence of opossums.

Reduce habitat by eliminating debris piles, stacking materials neatly (preferably off the ground), tightly covering or disposing of garbage, and trimming dense vegetation. Opossums can be trapped, or you can shoot them where hunting is permitted. No pesticides are registered for opossum control. Various suggested chemical repellants have not been found to be effective, for most purposes except for driving opossums from confined areas. For more information, consult publications such as *Opossum Pest Notes* (Salmon, Whisson, and Marsh 2005), online at www.ipm.ucdavis.edu.

Raccoon

Procyon lotor

The raccoon is a stocky mammal about 2 to 3 feet (60–90 cm) long and weighing about 10 to 30 pounds (5–14 kg). It is distinctively marked with a black "mask" over the eyes and is heavily furred, with alternating light and dark rings around its tail. Raccoons prefer groves near water and wooded or

Roof rats have a pointed muzzle and long, hairless tail. It is important to distinguish the species of rat present in order to select the most effective types and placements of baits or traps and to avoid killing nontarget species, some of which resemble pest rats.

Roof rats gnaw and eat fruit. Opossums and tree squirrels also chew fruit when it's still on the tree. Because their biology and management methods differ, correct identification of the species by direct observation of the pests and recognition of their signs is necessary before you can choose effective control actions.

natural areas. They den in hollow trees, ground burrows, brush or debris piles, and in attics or underneath buildings. They are nocturnal and eat small animals and plants such as avocado fruit. Raccoons are intelligent and clever animals. They are also powerful and can be vicious when trapped or cornered.

Reduce the availability of den space and cover by eliminating debris piles, stacking materials neatly, tightly covering or disposing of garbage and other potential foods, trimming dense vegetation, and making sure structures are sturdy and sealed well enough to exclude raccoons. Dogs kept outdoors may frighten some raccoons away, but raccoons sometimes cause serious injury to dogs. Large, sturdy traps with fruit or sweet food bait (to avoid attracting cats and dogs) are the primary control method. For more information, consult publications such as *Raccoon Pest Notes* (Salmon, Whisson, and Marsh 2004) online at www.ipm.ucdavis.edu.

Rats

Rattus spp.

Rats gnaw on electrical wires, wooden structures, and fruit on trees. After harvest, they damage fruit in bins by chewing it and leaving excrement. Rats are active throughout the year, and mostly at night.

The roof rat (*Rattus rattus*), sometimes called the black rat, is a common vertebrate pest in avocado groves. It builds leaf and twig nests in avocado trees or nearby trees or it can nest in debris piles or thick mulch on the ground. This agile, sleek rat has a pointed muzzle and tail that is longer than the body and head combined. The Norway rat (*Rattus norvegicus*), is an occasional pest. A mature Norway rat is larger and more stout than a roof rat, and has a blunt muzzle and a tail

JACK KELLY CLARK

JACK KELLY CLARK

Deer mice have relatively large, prominent ears and a long tail, more than 70% the length of their head and body. They sometimes strip bark from young trees, chew irrigation lines, and feed on fruit.

that is shorter than its body and head combined.

Be aware that endangered native kangaroo rats (*Dipodomys* spp.) and the riparian woodrat (*Neotoma fuscipes riparia*) resemble pest rats, but are protected by law. Unlike the hairless, scale-covered tail of Norway rats and roof rats, the tails of kangaroo rats and the riparian woodrat are covered with fur. The riparian woodrat is active mostly during the day, and its tail is somewhat shorter than the combined length of its body and head. A kangaroo rat's tail is noticeably longer than its body and head combined. Kangaroo rats are nocturnal, but unlike Norway rats and roof rats, which move on all four legs, kangaroo rats hold their front legs off the ground and travel by hopping on their hind legs. It is important to know which species of rat is present in order to choose the most effective types and placements of baits and traps, and to avoid killing nontarget or protected species.

Management Guidelines
Reduce vertebrate pest shelter and nesting sites. Eliminate debris and wood piles. Store materials neatly and off the ground. Thin and separate non-crop vegetation around groves where feasible. Baits and rat-sized snap traps placed in trees are the most effective control measures. Rats are wary, tending to avoid baits and traps for at least a few days after their initial placement. Fasten traps to limbs and bait them with sweet fruit or nut meats, but do not set the traps until after bait is readily eaten. Secure anticoagulant baits to limbs 6 feet (2 m) or more above the ground. Be aware that

certain types of single-dose rat baits for use inside buildings are not labeled for use outdoors in groves; these are hazardous to wildlife and should not be used. For more information, consult publications such as *Norway Rats* (Timm 1994), *Rats Pest Notes* (Salmon, Marsh, and Timm 2003), and *Roof Rats* (Marsh 1994), listed in the suggested reading.

Deer Mice
Peromyscus spp.

Deer mice sometimes strip bark from young trees, chew irrigation lines, and feed on fruit. Large membranous ears and a moderately to well-furred tail more than 70% the length of the head and body distinguish *Peromyscus* spp. from other small rodents also called mice. In contrast to their darker upper side, deer mice have distinctly lighter-colored fur on the underside of their body and tail.

Deer mouse refers to any of seven *Peromyscus* spp. that occur in California, and to the prevalent species *P. maniculatus*. At most locations, deer mice are less likely than voles (meadow mice) to be a problem in groves. Damage, and the situations where they become problems, are generally the same for deer mice and voles. Manage deer mice as discussed later in this chapter under "Voles," and in publications such as *House Mouse Pest Notes* (Timm 2000), online at www.ipm.ucdavis.edu.

Voles (Meadow Mice)
Microtus spp.

Voles, also called meadow voles or meadow mice, can be a particular problem where dense vegetation or cover crops grow around the base of trees. Voles damage trees by feeding on bark around the root crown, and sometimes they chew holes in irrigation lines. Small trees are most susceptible to being completely girdled and killed by voles. Large trees are susceptible to damage, for instance after severe pruning, when sufficient light penetrates the tree canopy for vegetation to grow near trunks, but vole damage to large avocado trees is uncommon and rarely kills the tree. Vegetation management and the proper use of trunk guards on young trees usually keep damage to a minimum. Bait can control populations that reach harmful levels.

Adult voles are larger than house mice but smaller than rats. Compared to deer mice, however, voles have a more robust body, less obvious ears, and a relatively shorter tail. Voles' ears are at least partly obscured by the hair in front of them and voles' tails are about one-half to one-quarter the length of their head and body combined. Deer mice have relatively large and prominent, fleshy ears and their tail is more than 70% the length of their head and body.

Voles are active both day and night and all year round.

Females bear several litters each year, with peaks of reproduction in spring and fall. Populations go through cycles, climaxing every 4 to 7 years and then declining fairly rapidly. Grasses and other dense ground covers provide food and cover that favor the buildup of vole populations. You can recognize vole activity by the presence of narrow runways in grass or other ground cover, connecting numerous shallow burrows with openings about 1½ inches (4 cm) in diameter. Voles seldom travel far from their burrows and runways.

Voles' ears are at least partly obscured by the hair in front, and their tail is relatively short, about ½ to ¼ the length of their head and body combined. Voles (meadow mice) are common pests when low-growing vegetation such as ground covers or extensive weed growth provides them shelter near young trunks.

Management Guidelines

Starting in midwinter, monitor monthly for active runways in cover crops or weedy areas. Look for fresh vole droppings and short pieces of clipped vegetation, especially grass stems, in runways. Look for burrow openings around the bases of grove trees. If you find burrows, remove the soil from around the base of the tree and look for bark damage. Voles usually start chewing on bark about 2 inches (5 cm) below the soil line and then move upward to about 2 to 4 inches (5–10 cm) aboveground. If you do not check carefully, you may not notice damage until late spring or summer, when it may be too late to prevent significant injury to the trees. Make sure to monitor ditch banks, fence rows, roadsides, and other areas around the grove where permanent vegetation favors the buildup of vole populations.

Habitat Management. Voles travel only a few feet from their burrows, so any destruction of vegetation will make the area less favorable to them. Use a hoe, herbicides, or other methods to keep an area reaching about 3 feet (90 cm) out from trunks free of vegetation. If you maintain ground cover or resident weeds in the row middles, keep it mowed fairly short to be less attractive to voles. A vegetation-free zone 30 to 40 feet (9–12 m) wide between the grove and adjacent areas helps reduce the potential for invasion by voles, but such a wide area is rarely practical. Bare soil borders may be undesirable where off-site movement of contaminated soil and water must be prevented with a vegetative border to filter runoff.

Tree Guards. Use wire or plastic trunk guards to protect young trees from voles and rabbits. An effective guard can be a 24-inch-tall (60 cm) cylinder made of ¼- or ½-inch (6–13 mm) mesh hardware cloth that is of sufficient diameter to

Ground covers and grassy weeds can harbor voles, as evidenced by these abundant runways and shallow burrows.

These heavy cardboard tree wrappers help protect against meadow mouse and rabbit damage. Correctly installed wire tree guards exclude vertebrates more effectively, but unlike these tree wrappers, wire screen does not protect trunks against sunburn.

allow several years' growth without crowding the tree. Bury the guards' bottom edge several inches below the soil surface if possible to discourage voles from burrowing beneath them. Plastic, heavy cardboard, or other fiber materials can also be used to make trunk guards. These materials are less expensive, also provide sunburn protection, and are more convenient to use; however, they provide less protection against vole damage since the voles can chew through them. Regularly check underneath any tree guards for evidence that voles are burrowing underneath them to gnaw on the tree trunk, looking also for the presence of other pests such as snails. Good weed control around trunks improves the effectiveness of trunk guards.

Baiting. If you find damaging infestations or population increases within the grove, poison baits can greatly reduce the vole population. Baiting can also reduce populations in adjacent areas before they have a chance to invade the grove. Single- and multiple-dose baits are available, but there may be baiting restrictions in some areas to protect endangered species. It is extremely important to understand and follow the label directions for use.

For small infestations, scatter the bait in or near active vole runways and burrows according to the bait's label directions. For larger areas and where the bait label permits it, you can make broadcast applications. For noncrop land, apply bait in fall or spring before the voles' reproduction peak. Bait acceptance will depend on the amount and kind of other food available.

Other Controls. Trapping is not practical for voles because so many individuals have to be controlled when they are causing problems in commercial groves. Fumigation is not effective because of the shallow, open nature of vole burrow systems and the large number of voles. Repellents are not considered effective in preventing damage. For more information, consult publications such as *Voles (Meadow Mice) Pest Notes* (Salmon and Gorenzel 2002), online at www.ipm.ucdavis.edu.

Black-Tailed Jackrabbit
Lepus californicus

Cottontail and Brush Rabbits
Sylvilagus spp.

Rabbits and hares (collectively called "rabbits" in this section) can severely damage young trees by chewing bark off the trunk and clipping off low branches to eat buds and young foliage. Rabbits may also gnaw drip irrigation lines. Jackrabbits prefer trees bordering open areas, such as grassy fields and rangeland. Cottontail and brush rabbits prefer groves near brushy habitats, ravines, riparian areas, and woodlands favored by these species.

A jackrabbit is a hare about the size of a large house cat. It has very long ears, short front legs, and long hind legs. Jackrabbits live in open areas of the Central Valley, coastal valleys, and foothills. They make a depression underneath bushes or other vegetation where they remain secluded during the day. Jackrabbit young are born fully haired, with open eyes, and become active within a few hours. Cottontail and brush rabbits are smaller than jackrabbits and have shorter ears. They nest where thick shrubs, woods, or rocks and debris provide dense cover. Their young are born naked and blind and stay in the nest for several weeks.

Rabbits are active all year. They often live outside of groves, moving in to feed from early evening to early morn-

Jackrabbits are the most common pest rabbit. In contrast to brush rabbits, jackrabbits live in areas that are more open and they have much longer ears and longer hind legs.

Cottontail rabbits are smaller than jackrabbits and have shorter ears. They feed primarily from dusk until early morning.

ing. They damage trees primarily in winter and early spring, when other sources of food are limited. You can prevent damage with proper fencing or tree guards. You can also bait, shoot, or trap rabbits, depending on the species and the size of the population.

Management Guidelines

Periodically examine young trees for rabbit damage. If you find damage, look for droppings and tracks that indicate rabbits as the cause. Voles also chew the bark from the trunk, but the bark damage caused by rabbits extends higher on the tree and the tooth marks are distinctly larger. If you find damage, monitor the grove perimeters in early morning or late evening to see where the rabbits are entering and to get an idea of how many rabbits are involved. You can also estimate the number of rabbits at night by using a spotlight, which produces readily observed "eye shine." Once the trees are 4 or 5 years old, rabbits usually do not present a serious problem.

Fencing. Rabbit-proof fencing prevents damage to young groves. Make the fence at least 3 feet (0.9 m) tall using woven wire or poultry netting with a mesh diameter of 1 inch (25 mm) or less. Bend the bottom 6 inches (15 cm) of mesh at a 90-degree angle and bury it 6 inches deep, facing away from the grove, to keep rabbits from digging under the fence. If you are building a fence to exclude deer, and rabbits are a potential problem, it is a good idea to add rabbit-proof fencing along the bottom. Unless you are already building a deer fence, the cost of a rabbit fence may be prohibitive for a large grove when you are only going to need it for a few years. Individual tree guards are a good alternative.

A cylinder of $^1/_4$- to 1-inch (6–25 mm) mesh wire protects trees from rabbits. Tree guards should be at least 24 inches tall and wide enough to allow several years' growth without crowding the tree. Bury the bottom of the cylinder 2 to 3 inches (5–8 cm) deep and stake the cylinder away from the trunk so rabbits cannot press it against foliage.

Droppings help you to identify the vertebrate species in your grove. Rabbits scatter coarse, circular fecal pellets. These jackrabbit pellets are about $^1/_2$ inch (13 mm) in diameter. Cottontail pellets average about $^1/_4$ inch (6 mm).

Tree Guards. Tree guards are useful when planting new groves or replanting trees in established groves. Cylinders made from wire mesh or some hard plastics provide the best protection against rabbits. Cardboard or heavy paper can also be used, but rabbits may chew through these. Make the cylinders at least 2½ feet (75 cm) tall to keep jackrabbits from reaching foliage and limbs by standing on their hind legs. Secure the tree guards with stakes or wooden spreaders. Use smaller-mesh wire and bury the bottom few inches of the cylinder if you also need protection against voles.

Baiting. Poison baits may be practical for controlling large numbers of jackrabbits or for jackrabbits that are damaging trees over a large area. Baits are not registered for use on cottontail or brush rabbits. Before baiting, consult the county agricultural commissioner for restrictions related to endangered species. Follow label directions carefully.

Multiple-dose baits for jackrabbit control must be placed in bait stations specifically designed for rabbits. Place bait stations containing bait near trails and secure them so they cannot easily be tipped over. Use as many stations as necessary to ensure that all jackrabbits have easy access to bait, spacing them 50 to 200 feet (15–60 m) apart along the perimeter where jackrabbits are entering the grove. Inspect the bait stations every morning for the first several days to keep bait supplies replenished; it may take this long before the jackrabbits become accustomed to feeding at the stations. Increase either the amount of bait in the stations or the number of stations if all the bait is consumed in a single night. Replace any bait that becomes wet or moldy. It usually takes 2 to 4 weeks or more before results are seen with multiple-dose baits. Continue baiting until feeding ceases and you no longer observe any jackrabbits. Make sure to take precautions to prevent domestic animals and wildlife from having access to the bait. Dispose of unused bait properly at the end of the baiting program. Bury the rabbit carcasses on a regular basis.

Other Methods. Shooting, applying repellents, and trapping may provide effective control for small populations of rabbits, or may be used to temporarily reduce damage until other measures such as fences or tree guards are installed.

You can shoot all types of rabbits if they are causing damage to your grove and if shooting is allowed in your area. If only a small number of rabbits is involved, shooting may be all that is necessary to prevent significant damage while the trees are young. For best results, patrol the groves at dusk and early in the morning.

Repellents sprayed on foliage or painted on trunks may temporarily prevent rabbit damage. Labels specify the proper application timing. Repeat applications as needed to protect new growth and to replenish any repellent that is washed off by rain or sprinkler irrigation.

Suitable live-catch or kill traps can provide effective control for small populations of cottontail or brush rabbits. Trapping generally is ineffective against jackrabbits because they do not readily enter traps. For more information, consult publications such as *Rabbits Pest Notes* (Salmon and Gorenzel 2002), online at www.ipm.ucdavis.edu.

Deer

Odocoileus hemionus

Mule deer, including the subspecies called black-tailed deer (*Odocoileus hemionus columbianus*), can be serious pests when trees are young. Deer occur in many foothill and coastal groves and sometimes in the Central Valley near riparian habitats. Young trees can be severely stunted, deformed, or killed when deer browse on new shoots. Bucks occasionally break limbs off of smaller trees or injure the bark when they use trees to rub the velvet off their antlers. Deer feeding on older trees seldom causes significant damage.

W. P. GORENZEL

Young trees can be severely stunted, deformed, or killed when mule deer browse on new shoots. Deer feeding on older trees seldom causes significant damage.

Management Guidelines

Deer feed mostly at night. To confirm their presence, look for tracks and fecal pellets in the vicinity of damaged trees. Deer hooves are split, pointed at the front and more rounded at the rear, and are about 2 to 3 inches (5–7.6 cm) long. The appearance of droppings varies, but commonly each fecal pellet is oblong, somewhat pointed at one or both ends, and ¼ to ½ inch (6–13 mm) long. You may also use spotlights to check for deer at night. If deer are causing significant damage, deer-proof fencing provides the most effective and lasting control. Fencing also substantially reduces crop theft and vandalism. Fencing is costly, but if you are planting groves where deer and uninvited people are likely to present continuing problems, it will likely pay for itself in the long run.

Fencing. Fencing is most effective for excluding deer when it is put in place before you plant the grove. Fences must be at least 7 feet (2.1 m) high in order to exclude deer. On sloping terrain, an 8-foot (2.4 m) or taller fence may be necessary. Woven wire fences are used most often in California. Electric fences and mesh fences made of polypropylene are also used. Your choice of fence will be influenced by the potential severity and cost of deer damage, how long you expect to require protection, and the topography of the area. When encountering a fence, a deer will try to go under first, through second, and over last; keep these priorities in mind when building fences.

Woven Wire Fences. A fence made of woven wire excludes deer if the fence is tall enough. You can use a 6-foot (1.8 m) fence of woven wire with several strands of smooth or barbed wire along the top to extend the height to 7 or 8 feet (2.1–2.4 m). Be sure the fence is tight to the ground or deer will crawl under. Check the fence periodically to make sure it is in good repair and that no areas have washed out, allowing deer to crawl under the fence. Smaller-mesh fencing installed and properly buried along the bottom of the taller fence will exclude rabbits as well as deer.

Wire mesh cylinders around individual trees may be effective where only a few new trees are being planted in a location subject to deer damage. Make the cylinders at least 6 feet (1.8 m) tall and large enough in diameter to keep deer from reaching over them to eat the foliage. Secure the cylinders with stakes so they cannot be tipped over.

Electric Fences. Electric fencing is less expensive to install than woven mesh fencing but it costs more to maintain. High-tensile wire is the best choice, as it is more resilient than other types; it can absorb the impact of deer, falling limbs, and farm equipment without stretching or breaking. Use a high-voltage, low-impedance power source that provides sufficient voltage to repel deer while being less likely to short out when vegetation touches the wires. Control vegetation around the base of the fence; in wet weather, contact with wet foliage can drain enough voltage from the fence to render it ineffective.

Other Controls. Habitat management usually is not feasible for deer control because deer travel long distances to reach food. Repellents may offer some protection to tree foliage, at least for a short time, but they must be reapplied after rains or as new foliage emerges. Noisemaking devices may be effective for a few days, but deer will quickly grow

A well-maintained, sturdy fence 7 to 8 feet (2.1–2.4 m) tall encircling trees is the only completely effective deer control. Where deer are abundant, the lush foliage of irrigated avocado trees is highly attractive, and it's best to install fencing before the groves are planted.

accustomed to them. If only a few deer are involved, having someone patrol newly planted groves at night with a spotlight to frighten deer away may prove effective, though expensive. The California Department of Fish and Game can issue depredation permits to allow you to shoot deer when they are causing damage. This may be necessary if a deer gets inside a fenced grove and is not able to escape. Shooting will not solve a serious deer problem; it may, however, prevent damage long enough to allow you to construct a fence. For more information, consult publications such as *Deer Pest Notes* (Salmon, Whisson, and Marsh 2004), online at www.ipm.ucdavis.edu.

These clipped terminal shoots on a young avocado are characteristic of mule deer feeding. Damage may be so extensive that small limbs are eaten or broken, causing severe stunting and poor structural development of scaffold branches.

Harvest Management for Fruit Quality

Fruit is especially susceptible to fruit rot diseases, injury, and contamination during harvest and handling, up until the fruit arrives at the packinghouse. Good harvest and handling practices can prevent blemishes to the skin, mechanical damage or rotten skin or pulp, and discolored, dry, or off-flavor pulp that commonly develop after improper harvest and fruit handling. Anthracnose, stem end rot, and Dothiorella and Phytophthora fruit rots are important fruit decay pathogens that can develop after harvest as a result of improper management and fruit handling in the grove.

California avocados have a well-deserved reputation for quality, but all growers are subject to increasing demands and regulations to make food safer. Food contamination incidents involving human pathogens occur every year in the United States. Some agricultural sectors have suffered major adverse economic impacts because of food safety incidents. Growers and pickers must strive diligently to preserve food safety and prevent fruit contamination by animal and human pathogens during production, harvest, and handling. For more discussion, consult the resources in the suggested reading, such as *Growing for Quality: A Good Agricultural Practices Manual for California Avocados* (Witney 2005), *Postharvest Handling Systems: Subtropical Fruits* (Kader and Arpaia 2002), and *Guidance for Industry: Guide to Minimize Microbial Food Safety Hazards for Fresh Fruits and Vegetables* (this one available online at www.fda.gov).

Prevent Fruit Quality Problems

Reduce the incidence of fruit rots by pruning out dead limbs and knocking dead twigs from the tree canopies. Adjust sprinklers and prune tree skirts to minimize irrigation wetting of canopies and to keep fruit and foliage from touching the ground. Maintain a thick layer of mulch beneath trees to reduce splashing of soil and to hasten decomposition of soilborne pathogen propagules. Consult the fifth chapter, "Diseases," for more discussion of fruit rot prevention and management.

Place a high priority on minimizing chances of contact between animal and human fecal material and avocados. Human pathogens can contaminate fertilizers, growing and harvesting equipment, soils, water, and the workers themselves. Examine in and around groves regularly during production to identify and remedy any obvious sources of potential contamination. Once fruit become contaminated, pathogens are very difficult to remove.

Manage vertebrates in and around groves. Keep dogs and other pets out of the grove and away from fruit handling and storage areas. Use only properly composted manures. Prevent any fruit contact with water, such as surface water irrigation sources that may be contaminated with human or animal waste in runoff. Do not let the fruit contact the ground or anything contaminated with soil. Prevent any fruit contact with dirty or wet surfaces. Equipment, harvest tools, workers' hands, the insides of bins should be clean and dry.

California avocados have a well-deserved reputation for quality. But growers and pickers must strive diligently to avoid damaging fruit and to prevent contamination that could cause foodborne illnesses.

This fruit arrived at the packinghouse with a barely visible dark blotch on its skin. Phytophthora fruit rot that began in the grove was revealed by a cut into the flesh. Fruit rot prevention requires good grove management practices and proper fruit handling during harvest.

Work with local watershed groups and upstream and upslope neighbors to prevent and mitigate soil and water contamination. Methods include good irrigation management to prevent runoff, maintenance of a thick layer of mulch beneath trees, cover cropping, and vegetative filter strips around borders. Test irrigation water for fecal coliform bacteria several times each year. Disinfect (e.g., chlorinate) contaminated water or switch to a different, uncontaminated source. Keep records of all water test results and management actions. Use potable (drinking) water or other high-quality sources when diluting pesticides and other sprays.

Pick a Good Harvest Time

Check grove treatment records before you schedule picking. Follow any preharvest intervals for pesticides (the minimum time, required by law, after the last application before harvest is permitted). Do not pick when tree canopies or fruit are wet. Handling wet fruit favors infection by stem-end rots

Keep dogs and other pets out of the grove and away from fruit handling and storage areas to reduce the chance of contamination. Instruct and supervise workers and provide them with proper sanitation facilities.

and other decay pathogens and dramatically increases the incidence of postharvest fruit rot diseases. If conditions have been wet, wait until the fruit dry and then be extra careful to minimize injury during harvest and transport. Stem-end rot fungi enter fruit through cut stems. Body fruit rots enter through lenticels and injuries in the skin. The risks of pathogen contamination and disease development are especially high after wet conditions.

Prevent heat injury to fruit. Place thermometers in the grove and monitor temperatures. Avoid picking during and 1 to 2 hours before and after air temperatures exceed 90°F (32°C). If picking during hot conditions, harvest only from well-shaded portions of the canopies. Shade the field bins and transport the fruit especially quickly to the packinghouse.

When Picking Fruit

Instruct workers not to pick fruit that show chewing damage or bird droppings on the surface. Select-pick fruit to thin the fruit clusters and avoid harvesting mechanically injured or rotted fruit. Do not place rotted fruit or fruit with fresh wounds into field bins. Damaged fruit produces excess ethylene gas, and that causes nearby fruit to ripen too quickly or unevenly. Fruit that is injured (especially from rodent chewing) may constitute a food safety hazard.

Prevent fruit from contacting the ground. Do not pick fruit that is on the ground, on downed branches, or on lower limbs that touch the ground. If this fruit is too valuable to discard, handle it separately: for instance, subject it to a chlorinated cooling rinse. Provide clean tarps and instruct your harvest crew that fruit should be placed on the tarps if they do not carry it continuously from the tree to the bin. Clean and sterilize or replace the tarps frequently.

Pick fruit using hand clippers or picking poles. Cut the button to ⅛ inch (3 mm) or less to minimize fruit handling injury from stem buttons. Snap-picked fruit (where the stem has been bent until it breaks) is acceptable to some packinghouses in limited situations, such as after extended dry periods when pathogen inoculum is low. Keep clippers, bags, and bins clean. Scrub blades clean and disinfect them periodically during harvest and before moving into a new grove. Soak cleaned clippers in a registered disinfectant, such as a chlorine solution or quaternary ammonium compound, following the products' label directions.

Keep picking bags completely dry during harvest. Wash and dry picking bags periodically. Direct workers to remove all plant debris each time the picking bag is emptied by moving away from the field bins, then shaking any debris or dust out of their empty bags before they begin to pick again. Keep

These avocado limbs touching the ground favor fruit rot diseases and potential contamination of avocados by animal pathogens. Prune any low limbs to at least 2 feet off the ground to reduce the chance that fungal spores will splash from the soil and to keep sprinkler wetting of canopies to a minimum.

Do not harvest fruit that has been chewed or fouled by animals, such as this avocado contaminated with bird excrement.

twigs and leaves out of the bins and remove them if you see them.

Do not allow workers to stand in bins. Shoes are a common source of soilborne pathogens. Clean bins with a high-pressure wash, rinse, and sanitizing treatment when you bring them in from offsite, before you move them into groves. Immediately cover clean bins that you are not using to keep them from being contaminated by birds and other animals.

Educate and Manage Field Workers

Workers can unintentionally contaminate equipment, produce, other workers, and water supplies if they fail to use good hygiene. Teach and enforce proper, regular hand washing. Direct all workers to wash their hands before starting or returning to work, before and after eating or smoking, and after using the restroom. Educate workers on the importance of using the restroom instead of relieving themselves in the grove. Provide all workers with conveniently located and adequate toilet and hand-washing facilities, including soap. Prevent anyone with a suspected infectious disease, diarrhea, or an open lesion (boil, sore, or infected wound) from having direct contact with fruit.

Clean toilets, sinks, and hand-washing stations on a regular schedule. Empty, clean, and sanitize water containers regularly and refill them with potable water. Make sure facilities are well-stocked with clean water, soap, toilet paper, disposable paper towels or other sanitary hand-drying materials, and a waste container. Dispose of toilet wastes regularly and safely. Make sure that groves and water are not contaminated when the portable toilets are serviced. Dispose of wastes through a municipal sewage system, a sub-surface septic tank system, or a professional porta-potty service. Document or keep a log of your employee training and the regular maintenance and servicing of sanitary facilities.

After Fruit Are Picked

Place picked avocados into rigid bins that do not flex or cause rubbing injury when bins are moved. Place bins in a cool, covered or shaded area with good air movement to prevent heat injury and sunburn and to reduce water loss. Do not use avocado foliage to cover bins as it may contaminate

Direct your picking crew to cut the button to $1/8$ inch (3 mm) or less. Long fruit stems can cause mechanical injury to adjacent fruit in bags and bins. Decay pathogens commonly infect fruit through wounds.

Pick only when canopies and fruit are dry. Handling wet fruit such as this dramatically increases the likelihood of postharvest fruit rot diseases. If conditions have been wet, wait until the fruit dry before you harvest and be extra careful to minimize injury during harvest and transport.

Keep fruit off the ground, for instance by placing picked fruit on a clean tarp until you transfer the avocados to a bin. Place bins in a shady location or cover them with a dry tarp that has not contacted soil.

Workers inspect avocados at the packinghouse and hand-cull blemished and damaged fruit. A high proportion of low-quality fruit substantially reduces the grower's revenue.

Keeping fruit cooled to the proper temperature until it is marketed is critical to preserving fruit quality. Transport fruit promptly to the packinghouse where it will be chilled to minimize fruit rots, water loss, and other causes of decline in fruit quality.

the fruit with insects or pathogens. Keeps bins clean and free of any protrusions that might injure fruit.

Cover and transport fruit promptly to the packinghouse where it will be chilled after harvest to minimize water loss, decline in fruit quality, and fruit rots. Investigate whether postharvest treatment is warranted, such as a cold chlorine solution rinse (hydrocooling) to reduce pathogen propagules on fruit surfaces and subsequent rots. Transport fruit to the packinghouse once or twice daily. Maintain smooth access roads to minimize fruit damage from rough handling during transport. Do not leave full bins in the grove overnight where fruit quality will decline, and where avocados are more susceptible to vertebrate pest damage, theft, and potential tampering.

World Wide Web Sites

The Internet's World Wide Web is a vast source of information on crop production and pest management. Among the many resources available online through the Web are color photographs of crop damage, pests, and natural enemies, information on biology, management recommendations, decision-making models, and communication channels for pest control experts and practitioners. Here are some relevant Web sites and their online addresses (URLs):

Avocado. University of California Cooperative Extension, Ventura County (http://ceventura.ucdavis.edu).

Avocado Information Home Page. University of California, Riverside (www.ucavo.ucr.edu).

Avocado Source. Library of avocado knowledge. The Hofshi Foundation (http://avocadosource.com).

California Avocado Commission. (www.avocado.org).

California Avocado Society. (www.californiaavocadosociety.org).

California Irrigation Management Information System, CIMIS. (www.cimis.water.ca.gov/).

Center for Irrigation Technology. California State University, Fresno (www.wateright.org).

Endangered Species Project. California Department of Pesticide Regulation (www.cdpr.ca.gov/docs/es).

Exotic Pests. California Department of Food and Agriculture (www.cdfa.ca.gov/phpps).

Fungicide Resistance Action Committee, FRAC. (www.frac.info).

Herbicide Resistance Action Committee, HRAC. (www.plantprotection.org/hrac).

Insecticide Resistance Action Committee, IRAC. (www.irac-online.org).

Red Imported Fire Ant (RIFA) Program. California Department of Food and Agriculture (www.fireant.ca.gov).

Statewide Integrated Pest Management Program. University of California (www.ipm.ucdavis.edu).

Sustainable Agriculture Research and Education. United States Department of Agriculture (www.sare.org).

Sustainable Agriculture Research and Education Program. University of California, Davis (http://sarep.ucdavis.edu).

Weed Research and Information Center. University of California, Davis (http://wric.ucdavis.edu).

Suggested Reading[1]

The publications listed below are sources for further information and are organized here by general topic. For a list of publications that are cited in figures and tables as the sources of data and illustrations, see the Literature Cited, following this list.

Cultural Practices, Abiotic Disorders, Horticulture, and Water

The Avocado: Botany, Production, and Uses. 2002. A. W. Whiley, B. Schaffer, and B. N. Wolstenholme, eds. CABI: New York.

Avocado Fertilization. 1978. G. E. Goodall, T. W. Embleton, and R. G. Platt. UC ANR Publication 2024.

Avocado Fruit Abnormalities and Defects Revisited. 2002. R. Hofshi and M. L. Arpaia. California Avocado Society 2002 Yearbook 86: 147–162. Online at www.avocadosource.com/CAS_Yearbooks/CAS_86_2002/CAS_2002_PG_147-162.pdf.

Avocado Handbook. 2005. B. Faber. UC Cooperative Extension, Ventura County. Online at http://ceventura.ucdavis.edu/Agriculture265/Avocado_Handbook.htm.

Avocados. 2002. D. Silva, C. Lovatt, and B. O. Bergh. In *California Master Gardener Handbook*, D. R. Pittenger, ed. UC ANR Publication 3382.

Determining Daily Reference Evapotranspiration (Eto). 1987. R. L. Snyder, W. O. Pruitt, and D. A. Shaw. UC ANR Publication 21426.

Evapotranspiration and Irrigation Water Requirements. 1990. M. E. Jensen, R. D. Burman, and R. G. Allen, eds. ASCE Manuals and Reports on Engineering Practices No. 70., Am. Soc. Civil Engrs., New York.

Irrigation Scheduling: A Guide for Efficient On-Farm Management. 1989. D. A. Goldhamer and R. L. Snyder, eds. UC ANR Publication 21454.

Propagating Avocados: Principles and Techniques of Nursery and Field Grafting. 1989. R. H. Whitsell, G. E. Martin, B. O. Bergh, A. V. Lypps, and W. H. Brokan. UC ANR Publication 21461.

Protecting Groundwater Quality in Citrus Production. 1994. C. Ingels. UC ANR Publication 21521.

Water Management. 2002. J. Hartin and B. Faber. In *California Master Gardener Handbook*, D. R. Pittenger, ed. UC ANR Publication 3382.

Water Quality for Agriculture. 1994. R. S. Ayers and D. W. Westcot. Irrigation and Drainage Paper 29. Food and Agriculture organization. Rome, Italy. Online at www.fao.org/DOCREP/003/T0234E/T0234E00.htm#TOC.

Watershed Function. 2002. M. Padgett-Johnson and T. Bedell. Farm Water Quality Planning Reference Sheet 10.1. UC ANR Publication 8064.

Wateright. 2005. Center for Irrigation Technology, California State University, Fresno, CA. Online at www.wateright.org.

Western Fertilizer Handbook: 9th Edition. 2001. California Plant Health Association. Interstate, Sacramento, CA.

Diseases

Avocado: UC IPM Pest Management Guidelines: Diseases. 2007. B. A. Faber, G. S. Bender, and H. D. Ohr. University of California Statewide Integrated Pest Management Program. UC ANR Publication 3436.

Avocado Root Rot. 1991. G. A. Zentmyer and H. D. Ohr. UC ANR Publication 2440.

Citrus: UC IPM Pest Management Guidelines: Diseases. 2003. H. D. Ohr and J. A. Menge. University of California Statewide Integrated Pest Management Program. UC ANR Publication 3441.

Diseases of Avocado. 2004. J. A. Menge and R. C. Ploetz. In *Diseases of Tropical Fruit Crops*, R. C. Ploetz, ed. CABI Publishing. Wallingford, Oxfordshire, UK.

Fungi on Plants and Plant Products in the United States. 1989. D. F. Farr, G. F. Bills, G. P. Chamuris, and A. Y. Rossman. American Phytopathological Society, St. Paul, MN.

Plant Pathology. 4th ed. 1997. G. N. Agrios. Academic Press. San Diego, CA.

Plants Resistant or Susceptible to Verticillium Wilt. 1981. A. H. McCain, R. D. Raabe, and S. Wilhelm. UC ANR Publication 2703.

Soil Solarization: A Natural Mechanism of Integrated Pest Management. 1995. J. J. Stapleton and J. E. DeVay. In *Novel Approaches to Integrated Pest Management*, R. Reuveni, ed. Lewis Publishers. Boca Raton, FL.

Economics

Economic Evaluation of California Avocado Industry Marketing Programs: 1961–1995. 1998. H. F. Carman and R. K. Craft. Univ. Calif. Giannini Foundation Research Reports 345. Davis, CA.

Economic Trends in the California Avocado Industry. Rev. 1988. E. Takele. UC ANR Publication 2356.

Growing Avocados in the San Joaquin Valley. 1983. J. H. LaRue. UC ANR Publication 2904.

---

1. Many University of California Publications are available for free download or purchase via the World Wide Web. Look online at http://anrcatalog.ucdavis.edu or www.ipm.ucdavis.edu.

2. Publication is out of print. You may be able to find a reference copy at a library.

Integrated Pest Managment

Avocado: UC IPM Pest Management Guidelines. 2007. B. A. Faber, G. S. Bender, and H. D. Ohr (Diseases); P. A. Phillips, B. A. Faber, J. G. Morse, and M. S. Hoddle (Insects and Mites); B. A. Faber, A. Shrestha, W. T. Lanini, C. A. Wilen, and P. A. Phillips (Weeds). University of California Statewide Integrated Pest Management Program. UC ANR Publication 3436.

Avocado Year-Round IPM Program. 2007. University of California Statewide Integrated Pest Management Program. Online at www.ipm.ucdavis.edu.

Citrus: UC IPM Pest Management Guidelines. 2003. H. D. Ohr and J. A. Menge (Diseases); E. E. Grafton-Cardwell, J. G. Morse, N. V. O'Connell, P. A. Phillips, C. E. Kallsen, and D. R. Haviland (Insects, Mites, and Snails); J. O. Becker and B. B. Westerdahl (Nematodes); C. W. Coggins and C. J. Lovatt (Plant Growth Regulators); A. Shrestha and N. V. O'Connell (Weeds). University of California Statewide Integrated Pest Management Program. UC ANR Publication 3441.

Diseases, Pests, and Natural Enemies of Coastal Avocados. 1996. P. Phillips. UC ANR Publication 21535.

Integrated Pest Management for Almonds. 2nd ed. 2002. L. L. Strand. University of California Statewide Integrated Pest Management Program. UC ANR Publication 3308.

Integrated Pest Management for Citrus. 2nd ed. 1991. University of California Statewide Integrated Pest Management Program. UC ANR Publication 3303.

Integrated Pest Management for Walnuts. 3rd ed. 2003. L. L. Strand. University of California Statewide Integrated Pest Management Program. UC ANR Publication 3270.

IPM in Practice: Principles and Methods of Integrated Pest Management. 2001. M. L. Flint and P. Gouveia. University of California Statewide Integrated Pest Management Program. UC ANR Publication 3418.

Invertebrates

Amorbia: A California Avocado Insect Pest. 1980. J. B. Bailey and M. P. Hoffmann. UC ANR Publication 21156.

Avocado: UC IPM Pest Management Guidelines: Insects and Mites. 2007. P. A. Phillips, B. A. Faber, J. G. Morse, and M. S. Hoddle. University of California Statewide Integrated Pest Management Program. UC ANR Publication 3436.

Citrus: UC IPM Pest Management Guidelines: Insects, Mites, and Snails. 2003. E. E. Grafton-Cardwell, J. G. Morse, N. V. O'Connell, P. A. Phillips, C. E. Kallsen, and D. R. Haviland. University of California Statewide Integrated Pest Management Program. UC ANR Publication 3441.

Color-Photo and Host Keys to California Whiteflies. 1982. R. J. Gill. Scale and Whitefly Key #2. Calif. Dept. Food Agric., Sacramento, CA.[2]

Color-Photo and Host Keys to the Armored Scales of California. 1982. R. J. Gill. Scale and Whitefly Key #5. Calif. Dept. Food Agric., Sacramento, CA.[2]

Color-Photo and Host Keys to the Mealybugs of California. 1982. R. J. Gill. Scale and Whitefly Key #3. Calif. Dept. Food Agric., Sacramento, CA.[2]

Color-Photo and Host Keys to the Soft Scales of California. 1982. R. J. Gill. Scale and Whitefly Key #4. Calif. Dept. Food Agric., Sacramento, CA.[2]

Common Names of Arachnids. 1995. R. G. Breene. American Tarantula Society. South Padre Island, TX.

Common Names of Insects & Related Organisms 1997. 1997. J. J. Bosik, ed. Entomological Society of America. Lanham, MD.

Destructive and Useful Insects. 5th ed. 1993. R. L. Metcalf and R. A. Metcalf. McGraw-Hill, New York.

Diaprepes Root Weevil. 2004. E. E. Grafton-Cardwell, K. E. Godfrey, J. E. Peña, C. W. McCoy, and R. F. Luck. UC ANR Publication 8131.

Key to Identifying Common Household Ants. 2004. C. A. Reynolds. University of California Statewide Integrated Pest Management Program. Online at www.ipm.ucdavis.edu/TOOLS/ANTKEY.

A Key to the Most Common and/or Economically Important Ants of California, with Color Photographs. 1983. P. Haney, P. A. Philips, and R. Wagner. UC ANR Publication 21433.

Life Stages of California Red Scale and Its Parasitoids. 1995. L. D. Forster, R. F. Luck, and E. E. Grafton-Cardwell. UC ANR Publication 21529.

Managing Insects and Mites with Spray Oils. 1991. N. A. Davidson, J. E. Dibble, M. L. Flint, P. J. Marer, and A. Guye. UC ANR Publication 3347.

Mealybugs in California Vineyards. 2002. K. E. Godfrey, K. M. Daane, W. J. Bentley, R. J. Gill, and R. Malakar-Kuenen. UC ANR Publication 21612.

Natural Enemies Are Your Allies! 1990. M. L. Flint and J. K. Clark. (Poster.) UC ANR Publication 21497.

Natural Enemies Handbook: The Illustrated Guide to Biological Pest Control. 1998. M. L. Flint and S. H. Dreistadt. UC ANR Publication 3386.

Omnivorous Looper on Avocados in California. 1979. J. B. Bailey and M. P. Hoffmann. UC ANR Publication 21101.

The Scale Insects of California, Part 1: The Soft Scales. R. J. Gill. 1988. Calif. Dept. of Food Agric. Sacramento, CA.

The Scale Insects of California, Part 2: The Minor Families. R. J. Gill. 1993. Calif. Dept. of Food Agric. Sacramento, CA.

The Scale Insects of California, Part 3: The Armored Scales. R. J. Gill. 1997. Calif. Dept. of Food Agric. Sacramento, CA.

1. Many University of California Publications are available for free download or purchase via the World Wide Web. Look online at http://anrcatalog.ucdavis.edu or www.ipm.ucdavis.edu.

2. Publication is out of print. You may be able to find a reference copy at a library.

Pesticides

Classification of Herbicides According to Mode of Action. 2005. Herbicide Resistance Action Committee (HRAC). Online at www.plantprotection.org/HRAC.

Classification of Insecticides According to Mode of Action. 2005. Insecticide Resistance Action Committee (IRAC). Online at www.irac-online.org.

Fungicides Sorted by Modes of Action. 2005. Fungicide Resistance Action Committee (FRAC). Online at www.frac.info.

Managing Insects and Mites with Spray Oils. 1991. N. A. Davidson, J. E. Dibble, M. L. Flint, P. J. Marer, and A. Guye. UC ANR Publication 3347.

Pesticide Safety: A Reference Manual for Growers. 1998. P. J. O'Connor-Marer. University of California Statewide Integrated Pest Management Program. UC ANR Publication 3383.

Pesticide Safety: A Reference Manual for Private Applicators. 2nd. ed. 2006. P. J. O'Connor-Marer and S. Cohen. University of California Statewide Integrated Pest Management Program. UC ANR Publication 3383.

Pesticides: Theory and Application. G. W. Ware. 1983. W. H. Freeman. San Francisco.

Plants Resistant or Susceptible to Verticillium Wilt. 1981. A. H. McCain, R. D. Raabe, and S. Wilhelm. UC ANR Publication 2703.

The Safe and Effective Use of Pesticides. 2nd ed. 2000. P. J. O'Connor-Marer. University of California Statewide Integrated Pest Management Program. UC ANR Publication 3324.

Postharvest Quality and Food Safety

Growing for Quality: A Good Agricultural Practices Manual for California Avocados. 2005. G. W. Witney. California Avocado Commission. Irvine, CA. Online at www.avocado.org/growers.

Guidance for Industry: Guide to Minimize Microbial Food Safety Hazards for Fresh Fruits and Vegetables. 1998. Food Safety Initiative Staff. U.S. Food and Drug Administration HFS-32. Washington, DC. Online at www.fda.gov.

Postharvest Handling Systems: Subtropical Fruits. 2002. A. A. Kader and M. L. Arpaia. In *Postharvest Technology of Horticultural Crops,* A. A. Kader, ed. UC ANR Publication 3311.

Vertebrates

California Ground Squirrel Pest Notes. 2002. T. P. Salmon and W. P. Gorenzel. University of California Statewide Integrated Pest Management Program. UC ANR Publication 7438.

Deer Pest Notes. 2004. T. P. Salmon, D. A. Whisson, and R. E. Marsh. University of California Statewide Integrated Pest Management Program. UC ANR Publication 74117.

House Mouse Pest Notes. 2000. R. M. Timm. University of California Statewide Integrated Pest Management Program. UC ANR Publication 7483.

Norway Rats. 1994. R. M. Timm. In *Prevention and Control of Wildlife Damage,* Vol. 1, S. E. Hygnstrom, R. M. Timm, and G. E. Larson, eds. Lincoln: Univ. Neb. Coop. Ext. pp. B.105–120.

Opossum Pest Notes. 2005. T. P. Salmon, D. A. Whisson, and R. W. Marsh. University of California Statewide Integrated Pest Management Program. UC ANR Publication 74123.

Pocket Gophers Pest Notes. 2002. T. P. Salmon and W. P. Gorenzel. University of California Statewide Integrated Pest Management Program. UC ANR Publication 7433.

Rabbits Pest Notes. 2002. T. P. Salmon and W. P. Gorenzel. University of California Statewide Integrated Pest Management Program. UC ANR Publication 7447.

Raccoon Pest Notes. 2004. T. P. Salmon, D. A. Whisson, and R. W. Marsh. University of California Statewide Integrated Pest Management Program. UC ANR Publication 74116.

Rats Pest Notes. 2003. T. P. Salmon, R. W. Marsh, and R. M. Timm. University of California Statewide Integrated Pest Management Program. UC ANR Publication 74106.

Roof Rats. 1994. R. E. Marsh. In *Prevention and Control of Wildlife Damage,* Vol. 1, S. E. Hygnstrom, R. M. Timm, and G. E. Larson, eds. Lincoln: Univ. Neb. Coop. Ext. pp. B.125–132.

Tree Squirrels Pest Notes. 2005. T. P. Salmon, D. A. Whisson, and R. W. Marsh. University of California Statewide Integrated Pest Management Program. UC ANR Publication 74122.

Voles (Meadow Mice) Pest Notes. 2002. T. P. Salmon and W. P. Gorenzel. University of California Statewide Integrated Pest Management Program. UC ANR Publication 7439.

Wildlife Pest Control around Gardens and Homes. 2nd ed. 2006. T. P. Salmon, D. A. Whisson, and R. E. Marsh. UC ANR Publication 21385.

Weeds

Annual Bluegrass Pest Notes. 2003. D. W. Cudney, C. L. Elmore, and V. A. Gibeault. University of California Statewide Integrated Pest Management Program. UC ANR Publication 7464.

Avocado: UC IPM Pest Management Guidelines: Weeds. 2007. B. A. Faber, A. Shrestha, W. T. Lanini, C. A. Wilen, and P. A. Phillips. University of California Statewide Integrated Pest Management Program. UC ANR Publication 3436.

Bermudagrass Pest Notes. 2002. C. L. Elmore and D. W. Cudney. University of California Statewide Integrated Pest Management Program. UC ANR Publication 7453.

1. Many University of California Publications are available for free download or purchase via the World Wide Web. Look online at http://anrcatalog.ucdavis.edu or www.ipm.ucdavis.edu.

2. Publication is out of print. You may be able to find a reference copy at a library.

Composite List of Weeds. 1989. J. F. Alex, G. A. Bozarth, C. T. Bryson, J. W. Everest, E. P. Flint, F. Forcella, D. W. Hall, H. F. Harrison, Jr., L. W. Hendrick, L. G. Holm, D. E. Seaman, V. Sorensen, H. V. Strek, R. H. Walker, and D. T. Patterson. Weed Science Society of America. Champaign, IL.

Cover Cropping in Vineyards. 1998. C. A. Ingels, R. L. Bugg, G. T. McGourty, and L. P. Christensen, eds. UC ANR Publication 3338.

Covercrops for California Agriculture. 1989. P. R. Miller, W. L. Graves, W. A. Williams, and B. A. Madison. UC ANR Publication 21471.

Crabgrass Pest Notes. 2002. C. L. Elmore. University of California Statewide Integrated Pest Management Program. UC ANR Publication 7456.

Field Bindweed Pest Notes. 2003. C. L. Elmore and D. W. Cudney. University of California Statewide Integrated Pest Management Program. UC ANR Publication 7462.

Managing Cover Crops Profitably. 2nd ed. 1998. Sustainable Agriculture Network. Beltsville, MD: USDA Sustainable Agriculture Research & Education. Online at www.sare.org.

Nutsedge Pest Notes. 2003. C. A. Wilen, M. E. McGiffen, and C. L. Elmore. University of California Statewide Integrated Pest Management Program. UC ANR Publication 7432.

Puncturevine Pest Notes. 2006. C. A. Wilen. University of California Statewide Integrated Pest Management Program. UC ANR Publication 74128.

Soil Solarization: A Natural Mechanism of Integrated Pest Management. 1995. J. J. Stapleton and J. E. DeVay. In *Novel Approaches to Integrated Pest Management,* R. Reuveni, ed. Lewis Publ. 309–322. Boca Raton, FL.

Soil Solarization: A Nonpesticidal Method for Controlling Diseases, Nematodes, and Weeds. 1997. C. L. Elmore, J. J. Stapleton, C. E. Bell, and J. E. DeVay. UC ANR Publication 21377.

Weeds of California. 1970. W. Robbins, M. Bellue, and W. Ball. State of California Documents and Publications. North Highlands, CA.

Weeds of California and Other Western States. 2007. J. M. DiTomaso and E. A. Healy. UC ANR Publication 3488.

Weeds of the West. 1991. T. D. Whitson, L. C. Burrill, S. A. Dewey, D. W. Cudney, B. E. Nelson, R. D. Lee, and R. Parker. Wyoming Agric. Extension. Jackson, WY. (Available as UC ANR Publication 3350.).

1. Many University of California Publications are available for free download or purchase via the World Wide Web. Look online at http://anrcatalog.ucdavis.edu or www.ipm.ucdavis.edu.
2. Publication is out of print. You may be able to find a reference copy at a library.

Literature Cited[1]

The publications listed here are cited in this book's figures and tables as the sources of information and illustrations. For publications referenced in the text as recommend sources for further information, see the Suggested Reading list.

Anonymous. 1952. *The Yearbook of Agriculture: Insects*. Washington, DC: U.S. Dept. Agric.

Aponte, O., and J. A. McMurtry. 1997. Biology, life table, and mating behavior of *Oligonychus perseae* (Acari: Tetranychidae). *International Journal of Acarology* 23:199–207.

Arpaia, M. L. 2000. *Enhancement of Avocado Productivity*. Proceedings of the California Avocado Research Symposium 2000. Carpinteria, CA: California Avocado Society.

Bailey, D., and T. Bilderback. 1998. *Alkalinity Control for Irrigation Water Used in Nurseries and Greenhouses*. Raleigh: North Carolina Cooperative Extension Service. Horticulture Information Leaflet HIL #558. Online at www.ces.ncsu.edu/depts/hort/hil/hil-558.html.

Bailey, L. H. 1941. *The Standard Cyclopedia of Horticulture*. Volume 3. New York: McMillan.

Bender, G., J. Menge, and M. L. Arpaia. 2003. Avocado Rootstocks. University of California Cooperative Extension. *Topics in Subtropics* 1(3):7–8.

Bettiga, L. J., H. Kido, and N. F. McCalley. 1992. Orange Tortrix. In *Grape Pest Management*, 2nd. ed. Oakland: UC ANR Publication 4105.

CAC and CMCC. 2003. *A Pest Management Strategic Plan for Avocado Production in California*. Irvine, CA: California Avocado Commission and California Minor Crops Council.

CAS. 1976. *Avocado Varieties for Commercial Planting in California*. Saticoy, CA: California Avocado Society.

Cutting, J., and J. Dixon, eds. 2001. *Growers' Manual*. Tauranga, New Zealand: New Zealand Avocado Growers Association.

Faber, B. 2005. *Avocado Handbook*. University of California Cooperative Extension, Ventura County. Online at http://ceventura.ucdavis.edu/Agriculture265/Avocado_Handbook.htm.

Flint, M. L. 1995. *Whiteflies in California: A Resource for Cooperative Extension*. Davis: University of California Statewide Integrated Pest Management Program Publication 19.

Food and Agriculture Organization. 1994, 2004. FAOSTAT. The United Nations. Online at http://faostat.fao.org.

FRAC. 2005. *Fungicides Sorted by Modes of Action*. Fungicide Resistance Action Committee. Online at www.frac.info.

Gill, R. J. 1997. Thrips. *Calif. Plant Pest Disease Report* 16(3–6):33.

Heidemann, O. 1909. *Two New Species of North American Tingidae*. Proc. Entomol. Soc. Washington. 10:103–9.

Hoddle, M. S. 2002. Developmental and reproductive biology of *Scirtothrips perseae* (Thysanoptera: Thripidae): A new avocado pest in California. *Bulletin of Entomological Research* 92:279–285.

Hoddle, M. S., and J. G. Morse. 2003. Avocado Thrips Biology and Control. *AvoResearch*. Santa Ana, CA: California Avocado Commission.

HRAC. 2005. *Classification of Herbicides According to Mode of Action*. Herbicide Resistance Action Committee. Online at www.plantprotection.org/hrac.

IRAC. 2005. *Classification of Insecticides According to Mode of Action*. Insecticide Resistance Action Committee. Online at www.irac-online.org.

Jones, T. W., and W. W. Embleton. 1966. Avocado and mango nutrition. In *Temperate to Tropical Fruit Nutrition*, N. F. Childers, ed., pp. 51–76. Hort. Publ., New Brunswick, NJ: Rutgers State Univ.

Klitz, B. F. 1930. Perennial weeds which spread vegetatively. *Journal of the American Society of Agronomy* 22:216–234.

Kono, T., and C. S. Papp. 1977. *Handbook of Agricultural Pests: Aphids, Thrips, Mites, Snails, and Slugs*. Sacramento, CA: Calif. Depart. Food Agric.

Lee, B. W. 1979. *Selection, Planting, and Care of Avocado Trees*. Oakland: UC ANR Publication 2208.

Lee, B. W. 1980. *Avocado Leaf Analysis Guide*. University of California Cooperative Extension, Ventura County. Online at http://ceventura.ucdavis.edu/ben/avo_handbook/fertilization/leaf_analysis.htm.

Marer, P. J. 1991. *Residential, Industrial, and Institutional Pest Control*. Oakland. UC ANR Publication 3334.

McGregor, S. E. 1976. *Insect Pollination of Cultivated Crop Plants*. U.S. Dept. Agric. Handb. 496. Washington, DC.

McKenzie. H. L. 1935. *Life History and Control of the Gladiolus Thrips in California*. Calif. Agric. Exp. Sta. Circ. 337:1–16.

Meyer, J. L., M. V. Yates, D. E. Stottlemyer, E. Takele, M. L. Arpaia, G. S. Bender, and G. W. Witney. 1992. *Irrigation and Fertilization Management of Avocados*. Proc. Second World Avocado Congress, pp. 281–288. Orange, CA.

Moznette, G. F. 1922. *The Red Spider Mite on the Avocado*. U.S. Dept. Agric. Bull. 1035.

National Agricultural Statistics Service. 2005. *Noncitrus Fruits and Nuts 2004 Summary*. Washington, DC: United States Department of Agriculture. Online at www.nass.usda.gov.

1. Many University of California Publications are available for free download or purchase via the World Wide Web. Look online at http://anrcatalog.ucdavis.edu or www.ipm.ucdavis.edu.

Padgett-Johnson, M., and T. Bedell. 2002. *Watershed Function*. Farm Water Quality Planning Reference Sheet 10.1. Oakland: UC ANR Publication 8064.

Salmon, T. P., and R. E. Lickliter. 1984. *Wildlife Pest Control around Gardens and Homes*. 1st ed. Oakland: UC ANR Publication 21385.

Salmon, T. P., D. A. Whisson, and R. E. Marsh. 2006. *Wildlife Pest Control around Gardens and Homes*. 2nd ed. Oakland: UC ANR Publication 21385.

Simanton, F. L. 1916. *Hyperaspis binotata*, a predatory enemy of the terrapin scale. *J. Agricultural Research* 6:197–204.

Smith, M. H. 1965. *House-Infesting Ants of the Eastern United States*. U. S. Dept. Agric. Tech. Bull. 1326.

Smith, R. F., and K. S. Hagen. 1956. Enemies of spotted alfalfa aphid. *Calif. Agric.* 10(4):8–10.

Strand, L. L. 2002. *Integrated Pest Management for Almonds*. 2nd ed. University of California Statewide Integrated Pest Management Program. Oakland: UC ANR Publication 3308.

Tomlinson, P. B. (with illustrations by P. Fawcett). 1980. *The Biology of Trees Native to Tropical Florida*. Allston, MA: Harvard University Printing Office.

Truog, E. 1948. Lime in relation to availability of plant nutrients. *Soil Science* 65:1–7.

Watson, G. W. 2005. *Neohydatothrips* sp. (probably *N. burungae* (Hood)) (Thripidae) A thrips. Sacramento, CA: Calif. Plant Pest Disease Report 22(1):21–23.

Whisson, D. 1997a. *Elevated Bait Station for Ground Squirrel Control in Kangaroo Rat Habitat*. Sacramento, CA: Calif. Dept. Pesticide Regulation Endangered Species Project. Online at www.cdpr.ca.gov/docs/es/espdfs/baitsta1.pdf.

Whisson, D. 1997b. *Modifying a "T" Bait Station for Ground Squirrel Control in Kangaroo Rat Habitat*. Sacramento, CA: Calif. Dept. Pesticide Regulation Endangered Species Project. Online at www.cdpr.ca.gov/docs/es/espdfs/baitsta2.pdf.

Wilcox, W. F. 1992. Phytophthora Root and Crown Rots, *Phytophthora* spp. (deBary). New York State Agricultural Experiment Station Tree Fruit Crops IPM Disease Identification Sheet No. 7. Geneva, NY: Cornell University.

List of Tables and Figures

Tables

Figures

Glossary

abdomen. the posterior of the three main body divisions of an insect.

abiotic disorder. a disease caused by factors other than pathogens.

aestivation (also estivation). a state of inactivity during the summer months.

annual. a plant that normally completes its life cycle of seed germination, vegetative growth, reproduction, and death in a single year.

anther. the pollen-producing organ of a flower (see Figure 4).

anticoagulant. a substance that prevents blood clotting, resulting in internal hemorrhaging; may be used as a rodenticide.

auricles. the earlike projections at the base of leaves of some grasses; used to identify species (see Figure 39).

axil. the upper angle between a leaf and the stem from which it is growing.

biofix. an identifiable event in the life cycle of a pest that signals when to begin degree-day accumulation or take a management action.

biotic disease. a disease caused by a pathogen, such as a bacterium, fungus, phytoplasma, or virus.

biotype. a strain of a species that has certain biological characters distinguishing it from other individuals of that species.

calcareous soils. soils containing high levels of calcium carbonate.

calibrate. to standardize or correct measuring devices on instruments; to properly adjust nozzles on a spray rig.

cambium. thin layer of undifferentiated, actively dividing cells that produces new bark (phloem) on the outside and new wood (xylem) on the inside (see Figure 5).

canker. a dead, discolored, and often sunken area (lesion) on a root, trunk, stem, or branch.

caterpillar. the larva of a butterfly or moth.

chlorophyll. the green pigment of plant cells, necessary for photosynthesis.

chlorosis. yellowing or bleaching of normally green plant tissue, usually caused by the loss of chlorophyll.

chorion. the outer membrane of an insect egg.

cocoon. a sheath, usually mostly of silk, formed by an insect larva as a chamber for pupation.

collar region. in grasses, the region where the leaf blade and sheath meet; used in identifying species (see Figure 39).

conidium (plural, conidia). an asexual fungal spore formed by fragmentation or budding at the tip of a specialized hypha.

cotyledons. the first leaves of the embryo formed within a seed and present on seedlings immediately after germination; seed leaves (see Figure 39).

crawler. the active first instar of a scale insect.

cross-resistance. in pest management, resistance of a pest population to a pesticide to which it *has not* been exposed that accompanies the development of resistance to a pesticide to which it *has* been exposed.

crown. the point at or just below the soil surface where the main stem (trunk) and roots join.

cultivar. a variety or strain developed and grown under cultivation.

degree-day (DD). a measurement unit that combines temperature and time; used in calculating growth rates.

developmental threshold. the lowest temperature at which growth occurs in a given species.

diapause. a period of physiologically controlled dormancy in insects.

disease. any disturbance of a plant that interferes with its normal structure, function, or economic value.

economic threshold. a level of pest population or damage at which the cost of a control action equals the crop value gained from that control action.

ectoparasite. a parasite that lives on the outside of its host.

endoparasite. a parasite that lives inside its host.

epidermis. the outermost layer of cells on the bodies of animals or on plant surfaces.

estivation. see *aestivation.*

evapotranspiration. the loss of soil moisture by the combined mechanisms of soil surface evaporation and transpiration by plants.

feeder roots. the youngest roots with root hairs, most important in absorption of water and minerals.

frass. a mixture of feces and food fragments produced by an insect in feeding.

fumigation. treatment with a pesticide active ingredient that is in gaseous form under treatment conditions.

girdle. to kill or damage a ring of bark tissue around a stem or root; such damage interrupts the transport of water and nutrients.

honeydew. an excretion from insects, such as aphids, mealybugs, whiteflies, and soft scales, consisting of modified plant sap.

hypha (plural, hyphae). a tubular filament that is the structural unit of a fungus.

indexing. testing a plant for a virus infection, usually by grafting tissue from it onto an indicator plant.

infection. the entry of a pathogen into a host and establishment of the pathogen as a parasite in the host.

inflorescence. a flower cluster.

inoculum. any part or stage of a pathogen, such as a spore or virus particle, that can infect a host.

instar. an insect between successive molts; the first instar is between hatching and the first molt.

internode. the area of a stem between nodes.

invertebrate. an animal having no internal skeleton.

larva (plural, larvae). the immature form of an insect that hatches from an egg, feeds, and then enters a pupal stage.

lesion. a well-defined area of diseased tissue, such as a canker or leaf spot.

ligule. in many grasses, a short, membranous projection on the inner side of the leaf blade at the junction where the leaf blade and leaf sheath meet (see Figure 39).

metamorphosis. a change in form during development.

microorganism. an organism of microscopic or small size.

molt. in insects and other arthropods, the shedding of skin before entering another stage of growth.

mutation. the abrupt appearance of a new, heritable characteristic as the result of a change in the genetic material of one individual cell.

mycelium (plural, mycelia). the vegetative body of a fungus, consisting of a mass of slender filaments called hyphae.

natural enemies. predators, parasites, or pathogens that are considered beneficial to crops because they attack and kill organisms that we normally consider to be pests.

necrosis. the death of tissue accompanied by dark brown discoloration, usually occurring in a well-defined part of a plant such as the portion of a leaf between leaf veins or in the xylem or phloem in a stem or tuber.

node. the slightly enlarged part of a stem where buds are formed and where leaves, stems, and flowers originate.

nymph. the immature stage of insects such as plant bugs and aphids that hatch from eggs and gradually acquire adult form through a series of molts without passing through a pupal stage.

oviposit. to lay or deposit eggs.

parasite. an organism that lives in or on the body of another organism (the host) without killing the host directly; in this manual the term is also used to refer to insect parasitoids, which spend their immature stages on or within the body of a single host that dies before the parasite emerges.

pathogen. a disease-causing organism.

pathogenic. capable of causing disease.

perennial. a plant that may live three or more seasons and flower at least twice.

pest resurgence. the increase of a pest population following a pesticide treatment to levels higher than before the treatment as a result of the pesticide having killed natural enemies of the pest.

petiole. the stalk connecting the leaf to a stem.

pheromone. a chemical produced by an animal to communicate with other members of its species. Sex pheromones that attract the opposite sex for mating are used in monitoring certain insects.

phloem. the food-conducting tissue of a plant's vascular system (see Figure 5).

photosynthesis. the process whereby plants use light energy to form sugars and other compounds needed to support growth and development.

phytotoxic. of a material such as a pesticide or fertilizer, causing injury to plants.

pistil. the female part of a flower, usually consisting of ovules, ovary, style, and stigma (see Figure 4).

predator. an animal that attacks and feeds on other animals (its prey), usually consuming many prey during its lifetime.

preemergence herbicide. an herbicide applied before target weeds emerge.

propagule. any part of a plant from which a new plant can grow, including seeds, bulbs, rootstocks, etc.

prothorax. the anterior of the three thoracic segments of an insect.

pupa (plural, pupae). the nonfeeding, inactive stage between larva and adult in insects with complete metamorphosis.

resistant. able to tolerate conditions harmful to other individuals of the same species.

rhizome. a horizontal underground stem, especially one that roots at the nodes to produce new plants (see Figures 35 and 39).

rootstock. an underground stem or rhizome; the lower portion of a graft that makes up the crown and root system.

rosette. a cluster of leaves arranged in a compact circular pattern, often at a shoot tip or on a shortened stem.

scion. the portion above a graft that becomes the trunk, branch, and tree top; the cultivar or variety used for that part of a graft.

secondary pest outbreak. the sudden increase in a pest population that is normally at low or nondamaging levels caused by the destruction of natural enemies by treatment with a nonselective pesticide to control a primary pest.

sedges. a group of grasslike, herbaceous plants that, unlike grasses, have unjointed stems. Stems are usually solid and often triangular in cross-section.

seed leaf. the first leaf (grasses) or first two leaves (broad-leaf plants) on a seedling; cotyledons (see Figure 39).

seedling rootstock. a rootstock propagated from seed.

seta (plural, setae). a bristle.

sheath. the part of a grass leaf that encloses the stem below the collar region (see Figure 39).

soil profile. a vertical section of the soil through all its horizontal layers, extending into the parent material.

spiracle. an external opening of the system of ducts, or tracheae, that serves as a respiratory system in insects.

sporangium. a structure containing asexual spores.

spore. a reproductive body produced by certain fungi and other organisms and capable of growing into a new individual under proper conditions.

stamen. a flower structure made up of the pollen-bearing anther and a stalk or filament (see Figure 4).

stigma. the receptive portion of the female flower part to which pollen adheres.

stolon. a stem that grows horizontally along the surface of the ground, often rooting at the nodes and forming new plants (see Figure 39).

stoma (plural, stomata or stomates). a natural opening in a leaf surface that serves for gas exchange and water evaporation and has the ability to open and close in response to environmental conditions.

systemic herbicide. an herbicide that is able to move throughout a plant after being applied to leaf surfaces (*translocated herbicide*).

taproot. a large primary root that grows vertically downward, giving off small lateral roots.

tensiometer. an instrument that measures how tightly water is held by the soil; used for estimating water content of the soil.

thorax. the second of three major divisions in the body of an insect, and the one bearing the legs and wings.

tolerant. able to withstand the effects of a condition without suffering serious injury or death.

translocated herbicide. a systemic herbicide.

transpiration. the evaporation of water from plant tissue, usually through stomata.

treatment threshold. a level of pest population or damage, usually measured by a specified monitoring method, at which a pesticide application is recommended.

true leaf. any leaf produced after the cotyledons (see Figure 39).

tuber. a much-enlarged, fleshy underground stem.

vascular system. the system of plant tissues that conducts water, mineral nutrients, and products of photosynthesis through the plant, consisting of the xylem and phloem.

vector. an organism able to transport and transmit a pathogen to a host.

vegetative growth. growth of stems, roots, and leaves, but not flowers and fruits.

virulent. capable of causing a severe disease; strongly pathogenic.

virus. a small infectious agent, consisting only of nucleic acid and a protein coat, that can reproduce only within the living cells of a host.

xylem. plant tissue that conducts water and nutrients from the roots up through the plant; the woody portion of a tree located inside the cambium (see Figure 5).

zoospore. a motile spore.

Index